The Bride

The
Bride

Rhonda Calhoun

THE BRIDE
4th edition
by Rhonda Calhoun

Other books by Rhonda Calhoun:
BLESSED ARE THE POOR
SIMON PETER AND THE MASTER
SIMON PETER AND THE KING
SIMON PETER AND THE SAVIOR
THE LAND WHERE DREAMS COME TRUE
THE GREAT I AM
BEAUTIFUL
VALIANT

Heart Publishing
harvesthome@juno.com
www.harvesthome.org
816-522-9011

Printed in Taiwan
International Standard Book Number: 0-9719140-1-X

Cover design by Dan Arnold
imdarnold@comcast.net

This book is dedicated to
my beloved King and Savior.
You gave Your life
to make me Your Bride
and I love You for it!

Contents

ACKNOWLEDGEMENTS
♥ ♥ ♥

I have been blessed by a number of people in many different ways during the writing of this book. I will begin with my dear friend, Diane Hallam, who encouraged and offered valuable insights throughout the writing process. Thank you, fellow Shulamite, you are a treasure, and I love you! "You are as beautiful as Tirzah, my darling, as lovely as Jerusalem, as awesome as an army with banners" (Sg. Sol. 6:4).

How can I ever thank Ken Lundeen enough? In the midst of pursuing his doctorate, he took the time to read *The Bride* and offer his insights. His knowledge of the Song of Solomon and of Hebrew customs was invaluble. His teaching and insights opened the Song of Solomon up to me in a greater way. Thank you so much for being such a wonderful teacher (rabbi). I know the following passage refers to Jesus, but it so speaks of you, my friend. "Like an apple tree among the trees of the forest, so is my Beloved among the young men. In his shade I took great delight and sat down, and his fruit was sweet to my taste" (Sg. Sol. 2:3).

I also want to thank my intercessors and friends. Their prayers have been the foundation for Harvest Home, which is the ministry to the poor that my husband and I founded in 1995. These ladies have invested so much into my life personally, into the ministry, and also into the creation of this book. The Lord used them in the birthing of my first book, *Blessed Are the Poor.* They have encouraged and believed in me when I did not. Thank you for constantly reminding me to"think big". I love you, Marie, Jan, Barb, Sue, Lydia, Elizabeth, Carla, Nancy, Bobbe, Alicia, Gloria, and Dana. "O my dove, in the clefts of the rock, in the secret place of the steep pathway, let me see your form, let me hear your voice; for your voice is sweet, and your form is lovely" (Sg. Sol. 2:14). How true that is of you all!

A special thanks to Nancy and Myrna for taking the time to sift through the pages of this book with your keen eyes. Your ability to spot things I overlooked was so helpful. Thank you and know that I love you!

I am so proud that my son-in-law, Dan Arnold, designed the book cover. Not only did you produce a work of art, but you did so with excellence. Your integrity and high standards make you the successful man of God that you are. My thanks and appreciation also go to your wife and my daughter, Misty, for sacrificing her time. You are truly beautiful and a delight to this mother's heart. I love you both very much.

I want to thank my daughters Dana, Molly, and Kaitlin for their suggestions, encouragement, and patience. And my husband, Danny, was amazing. How many times did you read this manuscript? I lost count. I could not have done it without you. I love you all!

I cannot close without thanking my Bridegroom King. You accepted this insignificant girl and poured into me love, grace, truth, and understanding beyond anything I ever dreamed possible. You helped me put into words what You are working in my life.You are outstanding among 10,000, and I owe everything to You!

FOREWORD
♥ ♥ ♥

It is a great pleasure for me to recommend Rhonda Calhoun's newest book, *The Bride*.

I have known Rhonda since 1993. In that time, I have found her to be a woman who deeply loves Jesus and moves in great compassion to the broken. She and her husband, Danny, are the directors of Harvest Home, which is a ministry that reaches out to men, women, and children living in poverty and hopelessness.

I thoroughly enjoyed reading this book; it is truly outstanding! Rhonda's gift of writing combined with her intimate relationship with her Bridegroom King has produced a most excellent resource for man, woman, old, or young. This book explains the Song of Solomon in an easy-to-understand format while maintaining scriptural integrity. Over 600 scripture references from both the Old and New Testament are used to paint a picture of the relationship between Jesus as the Bridegroom King and His Bride.

The Song of Solomon; it is a book I have devoted much time and energy to over many years. I believe Jesus is clearly highlighting this book at this time in our history. He is unlocking our hearts and revealing our identity as the Bride of Christ in greater ways than ever before. He is taking us to new levels of understanding and calling us to walk in deeper intimacy with our Bridegroom King.

As we give ourselves to the profound and life-changing truths found in the Song of Solomon, our love and devotion for the Man Christ Jesus grows in strength and depth and we are changed.

The Bride tells the story of a shepherd girl who is loved by the greatest King of all the ages. This unconquerable King is captivated by the shepherd girls beauty. He soon finds himself conquered by the devotion of this weak and immature girl. The message of God's love, which is infinite, unconditional and available to all is clearly portrayed throughout the story. You will experience the reality of how our Bridegroom King feels about His Bride. You will see how Jesus completely accepts us even in our weakness. As the Bride's journey unfolds, you will find your heart captivated by the glorious man Christ Jesus and ignited with greater passion.

There is a day coming when our Bridegroom King will return for His Bride. She will be without spot, wrinkle, or blemish—a perfect Bride for a perfect King!

So, sit back and relax as you stroll through the King's glorious gardens and run on the mountaintops with your Bridegroom. Allow Him to capture your heart as you have captured His. Prepare yourself for a grand adventure with the Trinity!

—Mike Bickle,
Director, International House of Prayer,
Kansas City, MO

INTRODUCTION

The idea that we, the church of Jesus Christ, are the Bride of Christ simply means we have a special place in God's heart - a place no other created being has! We have access to the heart of God that even the angels don't have. It has nothing to do with our gender or our ability to live perfectly, but it has everything to do with the way our heavenly King views us.

Our walk with God is a life of intimacy that leads to active partnership. The Bride of Christ, the church, is an eternal companion who does the work of God now and throughout eternity - a companion who is infinitely loved by her Bridegroom King.

The Song of Solomon is the story of unconditional love. The story unfolds as the King of all kings pursues a little shepherd girl. As she grows closer to His heart, He reveals Himself to her in all His glory, which causes her to surrender her life to Him completely and forever.

The Bride is an allegory based on the Song of Solomon, which clearly demonstrates the relationship between Jesus and His Bride. I had so much help from heaven writing this book that I dare not take any credit for any good that should come from it.

The night I finished writing this book I had a dream, which I would like to share with you.

In this dream, I sat in a room filled with people who are

aggressively discussing the various interpretations of the Song of Solomon. The more I listened, the more uncomfortable I became.

I looked around the room and saw the Lord sitting by a man who was known for his expertise on the Song of Solomon. The two looked at me and I could tell by their expressions that they were just as uncomfortable as I was.

I turned back to the debaters and said, "Excuse me, but you're missing the whole point of this book. You're so focused on getting the right interpretation that you have lost sight of the heart of this book.

"Song of Solomon is much more than symbolic language; it's about the heart of God. It is about the King of kings who loves His church, His Bride. This King loves His church so much that He gave up His throne and laid down His life for her, saving her from certain death and paying the bridal price.

"As you read and discuss the Song of Solomon, look for the gaps, the places in the book where it's obvious that something has taken place, but hasn't been revealed. Oftentimes, what isn't said is just as important as what is.

"Look for the heart of the book. In finding the heart, you will find keys that unlock a treasure chest filled with the goodness of a Bridegroom King who loves His Bride without measure, my friends."

And now, may He kiss you with the kisses of His word!

MAIN CHARACTERS

The Master Shepherd — Jesus
The King — Jesus
The Bridegroom — Jesus
The Ancient of Days — God, the Father
Comforter — the Holy Spirit
The shepherd girl — the Bride of Christ, the church
The Captain and guards — angels
Shepherds — pastors
David — a true pastor; one who lays down his life for his sheep
Saul — a pastor who is "a wolf in sheep's clothing"
Mother — the universal church
Brothers — leadership in the church
Charity & friends — daughters of Jerusalem, immature believers
Adversary — Satan

The

Cry For

Intimacy

Chapter One
DRAW ME AFTER YOU

The King has brought me into His chambers.

$\mathscr{S}$ince a young child, I have come to Hope Valley almost daily. I have loved this place for as long as I can remember. It was here I first met the Master Shepherd, and it was here, watching Him tenderly care for His sheep, that I decided to become a shepherdess; I was only five years old.

On this warm spring day, just as the noonday sun begins its slow, westward descent, I once again lead my tiny flock into the valley. An army of trees surround me, standing like soldiers, protecting this lovely sanctuary from outside intruders. Countless streams rush down from the surrounding mountains providing this valley and its inhabitants with all the water they could ever want or need. A multitude of brightly colored wildflowers sway in the breeze filling the air with a variety of sweet, intoxicating fragrances. This is such a wonderful place, much more desirable than the village where I live.

Hope Valley is not only beautiful, but it is also the most peaceful place in the entire kingdom, but neither of these things is what causes me to come here day after day. The real attraction and true beauty of this land is its King—a King more noble and gracious than any who has ever lived or ever will.

Rhonda Calhoun

This King is good to the just and the unjust. He considers no one too broken, poor, or insignificant to be treated with dignity, respect and unconditional love. He rules His kingdom with great kindness but is uncompromising when it comes to truth, justice and righteousness.

This King is wealthy beyond belief, owning everything that exists yet eagerly and generously sharing with the righteous and the unrighteous.[2]

Many call Him the King of love, for it is rumored that, once upon a time, He gave up everything in order to save the people of His kingdom from certain death.

Everyone in His kingdom is aware of His infinite wisdom and stand in awe of His judgements because they are always, without fail, just and true. This King moves among the nations in a manner most sovereign. Everyone knows that there is no enemy strong, wise or cunning enough to conquer Him.

It sounds as though I know this King. The truth is I have never even seen Him, but my childhood was filled with grand stories about Him. I would listen for hours in the village meeting hall as shepherds told of the King's great exploits and unrelenting love for weak, broken people.

My dream is to one day meet this King, but it is only a dream and one that I know will never happen for I am just a poor, fatherless girl who has charge over a few of the King's sheep. I dare not hope, for there is nothing special about me, nothing that would ever attract the attention of a King as perfect as He.

As my sheep lie down under the shade of a giant walnut tree, I sit on a large rock and rinse my dust-covered feet in the cool stream. A gentle breeze stirs the multitude of leaves overhead, and all around numerous flowers of various colors dance in the breeze. It is so peaceful here. What a wonderful place this is, a place that seems too good to be true!

The desperate bleating of a newly born lamb suddenly interrupts my thoughts. Snowflake has wandered away from her mother and is frantically and unsuccessfully trying to climb over a fallen log. Her plump, little belly is stuck causing all four legs to dangle in the air. Hurrying to her side, I say, "Snowflake, you're such an adventurous little lamb!"

Scooping her up, I check for injuries as her mother watches ever so closely. She is a lovely lamb—white as snow and just as soft. I love this lamb as I do all of the King's sheep in my care. Not that I have that many—just ten sheep and two lambs. My two brothers often tease me about my tiny flock, reminding me they have charge over more than two hundred of the King's best sheep. The size of my flock is not important to me. Whether I have one or one hundred matters not—I simply want to be with them, for I truly love being a shepherdess.

Leaving Snowflake with her mother, I walk back to my place of rest. On the other side of this stream, just a short distance away, are the King's palace and private garden. The locked garden is completely surrounded by a tall, ancient stone wall. It is said that every kind of flower imaginable and also every fruit, vegetable and herb ever created grows there. It is even rumored that there is a spring of water flowing from a rock that gives eternal life to those who drink from it. Behind the garden, situated at the base of the Lebanon Mountains, is the King's residence. Never has there ever been a palace built as grand as this one.

With each passing day, I grow more fascinated with the King and His kingdom. I have spent countless hours sitting by this stream imagining what it would be like to live in the palace and eat from the King's table. I am well aware that things like that never happen to poor shepherd girls like me, but that doesn't stop me from dreaming.

Scooping a handful of water, I am about to bring it to my parched lips, when, out of the corner of my eye, I see someone or something. There, standing just outside the garden gate, is the Master Shepherd. This highly skilled and tenderhearted Shepherd is in charge of the King's enormous flocks and their shepherds. He has always been extremely kind and good to me, unlike most of the other shepherds who are either rude or treat me as if I am a silly girl.

The Master Shepherd looks my way and waves. My youthful heart does somersaults—He is my dearest Friend and I love Him! Looking heavenward, I whisper, "God, I desire to love the Master Shepherd in the same way that He loves me. He is so kind and thoughtful, always esteeming others as greater than Himself. I would love to be like that.

"Oh, that He would kiss my heart, for His friendship is better than wine! I would love to run with Him on the mountains, caring for His sheep! Is it even remotely possible for someone like me to partner with someone like Him, someone who is so good and kind and absolutely wonderful? I know that I am asking a lot since I am just a simple shepherdess, but this is my greatest desire.

"God, would You look down on me with favor? Oh, that the Master Shepherd might flood me with His kindness! I long to do what He does and go where He goes, to run with Him on the mountaintops and through the valleys. Oh, that I might know the Master Shepherd intimately!"

I look back at this kind Shepherd and say to myself, "Draw me after You and let us run together![3] I understand that I am powerless to make this happen therefore I am asking for Your help."

As if He heard, the Master Shepherd beckons me to come. I hesitate. *Can it be true? Is He really asking me to come to Him?*

I look behind to make sure that someone has not walked up. No one there except my sheep.

The Master Shepherd stands with His hand resting on the iron gate that leads to the King's garden; peace covers Him like skin. He beckons me again. Trembling, I run through the stream and across the grassy field. My heart is pounding. As I draw near, He steps forward with His arms open. He laughs as I fall into them. Spinning around, He exclaims, "You are delightful!"

In this place, held in His arms, nothing else matters — every other thought flees as I am lost in His wonderful embrace. With my head nestled against His chest, I hear the steady beat of His heart reminding me of His constant faithfulness. Overcome with emotion, I say, "Your lovingkindness is intoxicating and more exhilarating than any pleasure, position, possession, or any other thing this world has to offer![4]

"And Your dedication is like sweet, fragrant oil; it

overwhelms me.[5] Your thoughts and affections toward me are perfect.

"Your character is like purified oil, which is poured from one vessel into another. You pour Your life into everyone who knows You, which transforms them into Your image. You are the source and fountain of all that is good in the earth. You are great beyond measure; this is why the pure of heart love You![6]

"Your thoughts and emotions toward me are pleasant, not harsh or critical. I can never get enough of You![7] The more time I spend with You, the more I want to be with You. Oh, how good You are—not just to me, but to all who know You."[8]

The Master Shepherd steps back and smiles the kindest of smiles. His eyes are filled with the purest love. My tender heart is easily captured and I plead, "If You draw me after You, I will follow You anywhere!"[9]

"You will follow Me anywhere?" He asks taking my hand. I nod.

Bowing slightly, He sweeps His arm toward the King's garden. "Then come with Me into My garden."[10]

"What do you mean into *Your* garden? That is the King's garden and only His family and most intimate friends are allowed inside. This cannot be *Your* garden; You are a Shepherd, not a King."

Without saying a word, this Shepherd, whom I have known for as long as I can remember, removes His simple linen garment. He now stands before me dressed in a purple and crimson robe; its sleeves and collar are trimmed in gold.

How? What?

The Master Shepherd wears the royal garments of the King! After a very long, awkward moment, I ask, "Are You trying to tell me You're...You're...the **King**?"

"I am," He answers, smiling broadly.

"Are...are You sure?"

Chuckling, He takes my hand and answers, "I was, I am and always will be the King." Tweaking the end of my nose He continues, "Yes, I'm sure that I am the King—there is none other. I am also sure that I would truly enjoy walking with you in My garden."

Rhonda Calhoun

"But, I can't leave my sheep."

"I have already made arrangements for them," he responds, pointing behind me to a young shepherd boy.

It feels as though I am dreaming as I place my hand in the crook of His arm. Around His neck, hanging on a thin scarlet cord, is a golden key, which He places in the lock.

Am I to not only see, but also walk in this very famous and intriguing garden?

The gate groans as it swings open. I feel faint; my palms are sweating. *Can this be real?*

A thick hedge grows just inside the gate, providing a wall of privacy from the outside world. As I am led around the hedge, I get my first glimpse of this garden paradise, which makes it impossible for me to take another step — such beauty is completely overwhelming! The finest artist in the entire world could never adequately capture the incredible beauty of this place. Before me, as far as I can see, are a multitude of plants and flowers in full bloom — flowers of every conceivable color, size, and shape. The colors are much richer and deeper than any flower I have ever seen. I have never seen a garden so beautiful or so well manicured. "This can't be real!" I whisper.

Squeezing my hand and giving my arm a gentle tug, He says, "This garden is more real than the world you live in...and, unlike the world you live in, this garden is eternal."

My head hurts as I try to process His words and the amazing sights before me.

He leads me deeper into this enormous paradise. I discover that the garden is actually made up of countless smaller gardens. There are flowers and trees beyond number, fruits of all shapes and kinds, plus every herb and vegetable imaginable. Every fruit-bearing plant is heavy with ripe produce, even though it is early spring. The same is true of the flowers — tulips, gladiolas, roses, chrysanthemums, lilacs, marigolds, daffodils, lilies and thousands more are all in full bloom.

How is this possible?

Lost in the wonder of it all, I spend most of my time merely staring. I have to constantly remind myself to close my mouth, for I am in awe.

My kind Friend leads me into a garden where roses of every variety and color grow in countless numbers. In the center of this rose garden is a marble fountain fashioned in the form of a man's cupped hands. A family of tiny sparrows sing as they bathe in its crystal clear shower. On the far side, near the stone wall, is the largest tree I have ever seen; its thick branches and dense foliage form a wonderful canopy from the noonday sun.

"Come, let us rest under the shade of that tree," my Shepherd says.

I spread my shawl on the thick grass and sit at His feet. Looking up at the towering tree, I see what at first glance appears to be apples, but a closer look reveals that my assumption was wrong. The fruit is rather odd shaped and anything but pleasing to the eye. Curious I ask, "What kind of fruit is this? What kind of tree is this?"

"This tree is one of a kind; it is called the Tree of Life. Anyone who eats from it will live forever; its leaves are for the healing of the nations."[11]

"How strange that something as valuable as a fruit that offers both eternal life and healing for nations would look so...well...so ugly," I say without thinking.

"Yes, that is different from the thinking of many, but most often that is the way it is in My kingdom. In this kingdom, it is never wise to judge anyone or anything by outward appearances. You will discover soon enough that My eyes are fixed on the condition and motives of your heart. Your accomplishments or lack thereof do not determine how I feel about you or how I see you. My love for you is based solely on who I am...not on what you do or don't do."

With a wink, He stands to His feet. Reaching into the branches. His arm disappears in the thick leaves only to reappear with a piece of the odd-shaped fruit. Rubbing its red flesh on His sleeve, He hands me the shiny fruit, saying, "Eat, My friend."

A family of rabbits suddenly hop out of a nearby bush, distracting me. The Master Shepherd sings softly, "Never sit under the apple tree with anyone else but Me, with anyone else but Me, with anyone else but Me."

I look into the eyes of this Man. He returns my gaze; it

9

feels as though He is peering into the very recesses of my soul. Unable to understand the love and kindness I see there, I quickly look away. Passing the ugly fruit from hand to hand, my mind tries to make some sense of all that is happening. *Who is this Man? And how is He able to search the very depths of my heart?*

I steal another look; He sits deep in thought twirling a golden leaf.

What holds His thoughts captive?

Without taking His eyes from the spinning leaf, He answers my unspoken question, "You wonder what consumes my thoughts. I am consumed with thoughts of You. My every thought is held captive by your pure heart and incredible beauty."

How did He know what I was thinking? Just who is this Shepherd? I thought I knew Him, but I had no idea the depth of His Spirit. He claims to be the King; I certainly don't understand how that could be possible.

If He isn't the King, then where did He get His clothes, and how does He have the key to the King's private garden? But if He really is the King, then why would He bother to bring someone like me into such a glorious place as this?

He looks up at me and smiles as if understanding the tug-of-war going on inside of me.

I just don't understand—everyone knows that king's do not spend time with peasants!

I smile back.

If He truly is the King, then how will I ever convince myself that He, the most wonderful King in the entire world, cares about me and wants to be my Friend?

Leaning towards me, He again answers the unspoken thoughts of my heart, "That is precisely the reason I first came to you as a Shepherd, but the time has now come for you to know Me as your King."

"It is true then?" I ask, so afraid to believe that it might be true.

"Do not be anxious, My love, for the day will come when you will not only believe that I find you breathtakingly beautiful, but you will also believe that My love for you is not based on how good you can be. You will come to understand that I love you even though you are not, and never will be, perfect—not in this life."

As usual, His words soothe my fearful heart. A gentle breeze blows several strands of my long, auburn hair across my face. He reaches out and brushes it away. I close my eyes and enjoy the intoxicating fragrance of thousands of roses in full bloom. Peace fills me. If I am dreaming, I pray that I never wake. This Man, whether Shepherd or King, is absolutely wonderful and ever so kind. He speaks words of life and never condemns or criticizes me. I know of no one like Him. I will rest in this fact. As for His claim to royalty, I will wait and see.

The cooing of a dove causes me to open my eyes. I can hardly believe what I am seeing—a snow-white dove is perched on His shoulder! The dove is beautiful, but not nearly as lovely as My Shepherd. His face is bathed in glorious light. His eyes are closed, and peace surrounds Him. I feel strangely warm and a new confidence fills me. Leaning forward, I ask, "I have known You since a young child. I watched You care for Your sheep and grew to care deeply for You. As one who longs to please You, may I be so bold as to ask what it is that You desire, my Friend?"

"There is one thing I desire above all else, My love, and that is for you to intimately know My Father and Me."[12]

"I have never met Your Father, and I already know You."

"But do you know Me with your eyes closed?" He asks, smiling.

"I don't understand...what do You mean?"

"Close your eyes and tell Me what your heart sees and believes to be true."

Somewhat reluctant, I close my eyes and begin, "Well, I see a beautiful garden filled with all kinds of roses and a very large tree with strange looking fruit, and I see You."

"And what do I look like?"

"I know You claim to be the King, but I see You as a Shepherd with a staff and a rod. Your hair is dark, and Your eyes are deep, dark brown. You're dressed in the garments of the—."

"Yes?"

I open my eyes and answer, "I can't do it! I have grown up knowing You as the Master Shepherd, but now You sit before me as a King. I guess I really don't know You after all."

Falling on my face, I cry out, "Help me to know You in Spirit and in truth!"

"Then come closer," He says, extending His hand.

My tender heart fills with longing. Trembling, I gather my shawl and spread it close to His side. Sitting this close to perfection fills me with extreme uneasiness, and I want to run. He takes my hand, and peace immediately fills me.

Who is this Man that is able to calm my fearful heart with just one touch?

"Please tell me, are You—are You *really and truly* the King?"

"I sit here before you as both a Shepherd and a King. Do not think that I am any different because I come to you dressed in royal attire. One's attire has absolutely nothing to do with one's heart or spirit. Do you not know that I am the same as I was yesterday, and I am the same today, and I will be the same tomorrow and forever?[13] Unlike the seasons, I change not."

Not understanding, but feeling quite encouraged I respond, "Oh, how good You are! Regardless of what comes my way, I will remember Your lovingkindness. How right it is that all the maidens love You, for Your love is better than the choicest wine! As a matter of fact, Your love is better than anything this world has to offer!"[14]

"O, how lovely you look!" He responds.

The bleating of my sheep suddenly interrupts my thoughts capturing my attention. It has grown quite late. Jumping to my feet, I grab my shawl and quickly shake the grass from it. "I must get the sheep back before dark," I explain.

My Friend stands and once more takes my hand. Looking into my eyes, He says, "The sun is fading, your sheep are calling, but My love for you only grows stronger."

I cannot reply; I simply return His gaze.

We walk arm in arm to the garden gate. Pushing it open, He says, "Come again tomorrow and I will feed you from My garden."

"You will be here tomorrow?" I ask.

"I am always here, but not always seen."

Puzzled, I shrug then hurry through the garden gate. Stopping midstream, I look back. The Master Shepherd stands just outside the gate dressed in the earthly garments of a simple shepherd. The sinking sun casts its golden light on His face. Oh, how glorious He looks! With His rod in one hand and His staff in the other, He smiles at me and nods. Turning toward the mountains, He quickly disappears from my sight.

Filled with great joy, I cross the stream. The young shepherd sits under the tree serenading my flock. His harp sounds heavenly, as does his song. I listen undetected until Snowflake sees me and runs to my side. I introduce myself while scratching Snowflake's neck. Laughing at my persistent little lamb, he responds, "I'm David."

"And this is Snowflake," I say, giving the lamb a playful hug.

David responds, "Snowflake is a very curious lamb."

"Yes, she is," I reply as she wanders off to explore a nearby turtle. "David, you have a great voice and you play that harp beautifully."

"Thank you, but I dare not take the credit. The Master Shepherd has taught me all that I know."

"How long have you known the Master Shepherd?"

"I was born in His house and plan to serve Him until I die," David answers.[15]

"I cannot imagine anything more wonderful than being able to spend your entire life with the Master Shepherd," I say, looking toward the mountains.

"I do not believe that there is anything on this earth that compares to the joy of being in His presence. For me, one day in His courts is better than a thousand days spent elsewhere."

"I can certainly believe that," I reply.

Hooking the crook of his staff around Snowflake's neck, he rescues her from the snapping turtle. "I must go, for my Shepherd waits, but I will return tomorrow to care for your sheep," David says.

"Why are you doing this?" I ask.

Rhonda Calhoun

"I am the King's shepherd, and all that I do, I do for Him. This is what He has asked me to do; therefore, it is my great pleasure and delight to serve you. In serving you, I serve Him and that makes my heart glad."

"Indeed." I respond, pondering his words.

Placing Snowflake and the other sheep back in my care, he bids me farewell. With rod and staff in hand, he follows the well-worn path the Master Shepherd took. As for me, I gather my sheep and lead them home, singing the entire way.

The
Tenderhearted
Shepherd

Chapter Two
GREENER PASTURES

For your love is better than wine. [16]

*T*he following day, eager to discover if my time in the garden was real or just a dream, I lead my flock to Hope Valley much earlier than usual. To my complete surprise and utter delight, David is already waiting for me under the walnut tree. He greets me warmly and then turns his attention to my sheep. He reminds me of the Master Shepherd.

Turning my attention to the garden gate, I can hardly believe my eyes—the Master Shepherd has arrived early as well! Saying a hasty farewell to David, I race across the stream and into the arms of my kind Friend.

"I was afraid that yesterday was just a dream. It is so difficult for me to believe that something as wonderful as all this is happening to someone like me," I say while trying to catch my breath.

Resting His hand on my shoulder, He replies, "Your life with Me will be filled with many great adventures and glorious encounters. No two days will ever be the same, but that is part of the beauty of being in relationship with Me. And not only that, but Goodness and Mercy will follow you all the days of your life and you will know true love, which is more real than the ground you stand on."

Stepping back, He removes His robe and drapes it over the branch of a nearby tree. Once again, dressed in the King's garments, He leads me through the gate as I whisper, "It's real; this is really real! Here I am, a simple shepherdess, walking with the Master Shepherd into the King's garden!"

"This is all a reflection of My love for you. Everything you see is meant to reveal the goodness of God. He loves you. He cares for you immensely...and so do I."

Looking at the ground, I respond, "I want to believe what You are saying is true, but it is difficult. I don't know how to make myself believe You."

"The only way to change what you believe is to discover the truth. Many people believe that truth is discovering the facts, but ultimate truth is only found in Me. And when you know Me, you know truth. Therefore, do not pursue information and facts, but pursue Me."

"I want to love You the same way You love me, for that is my heart's desire. You have always been so good to me and I want to return that lovingkindness, but I am weak."

"Look into My eyes and tell Me what you see."

Somewhat afraid, I slowly look up. He asks, "Now, what do you see there?"

"I see a reflection of me."

"That is because you are inside of Me. You are the apple of My eye, the jewel in My crown, the one I love. You have nothing to fear when the King is your care-taker, for I am able to do what you cannot. My Father promised me a bride who is pure, spotless and without blemish. One day you will understand the great price I paid to make you thus. I see you through the truth of eternity future. You are already My pure spotless bride not because of your efforts, but because of Mine."

"Oh, I do not understand!"

"That is because it is not time for you to know all things. Now is the time for you to simply trust Me with your life. Allow Me to orchestrate the events of your life in such a way that you will come to know Me intimately."

"I can do nothing but that, for I have no where else to

go. No one cares for me the way You do."

"That is true. Now look again and tell Me what you see."

I see what I can only describe as pure love and holy passion. His eyes invite me into wholehearted affection. "What is this that You ask of me?"

"I merely ask that you love Me regardless of what it will cost you."

"Am I able? Is my young heart able to suffer for the sake of another? Do I even have the capacity? Only You know!"

"You are more than what the circumstances of your life say. One day this existence you call life will fade away and all that will be left is your spirit. Do you not know that your life is more than what meets the eye?"

"What I do know is that I'm not the same when You look at me."

"When your heart condemns you on every side take refuge in the truth that I never condemn you. Child, My love is like the rain — it washes away the dirt and makes all things new. My love refreshes while restoring life. My love is also like the sunshine after the rain. It shines on all things and makes them beautiful, driving away the clouds and providing what is needed for growth. My love is everywhere. It is in the rain, the sunshine, the moonlight, the stars, the green meadows, the wildflowers and even in the thorns. My love consumes all that lives, for I am love personified and I am everywhere."

"What? How is that possible?"

"There are many things that you cannot understand, for My ways are higher than your ways, dear one."

"That is obvious," I reply.

Throughout the summer and well into fall, the Master Shepherd and I explore the wonders and beauties of this amazing garden. I never again mention His claim to royalty and neither does He. It is much easier and much more comfortable for me to believe that He is merely the Master Shepherd. After all, I am nothing more than a peasant.

Each day, without fail, He feeds me and my flock from the garden. Many in the village have commented about my healthy appearance. Each time, I tell them that the Master

Shepherd feeds me from the King's garden, but it is obvious from their responses that they do not believe me. Just this morning, I told a shepherd named Saul about the Master Shepherd feeding not only me, but also my flock. Saul proceeded to list all the reasons why someone as important as the Master Shepherd would never waste His time with someone as insignificant as me. I walked away while he was still talking.

When I was eight years old, my brothers put me in charge of the King's sheep that were handicapped, weak, barren, or sick. That was four years ago and my brother still refuses to trust me with anything other than what he calls the hopeless rejects. If it was up to him, these sheep would be killed, but the King refuses to do so and has ordered that all of His sheep, regardless of their condition, are to be well cared for their entire lives.

A strange thing has happened this past year—all of my barren sheep gave birth to strong, healthy lambs. Most had twins and several even had triplets. The sheep that were once sick and weak are now some of the strongest among my flock. Even the handicapped ones have made great improvements. I take no credit, for I know it is only because of the wonderful food the Master Shepherd has been feeding them.

Today is the last day of fall. The signs of the approaching winter season are all around. I pull my shawl over my head and lead my sheep out of the shade and into the sunshine. Once the snow comes, I won't be able to bring the flock to Hope Valley. I cannot bear to think of it, for I will greatly miss my time in the garden with my Beloved Shepherd.

It is nearly noon so I encourage my sheep to walk a little faster. Cresting the hill, I am surprised to see, not David, but my eldest brother waiting underneath the walnut tree. Fearing that tragedy has visited our family, I shout, "Brother, pray tell me that all is well?"

He shouts in return, "Fear not; all is well."

Relieved, I whistle for the sheep to follow me as I quickly descend the hill. I am eager to see what event has brought my brother here in the middle of the day.

He greets me with unusual kindness; I respond

halfheartedly because I am looking over his shoulder for the Master Shepherd. He stands by the gate; what a faithful Friend He is! Content, I focus my attention on my brother asking, "For what purpose have you come? What news do you bring?"

"Have no fear, little sister, all is well, for I am indeed the bearer of good news. I have come to rescue you from this God-forsaken valley and from a future of insignificance and boredom.

"Your brother and I have been watching you and your flock for some time now. It has come to our attention that those among your sheep that were barren have become quite fruitful and those that were sick have recovered.

"You've done so well with this pitiful little flock that we've decided to allow you to work alongside us. We will even give you charge over a large number of the King's flock in hopes that they will reproduce like these pitiful sheep have. Little sister, this is a great honor and one that you'd be foolish to refuse."

"It is quite an honor. I never dreamed I would ever be able to serve the King in such a magnificent way. Of course my answer is yes!"

"Good! Now help me get your flock up and moving," he replies.

"What? Why must they move?"

"You know that your brother and I feed our flocks in the pastures near Mount Hermon. You don't expect us to bring them here do you? Why, I have greater ambitions than can be found in this pitiful, insignificant valley."

Clutching my brother's sleeve, I cry out, "When I said yes to you I did not think that I would have to leave this place. I can't leave; this is where I meet the Master Shepherd each day, and I must remain close by His side if I am to become like Him!"

"Don't be silly. Either you come with me where you will have a chance at greatness, or you can stay here with your pitiful sheep. You can't have it both ways. Now, which will it be?"

Not waiting for an answer, he prods my resting sheep with the end of his staff. The tired sheep are not interested in moving. They, too, love this place and have certainly developed quite a taste for the fresh greens from the King's garden. Seeing their resistance, my brother shouts, "Help me get your stubborn

Rhonda Calhoun

sheep up!"

What should I do? I do not want to leave, but it would be foolish to pass up such a tremendous opportunity. I could learn a lot from my brothers, which would prepare me for greater service in the kingdom.

Perhaps, I could go with him...for a season. After all, the snows will be here soon, and I will not be able to come to Hope Valley anyway.

Justifying my prideful ambition, I call to my sheep and they immediately respond. Looking over my shoulder, I see that my Beloved Shepherd has walked to the edge of the stream. He waves to me.

"I can't go!" I cry out, agony filling my heart.

"You don't want to miss out on fame and fortune, now do you?" my brother asks as he places his arm around my shoulder. "Just don't look back, little sister. You must look forward, for your life is about to change dramatically."

At the time, I had no idea how true his words would prove to be. My life did change, but not in the way that he meant.

Tears pour down my face as we leave Hope Valley for bigger pastures and greater promises. As we make our way across the valley, their constant bleating and slow pace of my sheep cause my brother great agitation. I try my best to get them to hurry but am unsuccessful. They seem to understand that a great loss has occurred.

Snowflake keeps wandering off so I put her across my shoulders.

Oh, how I wish someone would pick me up and place me across their shoulders, for my heart grows heavier with each step.

After several days, the tears finally stop, but not so with the cries of my heart. I know that I will never stop longing to be with my Beloved Shepherd, for His love is better than anything.[17]

Chapter Three
COMPROMISE

They made me caretaker of the vineyards. [18]

*E*ach morning, I lead my large flock out to pasture. Because of all that the Master Shepherd has taught me, I am able to find the perfect kinds of grass for them. In just a few short weeks, the sheep in my care are much healthier and considerably more obedient than the ones in my my brothers care. I soon discover that my brothers are quite jealous and even feel threatened by me. That does not stop me from telling them about the Master Shepherd. They are not interested and continually make fun of me, but I know that He is their only answer. I long to see them come to know Him in the same way I know Him.

I ache for my brothers to accept me, but it does not happen. As the weeks go by, their jealousy only grows stronger; they treat me worse than a hired hand, yet I find myself striving more and more for their approval and acceptance but it doesn't happen.

The snow begins to fall and my despair deepens.

This morning, leading the sheep out to the south pasture where there is still some grass, I have the idea that if I work longer and harder then maybe my brothers will accept me. The

Rhonda Calhoun

following morning, I arrive at the sheep pen an hour before my brothers and stay an hour later than they. After a month of working like this, nothing changes, and I am quite discouraged and extremely exhausted. Things have only worsened between us. Now when I speak of the Master Shepherd they get angry. I try desperately to help them understand, but it seems as though they do not want to know Him.

The snow is now too deep to take the sheep out. I am busy cleaning their pen when my eldest brother joins me. With elbows propped on the gate, he says, "Mother just informed me that another worker has left the vineyards. I have no desire to work there and neither does our brother. Therefore, we have decided that since you enjoy working so much you should be the one to help her in the vineyards. Your brother and I will see to the sheep."

"But, I know absolutely nothing about taking care of vineyards. All I have ever done is care for sheep," I respond, leaning against my pitchfork.

"Then it's time you learned. You can start as soon as you finish mucking out the pen. And who knows, you might even be good at it. Besides, it might help take your mind off your *Beloved*," he says mockingly.

Driven by a strong desire for my brother's approval, I keep silent, but inwardly I am furious. Throwing down the pitchfork I walk to the back of the pen. Sitting on a pile of hay in the midst of the sheep, I pick up a black lamb named, "Midnight". Rubbing his soft wool, I whisper, "It appears that my love for the Master Shepherd makes people jealous or something. The Master Shepherd told me that dull hearts are uncomfortable around burning hearts. I guess He was right, but then, He always is, isn't He?"

Midnight scrambles out of my arms.

Sighing deeply, I announce, "I have to work in the vineyards, so I won't be able to take care of you anymore, but I will do my best to see you whenever I can."[19]

My heart is broken. I just cannot understand why my brothers treat me this way.[20] I do my best to please them, but nothing works.

Each morning, just before sunrise, I head out to the vineyards. My primary job is to keep debris from collecting around the vines and to set traps for the foxes that will eat the budding grapes in the spring.[21] I learn what I need to know, but this is not who I am, this is not what I was called to do; I am a shepherdess not a vineyard caretaker.

Each day, I work until it is too dark to see, and then collapse on my cot. Often, I find it impossible to rest because visions of my Shepherd invade my mind. The sound of His voice echoes through my dreams, and I awake feeling exhausted and ever so lonely.

I sit at my mother's table every day surrounded by family but feel empty. My heart aches to be loved, but my family is more interested in discussing new ways to earn money than they are in me.

Oh, to be back in Hope Valley with my Shepherd where I am loved! One day, I will go back and what a day that will be!

The winter was the longest I have ever known, and the dreary, wet spring only reflects the desperate state of my heart. I have spoken several times of returning to Hope Valley, but each time my mother and brothers respond in anger. I know the work here is overwhelming and their needs are great, but I long for the peace and love that I had with the Master Shepherd. I grow more and more miserable with each passing day.

Summer finally makes its way to the village, and my brothers announce that I will no longer have Sundays in which to be "lazy". They tell me that from now on I must take care of the sheep on Sundays. I respond with mixed feelings, for I am overjoyed at the thought of being able to care for sheep again, but Sunday is the only day I have to wander through the fields and dream of being with my Beloved Shepherd. But it matters not, for I have no say in the matter.

July arrives and brings with it unusually dry, hot weather. It hasn't rained in weeks, so finding suitable pasture and water for the sheep is proving to be quite a challenge. The drought causes the wolves and other predators to come down from the surrounding mountains in search of food and water, making the sheep more vulnerable than ever. Working seven days a week

Rhonda Calhoun

is exhausting and leaves me little time to look after myself, but I enjoy being with the sheep so much that I am able to ignore my fatigue. They bring what little happiness there is to my otherwise dreary existence.

My family continues to deny that the Master Shepherd took me into the King's garden. The one time I dared to mention that the Master Shepherd wears the King's garments, they ridiculed me for weeks. 'Tis a strange thing — my mother and brothers know quite a lot *about* the Master Shepherd, but they do not really know Him. Because of their cruel remarks, I have decided, from this day forth, I will remain silent concerning Him.

It is still dark outside when I wake to someone jabbing me in the side. My eyes strain to focus. "Get up, you lazy girl!" my brother shouts.

The only light in my room comes from the small oil lamp he holds. "Get up and go after the lost lamb!" he shouts.

"Which lamb is it?" I ask, suddenly wide awake.

"The stupid one, that's which one. Now, go fetch it!"

He leaves mumbling something about me being just as stupid as the sheep. I quickly stuff bread and cheese in my satchel, grab my rod and staff, and head out into the darkness.

Stopping just outside the village gate, I fill my water bag from the slow moving stream. Looking back at the sleeping village, I sigh. I never would have accepted my brother's offer if I had known my life was going to be like this. I miss the Master Shepherd much more than I ever thought possible.

With a heavy heart, I start out. It is very dangerous for any animal to be out at night, but even more so for a lamb. Lambs are vulnerable and easy prey for the lions and leopards that infest the surrounding Hermon Mountains. Anxious for the well-being of the little one, I pick up my pace.

It is mid-morning, and I still have not found the lamb. The sun is scorching. I kneel at a river's edge to fill my water bag and wash my face. Just ahead, over the hill, is Hope Valley. It has been nine long months since I have seen my Beloved Shepherd. I miss Him greatly and long to return, but dare not for fear of what He will say. Oh, how I wish I had never left!

Suddenly, I tumble face first in the water. I come up

sputtering. Angry, I turn to see who shoved me. Grinning from ear to ear is Compromise, an old acquaintance from my childhood. "Compromise, what'd you do that for?"

He offers me his hand, which I blatantly refuse. "Oh, come on. Where's the fun-loving girl I use to know? Be a good sport. It's hot out here so I thought I'd help you cool off, that's all."

"Yeah, it is hot, but I didn't plan on going for a swim. I have a lamb to find."

"Hey, I will help you find it. Finding lost lambs was always my specialty."

"Since when have you ever cared for anyone or anything other than yourself?"I ask.

Filling my water bag, I grab my staff and head for the hills, dripping wet. He follows. We travel quite a distance in silence, or rather, I walk in silence as he talks continuously.

Well past noon, I see a very large tree in the midst of this dry, barren wilderness. It stands alone, tall and proud. Its thick, twisted branches have grown in such a way that they give the appearance of arms reaching toward heaven.

I drag a hollow log under its tempting shade and sit. Compromise wastes no time sitting close beside me. Each time I move further away, but he inches closer.

"Do you know what kind of tree this is?" he asks.

I shrug, not really caring.

Ignoring my lack of interest, he stands and picks a piece of fruit hanging from the tree's heavy-laden branches. With prize in hand, he takes his seat beside me. Rubbing the beautiful looking piece of fruit on his sleeve, he offers it to me, but I refuse hoping to discourage any further invitations. "Suit yourself," he says taking a bite.

Patting the tree trunk, he continues, "This is the Tree of the Knowledge of Good and Evil. Do you want to know why it's called that?"

"Not really," I answer, looking the other way.

"Well, since you're so interested, I'll tell you. Anyone who eats from this tree will become like God," he states matter-of-factly.

Rhonda Calhoun

"Oh, really?"

"Really. And this," he says as he holds out the fruit, "will make you wise."

"Everyone knows that the fruit from the Tree of Knowledge of Good and Evil is forbidden fruit. If you eat it, you will die," I respond.

"But do you know why it's forbidden?"

"I have never really thought about it." I answer, suddenly growing curious.

"Well, I know why. It's because God understands that in the day you eat from it your eyes will be opened, and you will be like Him, knowing good and evil. If you eat this fruit, you will be able to appreciate and know the pleasures this earth has to offer. You will be free to decide for yourself what is good and what is evil. You will be able to make your own choices and do whatever you want to do, just like me."

His words intrigue me greatly.

When I was young, I heard many stories about this tree. It is rumored that God proclaimed that if anyone eats or touches the fruit from this tree they will surely die. I have often wondered where the tree grew and what its fruit looked like. Now I know.

It certainly looks a lot better than the fruit from the Tree of Life.

I look at the fruit Compromise holds. Before I can say anything, he tosses it in my lap. Terrified, I throw my hands in the air. The highly polished, perfect looking fruit sits nestled in the folds of my robe. I dare not touch it, for I know the result would be my death. I simply stare at the delightful piece of fruit.

It does look delicious and the bread I brought to eat is a bit stale. And it would be nice to be wise and make my own choices. I am a bit tired of having my brothers always telling me what to do.

I look at Compromise. He took a bite, and he's still alive. As if he knew what I was thinking, Compromise laughs and says, "You won't die! Look at me, I'm just fine!"

He reaches out and takes my hand in his. Pulling my hand out of his clutches and feeling quite panicked, I ask, "What do you want from me?"

"I don't want anything from you. I just want to be your

friend. I've been looking for you for quite some time and only recently learned where you had gone. I came as soon as I could," he answers, moving closer.

Brushing his arm against mine, he continues, "I hear that you're not only a fine shepherdess, but also a marvelous caretaker of vineyards. I'm so very proud of you and all that you've become. I always knew you had it in you to make something of yourself."

He lays his hand on top of mine. My heart races. He continues, "You've become quite lovely and very desirable."

What am I feeling? It has been so long since I have heard kind words. He squeezes my hand ever so gently and whispers my name.

There is something very familiar about his touch, his words. What is it?

My head is swimming. I cannot think.

"Wh-what do you want from me?" I ask, ever so weakly.

"I want you, that's all. I want to spend the rest of my life with you. You desire me; I can see it in your eyes. You want to be free, don't you? You want to be loved, don't you? You want to know pleasure, don't you?"

The fruit rolls onto the ground. Without thinking, I reach out and pick it up. Something cold and sinister courses through my veins. My head is swimming and my heart is racing.

Compromise holds the fruit next to my lips. I feel quite intoxicated. I take a bite. Immediately, he throws it to the ground. Taking my hand in his, he ever so gently kisses my fingertips, my hand, my neck, my cheek, and then my lips.

Rhonda Calhoun

Chapter Four
THE LAMB

The sun has burned me. [22]

$\mathcal{T}$he distant, desperate bleating of a lamb fills my ears, bringing me to my senses. In my weakness, for a brief moment, I forgot the lamb, the precious lamb!

I gather my things and run as fast as I can from Compromise, but it is too late; I gave myself to him under that awful tree!

Oh, what have I done? What have I done?

Love burns in my heart, but not for Compromise. I could never love him! There is only One I could ever really love, but I just ruined any chance I ever had of being loved by Him. I will never know true love again; my hope for a decent future just died.

What was I thinking! How could I trade perfect love for something so fleeting and so cheap?

The excruciating pain of my betrayal consumes me. Shame covers me like a wet, cold blanket.

Why did Compromise come to me when I was so weak and vulnerable? Why did I not run from him?

I know what Compromise is like; he never changes.

Why did I do the very thing that I said I would never do?

Rhonda Calhoun

All these questions and many more flood my mind, tormenting me. Blinded by my tears, I continue toward the lamb's continual cries, which grow weaker by the moment. Excruciating pain, crippling shame and deep hopelessness consume me like fire consumes dry grass.

Minutes seem like hours. The lamb's cries cease, and I fear that I am too late. Cresting the next hill, I see him just a few feet away tangled in a thorn bush. He appears to be lifeless.

"Oh, please not this too!" I cry out.

Rushing to his side, I thrust my trembling hands through the thorns ignoring the pain. His heart still beats; I let out a long, deep cry. The little guy lifts his head and looks at me. There is so much trust in his look that it takes my breath. I whisper, "I'm here now and I will get you out of this." My tears flow freely.

I quickly set about the difficult task of untangling him without causing him further injury. Thorns have pierced his brow and all four limbs. His back and belly are bleeding profusely from his struggle to be free.

My hands are shaking and my heart is breaking. Overcome by my own inner torment, I cry out, "Oh, God, I am so sorry! Please forgive me and help me! I have wandered far from home and lost my way like this lamb—I am hopelessly tangled in the thicket. I am broken in heart, soul and body. Would You untangle the mess I've made of my life and lead me back to Hope Valley and to my Beloved Shepherd? Perhaps, He will deal kindly with me...."

I finally pull the lamb out; he is as limp as a willow branch. For a long moment I simply hold him close, praying for his healing. I then wash his wounds and pour oil on them. Satisfied that every wound is clean and disinfected, I carefully wrap strips of cloth around most of his body, for his wounds are many. Laying him on my cloak, I then tend to the numerous cuts on my own arms and hands.

We are both trembling. Carefully picking him up and holding him close, I whisper, "It's okay little guy. You're going to be just fine...I only wish I could say the same about myself."

After much coaxing, I get him to drink a little water from my hand. Confident that all has been done, I gently place the lamb in a sling made from my cloak and then set out for the village. The long walk gives me plenty of time to think. I realize my dream of returning to Hope Valley and to my Beloved Shepherd is now just that, a dream—a dream that will never see the light of day, not after what I have done. I resign myself to the fact that I will spend the rest of my life working in the vineyard for my brothers and occasionally being allowed to care for sheep. That is the best I can hope for.

It is mid-afternoon when I return home. I quickly take the lamb to its mother who wastes no time inspecting the little one. Instead of expressing gratitude, my brothers chastise me for taking so long and send me off to work in the vineyard.[23] My tears fall like rain as I walk away.

Will this day never end?

The sun finally sets. Skipping the family meal, I hurry to my cot where I can be alone with my pain and shame. With my face buried in my pillow, I cry until I can cry no more. Oh, the pain that fills my soul!

What have I done? Whatever will I do? I have ruined my entire life. I am without hope. How could I have been so weak, so careless?

My heart and soul are in agony, preventing me from sleep, so I rise while it is still dark. Sitting before my tiny window, staring into the never ending night, I think back to the glorious days I spent with my Beloved Shepherd in the garden. He is so good and kind, so gentle and loving.

Why did I ever leave Him? What was I thinking? How will I ever endure the pain in my heart?

The longing and lovesickness I feel for my Beloved is replaced with guilt and shame.

I am forever ruined. I can never go back to Hope Valley, neither can I go forward. I am hopelessly trapped and destined to a future filled with pain and loneliness. If only I could go back in time and change the decisions I made, starting with my decision to leave Hope Valley and the Master Shepherd. But, that is impossible. I must face the reality that my actions have forever ruined any chance I ever had of knowing true happiness, of knowing true love.

I watch as the rising sun quickly consumes the deep

Rhonda Calhoun

darkness.

Oh, how I wish someone could do that for me!

There was a time when all I wanted was to be with my Beloved Shepherd and care for His flock. How peaceful and wonderful those days were! I cannot believe that I left Him in search of fame and fortune. I have compromised all that I hold dear.

It is sad, but I finally know who I am and what I truly desire and it is too late. The truth is I am a shepherdess who deeply loves the Master Shepherd, not a girl in love with the praise of men. I whisper to myself, "I would give anything if I could have a second chance."

The following weeks drag painfully by, and I find myself dreading each sunrise, for it only brings more shame and heartache. I have nothing to look forward to and everything to regret.

Compromise visits from time to time. He spends hours talking about things he knows nothing about, things like love, integrity, truth and honor. I listen, but say nothing. He does not love me, that is obvious, yet he relentlessly pursues me. I am nothing more than a trophy to be had, for he loves only one thing and that is himself. I know that now.

When Compromise is near I feel like a ship tossed on the ocean waves, like a reed blowing in the wind. My heart is desperately weak and I know it, so I refuse to be alone with him. There is only one good thing about his appearances; they remind me that a distracted heart soon becomes weak and its love can suddenly grow cold.[24]

Chapter Five
LILY OF THE VALLEY

Why should I be like one who veils herself? [25]

$\mathcal{I}$t has been ten months, two weeks, three days and twelve hours since my life ended under that awful tree. I cannot bear to think of it, yet I find myself thinking of it frequently because that brief moment in time changed my life forever.

It is Sunday morning, and I wake well before sunrise. I struggle to get out of bed. Until recently, being with the sheep was a source of comfort and medicine to my aching heart, but not anymore. I still love them, but the sense of joy and accomplishment that I felt from taking care of them is gone. Nothing matters anymore.

The flock seems anxious this morning. The sky is an angry grey color; a storm is clearly brewing and they know it.

After several hours of prodding, we finally arrive at the pasture near Mount Hermon. The sheep graze while I keep an eye out for predators. Because of the drought, the streams are dry, and the grass is sparse.

Once my flock has eaten what little grass there is, I lead them to the base of Mount Hermon. This mountain is quite steep and its barren, rocky terrain is very dangerous. People in these

Rhonda Calhoun

parts call this place the Mountain of Myrrh. Myrrh is the spice we use in our burial ceremonies. Everyone who has ever dared climb the Mountain of Myrrh has never been seen or heard from again. Whether it is the leopards, lions, or rugged terrain that devours them, no one really knows. The one thing that is certain is that no one climbs the Mountain of Myrrh and lives to tell about it.[26]

There is only one reason I bring my sheep to such a dangerous place and that is because of the calm pool of water situated at its base. Sheep will not drink from swift running water, which is a good thing because their heavy wool coats would cause them to drown if they were to get caught in a strong current. This pool is the only calm water for miles.

The arduous trek across the valley has exhausted my sheep so I make them lie down under a cleft in the rock. I dare not allow them to drink while they are so hot because it would make them quite ill and could possibly kill them.[27]

Exhausted more from the guilt and shame I feel than from my journey, I sit on a nearby rock and close my eyes. I must have dozed off because the next thing I know I wake to a sharp pain in my side.

Standing over me are my two brothers. The younger one says, "You're in trouble now, for you are asleep while the King's sheep have been devoured by wild animals."

I jump up looking for my flock. I quickly count them and find that none are missing. Giving my brother a dirty look, I grab my rod and staff and rouse the sheep. I lead them to the water's edge where they eagerly drink. I see Snowflake and her newly born twins, Faith and Hope. I push my way through the mass of sheep to their side. Scratching Snowflake's ear, I whisper, "You've grown to be such a pretty girl, and your babies are absolutely adorable."

With my other hand, I scratch Hope's belly. "You love being scratched just like your mother."

I laugh as she nestles closer. Out of the corner of my eye, I see my brothers watering the handful of sheep they brought with them. Hopefully, they will leave soon.

Once the sheep are satisfied, I gather them together and

call for them to follow me. They know my voice and quickly scramble behind me as I lead them on to the high pastures. My brothers follow.

I decide to be nice and try several times to have a friendly conversation with them, but it matters not what I say, they always find something to use against me. I finally give up and continue on in silence.

We arrive in the high pasture. It is quite lovely, and there is plenty of grass for the flock, but it is not nearly as lovely as Hope Valley. While the flock grazes, I sit on a fallen log and take out my lunch. My older brother sits beside me, clears his throat and says, "Little sister, I have a question for you. All this talk about the Master Shepherd loving you and feeding you from the King's garden. Do you really believe it, or are you just an ignorant girl living in a fantasy world?"

Unable to take anymore of their abuse, I shout, "Why must you constantly pick on me? And why do you treat me with such contempt? What have I ever done to you?"

He answers, "I'll tell you what you've done. All you do is talk about the Master Shepherd and how much he loves you. You think you're special, but you're not! You're no different from us. You work for the Master Shepherd taking care of his sheep, just like your brother and me. What makes you think he would want to spend time with you anyway? As for you being special, well, you can just forget that. You'll never be good enough to take our place!"[28]

"What? I've never tried to take your place and I've never claimed to be special! I don't even want your precious position! I don't even want the one I have!"

Talking more to myself than to them, I say, "There are only two things that I have ever really wanted and that is to know the Master Shepherd intimately and to become a good, kind shepherd like Him."

Overwhelmed by all that has happened, all that I have lost and my incredible failure, I throw my rod and staff down at their feet and shout, "You can have your precious job! I refuse to work for you one day more!"

My brother grabs my arm, but I pull myself free, leaving

my shawl in his hand. I run. I have no idea where I am going or what I will do. I just know that I have to get away. I run over the hills and through the valleys until I am unable to run anymore. I finally collapse in the midst of a deep valley where the tears that have been buried for months flow unhindered and without restraint until there are no more. Thoroughly exhausted, I roll onto my back. I am laying in a very large patch of snow-white lilies. There must be at least a hundred of them. I sit up and see that encircling the flowers are what appears to be thorn bushes.

That explains why my legs are cut and bleeding.

It seems strange to see such incredible beauty in the midst of such a dismal looking valley.[29]

It will be night soon, but that does not matter. Nothing matters anymore. Exhausted and feeling hopeless, I cry out, "Oh God, what have I done? What have I done?"

I watch as the sun slides behind the surrounding mountains. The moon and stars have not yet made their appearance. Surrounded by darkness, this valley appears even more foreboding.

I am alone, so painfully alone! Falling back, looking to heaven, I pray, "I am weak; I have failed You. I traded pure Love for a moment of earthly pleasure. Can You ever forgive me? I know that I don't deserve Your attention and I certainly don't deserve Your love, but I have nowhere else to turn. You are my only hope. If You won't come to me, if You won't embrace me, then my life is over."

Somehow the tears return.

After quite some time, the stars begin to peek out from behind the clouds. *I wonder if God even heard me, but then, why would He? I certainly have not done anything that would be worthy of His attention.*

In the distance, I hear something. It is quite faint, but grows closer and more distinct with each passing moment. Every nerve in my body is on high alert. I think I know this voice.

Can it be? Oh, I hope it is not!

Sitting up, I strain to hear. The words are now quite clear... I know this song—it is the Master Shepherd's song, and it is none other than He who approaches. My mind, filled with guilt and shame, demands that I run away, but my love-starved heart compels me to wait and hope and believe that maybe, just maybe He will be merciful to me and forgive me.

My shattered heart wins the tug-of-war as I scramble to my feet. Ever so weak, yet fueled by childlike devotion, I run and fall on my face before Him. In a matter of minutes, a river of tears wash the dust from His feet. I dry them with the only thing I have—my hair.[30] I am filled with a mixture of love, guilt, joy, fear, hope and shame.

What will He do; what will He say when I tell Him what I have done? Will He reject me? Will He tell me how awful I am? Will He punish me? Will He send me away?

Taking a deep breath, I dare to look up. His look is one of great tenderness. Quickly lowering my eyes, I plead, "Oh please, Good Shepherd, do not look at me for I have been unfaithful to You. I return to You covered in shame. My garments are filthy rags. If I had a veil, I would cover my face from Your loving gaze."[31]

Quietly and ever so gently, He responds, "And that would be a shame because you look so beautiful to Me!"

He kneels before me, taking my rough, calloused hands in His. My hands reveal how diligently I have labored, and for what? For nothing more than a few shiny trinkets that were quickly spent and for the ever elusive praise of man that brings only momentary satisfaction. How empty, how vain it all seems now!

My guilty heart agonizes over being so close to Him, and I pull my hands from His grasp, hiding them beneath my skirt. Looking up, I say, "Please, kind Shepherd, if You knew what I have done, You would send me away and rightfully so."

"Child, I know everything—every act, every thought, every motive and every heartache. I know it all, and I forgive you," He says gently.

"But I have done all the wrong things. I left You for the things this world has to offer. I soon discovered the pleasures of this world were fleeting, so I tried to fill my emptiness with the approval of man. And, if that wasn't bad enough, I gave in to Compromise, and the sun burned me, and now—. Well, now I am dark and—."[32]

"And, you look lovely," He states, taking my hands in His again.

"I don't understand? How can I look lovely to You when I have been unfaithful?"

"I look at your heart."

"My heart is deceitfully wicked,"

"I have covered you with garments of salvation and wrapped you with My robe of righteousness.[33] When I look at you, I see *My* beauty and *My* righteousness, which makes you as lovely as these pure, white lilies." He says as He picks one and hands it to me.

"But, I have betrayed You in the worst way," I respond, trembling.

Pressing His finger ever so gently against my lips, He whispers, "Shhhhh."

"But...."

"Welcome back, dear one. I have missed you greatly and love you still!"

"But...."

"There is nothing for you to worry about. You are forgiven and when I forgive sins, they are remembered no more. In My eyes, it is the same as if it never happened," He says.

"But I...."

He brushes His hand against my cheek saying, "If you were to ask Me about your sins, I could not recall them. My blood doesn't just cover sins, it washes them away, making you clean and brand new. All that consumes My thoughts now is the fact that you have returned to Me; you have come home."

He wraps His arms around me; I fall back against His chest and allow myself to be held in His warm embrace for a long, long time.

"You must be thirsty," He says.

"I feel nothing but peace and safety."

"That is how it should be, My love."

"It has been so long. I didn't believe I would ever feel this way again," I say.

"I have missed you greatly," He whispers.

"There's no place like home," I say as tears stream down my face. He holds me until I let Him go. He then hands me His water pouch. My hands are shaking so much that I spill water all over myself.

He wipes my chin with the back of His hand and says, "As far as the east is from the west, that is how far I have removed your sins.[34] I do not dwell on them, neither do I remember them. I love you dearly and am so happy you have returned to Me. I have missed you more than you can comprehend."

Whether it is His words, the refreshing water, or both, I do not know, but my weary heart and body suddenly feel energized. "If You say that I look lovely...."

"Yes?"

"Then, I must be lovely, for everyone knows that it is impossible for the Master Shepherd to lie."[35]

"You are right; it is impossible for Me to lie, and you do look lovely."

Joy floods my heart and I jump to my feet. Running and spinning and laughing, I shout, "I look lovely! The Master Shepherd says I look lovely!"

Dizzy, I fall to the grass, laughing and crying all at once. My Beloved Shepherd sits beside me; He is smiling. I force myself to look into His eyes. I can still see the love I knew before, but something is different; He is different. What is it about His face?

I sit up. In the darkness, I see horrible looking scars across His forehead. "What has happened to You? What are those wounds?" I ask.

"These wounds are evidence of the magnitude of My love for you."

"I don't understand."

"You will, but now is not the time to talk of such things."

I suddenly feel totally exhausted and quite chilly. My Beloved covers me with His cloak. "We will talk more later. It is time for you to rest now, My love."

I curl up next to Him. Brushing my hair from my face, He says, "My mercy is new every morning; therefore, hope in Me. Great is My faithfulness. Sleep well, My love."[36]

Rhonda Calhoun

I look into the eyes of pure love and whisper, "I am refreshed, even though my body is exhausted. I am at peace, even though my heart is dark. I am filled with hope, even though my future is uncertain. And I am at rest, for my Beloved is with me."

I sleep peacefully for the first time since leaving Hope Valley. I wake a couple of times during the night and, each time, the Master Shepherd is singing over me, washing and flooding my heart with the unconditional love I so desperately need and have been secretly longing for.

How good it is to be back with my Friend. There is no place on earth I would rather be.

Chapter Six
DARK BUT LOVELY

Do not stare at me because I am black. [37]

$\mathcal{I}$ wake to the sound of distant laughter. Disoriented, I look around and discover that the Master Shepherd is gone and I am alone. Images of Him singing over me flood my heart and soul.

Was it all just a dream?

I scan the valley for Him but see only a group of young girls quickly approaching. Smoothing my tangled hair and wrinkled robe, I stand; something falls at my feet. Joy of all joys — it is my Beloved Shepherd's cloak! Hugging it, I spin around exclaiming, "It's true; it's really true! The Master Shepherd was here! He did sing over me! He does care about me! He did forgive me! He loves me still!"

As the girls draw near, I work hard at gathering my composure. I manage to do so with the exception of my face; I am sure that I am glowing. They call out to me. I recognize most of them. They are friends from my village — innocent and sweet, but painfully immature. At first they do not recognize me, and when they do, they draw back in fear, except for Charity who charges up to me saying, "Look at you! Whatever has happened to you?! Your fair complexion is ruined. The sun has burned you and you're so dark and you're so —."

Untouched by her rude remarks, I interrupt. "Charity, don't look at me like that. I know I'm dark.[38] My brothers[39] were jealous of me. Their jealousy quickly turned to anger so they made me caretaker of the vineyard, which is the lowly work of a servant. I was made to bear the burden and heat of the day. My own family rejected me so I worked even longer and harder in an effort to earn their approval. I did whatever they asked me to do. I tried to be the best worker they had ever had. In the process, I neglected to cultivate my relationship with the Master Shepherd, which was a fatal mistake.

"You see, Charity, in pursuing the approval of man, I forgot about the most important thing in life and that is being a friend to my beloved Shepherd. I was so busy working that I didn't take care of my own heart, therefore the love I felt for the Master Shepherd soon grew cold. It wasn't very long before I found myself surrendering to Compromise."[40]

Shaking her head, Charity responds, "Oh, you poor, pitiful thing."

"Charity, don't feel sorry for me. It is true that, on the outside, I am as dark and rough as the goatskin tents of the nomads,[41] which are weather-beaten and burned by the sun. But, because of the great mercies of the Master Shepherd, on the inside, I am as white and smooth as the curtains hanging in the most Holy Place.[42]"

"How is that possible? You should find a pond and take a good look at yourself! You are dark! And you certainly don't look anything like the beautiful, wrinkle-free curtain hanging in the temple!" she replies.

"You don't have to tell me that I'm dark — I know that all too well. I also know that I am like the rose of Sharon, a simple, insignificant, blood-red flower that creeps along the ground, a flower that people walk on, a flower that is considered a weed and is hidden from the eyes of man. I have been a rose of Sharon my whole life. But, I am also like a snow-white lily growing in a beautiful valley, for the Master Shepherd told me so."[43]

"Are you saying that the Master Shepherd told you that

you were like a lily? Have you lost your mind? He finds *you* lovely? What is this ridiculous talk? The Master Shepherd is the greatest shepherd in the entire world. He would never call you beautiful!"

"But, He did!"

"In your dreams maybe, but certainly not in real life. He is important and He is kind, but He's not that kind!" she replies.

"But Charity, He was here last night and I told Him how I left Him to pursue my own pleasures. He forgave me and He...."

Charity interrupts, "He forgave you? What is this talk? You are a silly girl, one not worth wasting my time on and certainly not worth the time of the Master Shepherd."

"Charity, you don't know Him like I do. If you did, you could believe what I am saying. He is kind and loving and forgiving. He is patient and unselfish and not willing for anyone to leave His side."

"I do not care to hear any more of your crazy talk," she says as she arrogantly spins around and rejoins her friends. They walk away laughing and talking about some childish game they cannot wait to play. There was a time in my life when such trivial things consumed my thoughts and my time, but not anymore—I now love too much and feel too deeply. I am held captive by the love of a Shepherd.

Collapsing on the ground, clutching His cloak close to my heart, I whisper, "Master Shepherd, I love You, and I will wait forever for You to come."

I soon fall asleep and dream of running with my Beloved Shepherd on the mountains and in the valleys.

Rhonda Calhoun

Chapter Seven
MOST BEAUTIFUL AMONG WOMEN

Where do you pasture your flock?[44]

I hear His voice. Searching the valley, I see Him walking towards me. Not waiting for Him to come, I hurry to meet Him. I am well aware that I do not deserve His kind affections, which only causes me to love Him all the more. Falling at His feet, I cry out, "I am lost without You!"

"No longer lost, but found by Me."

"May I never be separated from You again!"

"Nothing can separate you from My love. Now rise up, My beautiful one and come away with Me," He responds as He takes me by the hand and helps me to my feet.

"I know that I'm like a small, insignificant flower surrounded by incredible beauty. I am like this lily with a weak stem growing in the midst of a green, lush valley. I am nothing when compared to others. I wish I had not left You, but I pray that from this day forward, anytime I run, it will be to You and not away from You. May I never run into the arms of another for as long as I live! Do whatever You need to do in my life to keep me, I pray!"

"How lovely you look!" He responds. "It is true; you are

like a lily among thorns. You believe that everyone else is beautiful, valuable and desirable. You see yourself as dark, insignificant and simple. You say that you are insignificant, but I say that you are the most noble of all flowers. You are tall and stately like the lily. You are dressed in My righteousness and are being transformed into My likeness. You are pure, humble and lovely. There is no flower as productive as the lily, which can have as many as fifty bulbs hidden underground. It is true that it has a weak stem; I created it that way. I am not asking you to be strong in yourself, but to lean on Me and allow Me to be your strength. You look beautiful even in your weakness.

"I do not wait for you to become perfect before enjoying you. On the contrary, I enjoy you just as you are, while you are growing and maturing into the glorious bride that you are destined to be. You are a lily among thorns, My love. The truth is that your outstanding beauty causes everyone and everything outside of My kingdom to look like thorns."[45]

I reply, "You are indeed kind to me."

"I am kind, but it is not My kindness that causes Me to proclaim your beauty. I call you lovely because I see the end from the beginning. When I look at you, I see who you will be for all eternity. In My eyes, believing souls are absolutely beautiful and completely desirable. I do not wait until you have matured and are wholeheartedly devoted to Me before I am able to enjoy you. On the contrary, I enjoy watching you grow and thoroughly delight in you just as you are."

I ponder His words. *What kind of Man is this?*

I have never known such love, such kindness, such mercy, such grace. "Tell me, You whom my soul loves, where do You feed those You love? For I am hungry, and only Your food can satisfy this poor heart. Tell me, where do You make Your sheep lie down during the hottest part of the day? For I am weary and in need of rest that only You can give. Tell me where I can go to fellowship with You, for I am in great need of Your company.

"In the midst of my failures, I have discovered that You are all I need. Why should I go elsewhere to search for what only You have? To do so would be shameful."[46]

He responds, "You ask where I feed My flock? Oh most

beautiful among women, if you do not know then follow the well-worn path of the shepherds. Follow those who have gone before you, and they will lead you to My feeding place. Do not withdraw in isolation, but stay in relationship with those who have charge over you. Pitch your tent beside the shepherds,[47] for that is where you will find Me and that is where you will find nourishment for your soul."[48]

I take a step back. *Is He telling me to return to my brothers? I cannot do that. They rejected me and overworked me and certainly did not understand or support me. And besides, the thought of leaving my Beloved Shepherd is unbearable.*

He takes my trembling hand and says, "Dull hearts are uncomfortable around burning hearts; you experienced that with your family. I know you have been hurt and rejected, but you must not forsake or reject them.

"It is important for you to do only what I ask you to do, nothing more and nothing less. Do not work to please man and do not work to please Me, for you already please Me. Seek love first. Love Me and love others, for that is why you were created. I am all you need. I will care for you just as I care for the lilies of the field. Seek Me first, and I will meet all your needs.

"Now is not the time to draw back in fear. Now is the time to move forward empowered by My great love. It is time for you to rise up and overcome those things that hinder you from walking in full partnership with Me. You must not fear, for I am always with you and will provide all that you need."[49]

I know His words are true, but I cannot bear the thought of returning to my family. They hurt, used and rejected me. I whisper, "Master Shepherd, I love you, but I cannot go back. I just can't."

For the longest time He stares into my pain-filled eyes. Then, without a word, He brings my hand to His lips. He lightly kisses my fingertips, my hand, my arm, my forehead and then steps back. I remember my failure with Compromise. The huge, gaping wound in my heart causes me to look away filled with shame and fear.

My Shepherd responds, "My love, you need to know that I am not like any other on this earth. There is no one like Me, for

Rhonda Calhoun

I am gracious and merciful, slow to anger, and abounding in lovingkindness.[50] I am your keeper, your shade from the sun. I will protect you from all evil and keep your soul. I will guard your going out and your coming in from this time forth and forever.[51] You have nothing to fear and no reason to be ashamed, for I am your righteousness."

Lifting my chin, He follows the tracks of my tears with His fingers. "You need not cry, for I love you with the purest of love, and I will heal your broken heart and restore to you all that was lost."

I fall into His arms. He holds me close while humming a most wonderful tune. I quickly forget my pain as He comforts my soul, filling me with love and peace.

"That is the most beautiful tune I have ever heard. What is it called?" I ask.

"It is called the Song of the Lamb," He answers, as He picks one of the many lilies growing all around us.

Handing it to me, He says, "I give you this lily as a reminder that you are like this flower. And to remind you that I will take care of you, that I am all you need.[52]

"I know it is difficult for you to trust Me, but look at these lilies. They do not work neither, do they sow, yet they are gloriously arrayed. I tell you, even king Solomon in all his glory was not dressed as well as one of these.

"Look how well My Father clothes the grass of the field, which is alive today and tomorrow is thrown into the furnace. Will He not much more do so for you? He is able to not only provide you with food, clothing, and shelter, but He will also provide you with beautiful garments of righteousness. He will make you like this lily, productive, pure and innocent. You have nothing to fear, for you will be well cared for."

His words are like fresh water to my parched soul. Shame and fear are dealt a crushing blow as my heart soars. "Thank You for loving me!"

"It is My pleasure," He says, smiling.

Picking a handful of lilies, He says, "Now, come with Me, for we have a long journey ahead of us. Tomorrow you shall dine with My Father."

"Your Father?"

"Yes, My Father!"

As we travel, my Beloved tells me many stories of His Father's awesome power and generous exploits, which makes the miles pass so quickly that I am unaware of the fact that we just climbed the last mountain separating us from Hope Valley. I look up and my breath catches in my throat. There, stretched before me, is the most beautiful place on earth, the place I thought I would never see again!

The sun is just beginning to disappear behind the snow-capped mountains. The sun paints the sky with various shades of pink, red, and gold. The winding river reflects the breathtaking sky like a mirror. A friendly breeze causes the knee-high grass to wave a thousand welcomes.

How beautiful and wonderful this place is!

I fall on my knees weeping.

How could I have ever left?

Taking my hand, my Shepherd says, "All is well now. Come, I have built a place for you.[53] There you will be safe and well cared for and will find healing for your wounded heart. In this place, you will find perfect love, which casts out all fear."

My Shepherd leads me to a quaint cottage hidden just under the clefts of the Lebanon Mountain and overlooking the King's garden. A Man dressed in a white linen robe waits at the door. My Beloved embraces Him with great affection. Taking my hand, He says, "I would like you to meet Comforter. He is My best Friend and will soon be yours. He will help prepare you for the days that are yet to be."[54]

Comforter extends His hand. I nervously take it. He bears an amazing resemblance to the Master Shepherd—they could be twins. My Beloved bids me good-night, promising to return for me on the morrow. I watch as He crosses the palace grounds and disappears into the darkness.

"You will see Him tomorrow, Lovely Lady," Comforter says.

Startled, I jump; I had forgotten He was here.

"Perhaps you would like something to eat after your long journey?" He asks.

Rhonda Calhoun

"Yes, thank You. I am quite hungry."

The cottage is lovely. Its beams are made of cedar and its rafters of cypress.[55] What a lovely dwelling place! One that is expertly crafted and will never rot. It is pleasing to both sight and smell. It brings me great comfort to know that my Shepherd chose a permanent dwelling place for me and not a tent. And to think that He built this just for me is almost more than I can imagine.

Comforter leads me to a small table, which is covered with delicious looking food. He holds my chair and then fills my cup, saying, "True service, Lovely Lady, is pouring out all you have, your very self, on the ones you love. And if that should be all that He allows you to do in this life, then it is enough."

I know not how to respond.

Comforter continues, "At the end of the day, when the darkness falls, the real question is, has the King been satisfied?'"

"I do not know how to love this way, Comforter."

"You will, Lovely Lady, you will," He says as He fills my plate.

"Kind Sir, I am not accustomed to being waited on, for I am the one who has served others."

"It is my joy and pleasure to serve you, Lovely Lady."

The food tastes better than any meal I have ever eaten. I am much hungrier than I realized and eat more than I ever thought possible. Afterwards, I rise to clear the table, but Comforter stops me, saying, "I will do that. You must be exhausted. Come, I will show you to your room."

Opening the door at the end of a short hallway, He says, "Let me know if there is anything else you need."

"Good-night and thank You for everything."

"Good-night, Lovely Lady."

I shut the door and fall back against it. "He called me, "Lovely Lady'!"

The sweet fragrance of flowers fills the air. A blazing fire casts its golden, dancing light throughout the room. Numerous oil lamps, strategically placed around the room, drive out the darkness. A dozen or so vases, filled with miniature lilies, remind me of my Beloved's words. In the center of the room is a large mahogany bed with a most beautiful white lace canopy. The covers are folded back and lying on the pillow is a large bouquet of beautiful, snow-white lilies.

Is this real, or am I dreaming?

The crackling of the fire seems real enough. The door handle feels real in my hand. The smooth, wooden floor feels real enough under my bare feet. Perhaps, it is true that I have been rescued from a life of hopelessness and despair and brought to a place where I can find healing and restoration. Maybe, just maybe I will find true love.

Sitting on the edge of the bed, I bury my face in the bouquet enjoying its sweet fragrance.

How wonderful!

On the night table is a golden vase filled with water just waiting for the flowers. I make them wait no longer, placing the lilies in their new home.

I am a lily in a new home, drinking deeply of kindness. I have done nothing to deserve the Master Shepherd's forgiveness and acceptance. I actually deserve just the opposite; I deserve to be punished because I was guilty. But, the lovingkindness of the Master Shepherd is greater than my sins and greater than any love I have ever known.

I look up and see, draped over the back of a chair, an elegant nightgown. A pair of matching slippers are tucked just under the edge of the chair. "Someone has thought of everything," I whisper.

Looking around the room, I say to myself, "I only wish I had some water."

Seeing a wash basin, I hurry over expecting to find it empty, but to my surprise and delight, it is filled with warm water. A bar of soap lies on a cloth beside a neatly folded towel. The soap smells wonderful.

It feels so good to wash away the dust from my journey, to have a new start.

Ready for bed and suddenly feeling quite exhausted, I slide my feet under the bed covers. To my surprise, a scroll is tucked just under the edge of my pillow. The scroll is sealed with wax and bears the mark of the King. Trembling, I read:

Rhonda Calhoun

The Lion and the Lamb

My Beautiful One,

I am so happy you have returned to Me; I knew you would. You look just as beautiful as ever, even more so, if that is possible.

How can I describe your beauty? If I compared you to My favorite mare, which is adorned with splendid jewels and golden tassels, a most elegant, valuable, beautiful and outstanding mare—even then, My description would be grossly lacking. You are unaware of the strength of your heart and the beauty that I see within you.[56]

Your emotions are lovely to Me. Your cheeks, stained with tears of lovesickness, adorn you with great beauty.[57] On your neck are chains of gold; My divine character is being formed in you. You belong to royalty. You are loyal, true and resolute in your devotion to Me. You may feel weak and unworthy, but you are growing in grace and truth. I see the desire in your heart to please Me and that delights My heart more than you will ever know.[58]

My darling, you are already so beautiful, but how much more beautiful you will be in the days to come! My Father, Comforter and I will bestow upon you our richest gifts and greatest virtues.[59] We will make you an extravagant worshipper, for you have been redeemed by My life. You will become a woman of excellence who is fully devoted to Me and We will purify your heart.[60]

I want you to know that you are not a failure—one never fails until one fails to get up. Right now, because of what you have gone through, you view yourself as a sinner who sometimes loves God, but the truth is you are a lover of God who sometimes sins. Your true identity is that of a lover, not a sinner. Just like the lily, you are lovely, fragrant, innocent, pure and clothed in My splendor.

So, rest under the canopy of My love and dream of better days. Sleep well, most beautiful among women, for I am with you.[61]

Forever Yours,
The Master Shepherd

Chapter Eight
ROYAL GARMENTS

We will make for you ornaments of gold. [62]

$\mathscr{I}$ wake early, fully rested. Rays of sunlight stream through my open window, flooding my beautiful room with glorious light. I was so tired last night that I did not notice that the room is filled with lilies—the wallpaper, paintings, coverlet, curtains, everything. On the mantle, in a golden vase, is a huge arrangement of lilies.

Eager to see my surroundings in the light of day, I hurry to the window. A small, brown dog scampers across the yard surprising a flock of sleeping ducks. A shepherd, leading his sheep out of the sheepfold, calls to a wandering lamb. Not so far away, a rooster announces the arrival of a new day.

I turn to put on my tattered clothes and see draped across the back of the chair a beautiful lavender dress. Its exquisite beauty captivates me so I hurry for a closer look.

Carefully running my fingertips along the bodice, I am in awe of the workmanship. I have never seen such wonderful embroidery or finery. The lace-covered bodice is adorned with hundreds of miniature pearls and tiny gemstones. Threads of gold are woven throughout the bodice. [63]

Rhonda Calhoun

I hold it against my body and look in the mirror. The skirt is ever so full and appears to be made of satin. At least, I think it's satin. I have never really seen satin so I can only guess.

I can only imagine what it would be like to wear something this extravagant. I quickly and carefully lay it back on the chair smoothing out the skirt. That is when I see the note lying on the nearby table. It reads:

My Love,
　　I pray that you slept well. I so look forward to introducing you to My Father; He already loves you so.
　　This dress is My gift to you. I purchased it at a dear price. It was made exclusively for you; it fits none other. It is with great joy and a thankful heart that I give it to you.
　　Enjoy your day. Rest, and allow Comforter to do what He does best and that is to serve you. See you at My Father's house this evening.

Forever,
Your Shepherd and Friend

This elegant dress is for me? I can hardly believe it! With great care and trembling hands, I try it on. It is a perfect fit and so beautiful! Looking in the mirror, I cannot believe my eyes—I actually look a little pretty!

Can this be real?

I twirl around, enjoying the swishing sound the layers of fabric make as they sweep through the air. Growing dizzy I stop, but my dress does not, and I find myself giggling like a school girl. But, my joy quickly fades away as I look down at my bare feet. I have neither sandals nor shoes, for poor servants wear neither.

Whatever will I do?

A knock on the door interrupts my anxious thoughts. Composing myself, I open the door and find Comforter holding a pair of beautiful white slippers. He smiles and says, "You look lovely."

Blushing, I look away.

"I thought you might like these," He says as He hands me the shoes.

"Are...are these really for me?" I ask, looking up.

"They are indeed."

I have never worn shoes. *What is happening? Am I awake or am I dreaming?*

I slip my foot into the shoe. "Thank You, Comforter!"

I look into the kind eyes of my newly found Friend and say, "I'm not yet convinced that I am not dreaming, Comforter. I'm so afraid that I am going to wake and find myself back in the vineyard chasing foxes and pruning vines."

"Have no fear, Lovely Lady; you have only just begun to live."

Admiring my beautiful dress and fancy shoes, I ask, "How did You know what size I wear?"

Smiling broadly He answers, "Lovely Lady, I know everything there is to know about you. You will find all the apparel that you need, including more shoes, in the closet."

"Oh, thank You, Comforter!"

"Once you have changed, perhaps you would like some fruit from the King's garden?"

"I would love some."

I quickly, but ever so carefully lay my gown across the bed, choosing instead a simple, light blue linen dress. Rinsing my face in the basin, I am shocked to find that the water is still warm.

How is that possible?

This is another one of the many mysteries that seem to be increasingcoming fairly common.

Hurrying down the hallway, I am flooded by the delicious aroma of fresh baked bread. The table is set with milk, a large variety of fresh fruits and hot bread complete with butter and jam. Everything tastes wonderful, and I eat until I can eat no more.

"Lovely Lady, you have been invited to dine with the King of kings this evening. What would you like to do until then?" Comforter asks.

"If I could choose, then I would do nothing but sit under the shade of that old walnut tree by the stream."

Rhonda Calhoun

"Then that is exactly what we will do. I will prepare a picnic lunch for you."

"Comforter, you are such a dear servant to me. Why?"

"All that I do, I do for love, " He answers.

I look at this Man who looks so much like my Shepherd and wonder how He could love me so quickly. He barely knows me, yet He seems to know everything about me.

"It is rare to find love that is given without strings attached or demands made," I respond.

Holding the chair for me, He replies, "In this world, sadly, that is often true, but there is a place where love of this nature rules and reigns. There is a place that is filled with a love that is not self-serving but pure and peaceable, esteeming others as greater than oneself rather than using them for selfish gain."

"I would love to live in a place like that. I would also love to know this kind of love and be able to love that way," I respond.

"And so you shall, Lovely Lady. The day will come when you will walk in the love of your King. You will freely give yourself away for His sake and for the sake of others."

After clearing the table, Comforter leads me to my old, familiar tree. I soon discover that Comforter is quite delightful and so much like the Master Shepherd.

Comforter talks to me of many things, things like love, commitment and truth. He has tremendous insights into every subject I introduce and is a wonderful Teacher. He remains close by my side throughout the day. This brings much peace to my timid and still very fragile heart. He seems to know just when I need to talk and when I need to be quiet. He has the most amazing ability to say just the right things at just the right time.

The day passes rather quickly, and Comforter announces that it is time to return to the cottage and dress for dinner. Walking barefoot across the valley, sandals in hand, Comforter singing softly by my side, it suddenly occurs to me that I am about to meet the King. Not just any king, but *the* King! I exclaim, "Oh, my, this is really happening! It is real! I am really here, and I am really going to meet the King!"

Twirling around, I laugh with the freedom of a young child. Comforter laughs with me and responds, "Yes, Lovely

Lady, this is more real than anything you have ever known, and you will dine with the King this day."

"Comforter, what will I do? I don't know how to act around a King! I know nothing about proper manners and social graces. I don't know which fork to use on what food," I say, acknowledging just how unrefined I am.

Comforter seems to be quite amused by my dilemma. "You will be just fine, Lovely Lady. Remember that I am here to help you. Speaking of helping you, perhaps you would like Me to assist in styling your hair for your dinner party?"

"Is there anything You don't do, Comforter?"

"Yes, there are limits to what I will do. For example, I will never go against your will. Throughout your life, I will encourage you and speak plainly to you, but you will be the one who must decide whether or not you are going to listen to My counsel. The decision will always be yours."

Having said that, Comforter reaches out and touches my shoulder saying, "Tag, you're it!" He then takes off running. Wasting no time, I set out after Him. Grabbing His sleeve, I say, "Now, You're it," and I run like the wind, but not fast enough. Within minutes, He tags me saying, "Lovely Lady, always run after Me, and I will always make sure you catch Me."

His words impact me greatly. I file them away knowing that I am receiving nuggets of infinite wisdom.

We laugh most of the way back to the cottage. Comforter loves to laugh, and I am beginning to remember just how wonderful it is myself.

As Comforter styles my hair, I ask him a million questions about the King. He enjoys talking about Him as much as I love hearing about Him. Laying down my brush, He says, "My favorite thing to do in this life is to reveal the character, beauty and nature of your King. Speaking of beauty—look in the mirror, Lovely Lady."

Looking up, I cannot believe my eyes! My auburn hair looks stunning! Delicate curls frame my face and neck. Comforter has placed tiny gemstones throughout my hair. It looks absolutely perfect and so does my dress and shoes—everything is perfect, everything, that is, except me. I know I will never be perfect, I proved that with Compromise. Sadness fills my heart. Comforter lovingly places His hand on my shoulder.

"Comforter, I do not belong here. I don't deserve any of this. I am just a poor shepherd girl who has nothing to offer the King except a horribly flawed and extremely weak heart. I am certain there has been some awful mistake. The King will take one look at me and tell the Master Shepherd to send me home."

"You love the Master Shepherd, is that not true?"

"It is true that I love Him, but I lack any virtue, and I am dreadfully weak."

"When your Beloved Shepherd looks at you, He sees the desire to please Him that resides in your heart, Lovely Lady."

"It is all I have to give, Comforter. I can pledge nothing more than the heartfelt love that grows within."

"And that is the most important thing your Beloved desires, for He knows that if you love Him, you will obey Him."

I respond, "It is my only treasure, but I cannot truly say that it is mine, for my Beloved is the One who placed this love in my heart, and He is the One who continues to fan its flame. Without Him, it would surely die, as I painfully experienced so many months ago. Comforter, I so wish I had something grand to give the Master Shepherd."

"Lovely Lady, your voluntary love is what He most desires, for a heart in love will give everything to the object of its affection."

"Oh, that I might love Him in such a way that, even if I should ever desire to leave Him, I would not succeed in doing so. Comforter, would you fan the tiny flame of love in my heart in such a way that I would never again be focused on myself or on my own ambitions? From this day forward, I desire to walk in my Shepherd's footsteps and love Him without reservation," I reply.

"And so you shall, Lovely Lady."

Comforter reaches into His pocket and removes a small leather pouch tied with a red ribbon. Placing it in my hand He says, "I have a gift for you from your Shepherd, His Father and Myself."

Nestled in the bottom of the pouch is a beautiful gold

bracelet. The delicate chain is adorned with three silver hearts.[64]

"Comforter, it is so lovely," I say as I stand before Him, "but I could never wear anything this valuable," I say, handing it back.

His eyes are filled with acceptance, kindness and love. "You are the one who is valuable," Comforter says as He places the bracelet back in my hand.

My tears flow like a river as shame and unworthiness weigh heavy on my heart. Comforter holds me close while humming a song that the Master Shepherd has sung to me many times. Knowing my thoughts, He whispers, "Your Shepherd's song is true. Allow me to sing it over you, Lovely Lady.

The King's daughter is all glorious within;
Your clothing is interwoven with gold.
You will be led to the King dressed in beautiful,
embroidered garments.

The maidens who follow you,[65]
Will be brought to the King as well.
They will be led forth with gladness and rejoicing;
They will enter into the King's palace.[66]

"No one here expects you to be perfect. Your imperfections have already been taken care of. You must not trust in your ability to be good or to live a perfect life, but rather trust in your King's ability to be your strength, your source, your everything. This is the only true security there is. You will become all that you were created to be, not because of your strength or determination, but because He is Life itself. Remember the lilies of the field, they neither toil nor spin and your Father adorns them with garments much finer than king Solomon's. If He adorns the flowers in such a glorious way, how much more will He do for you, the one He loves?

"The beauty of your heart will cause many to follow you into the King's chambers. You will be transformed because of perfect love. We will see to that."[67]

Rhonda Calhoun

"Comforter, I feel so frightened and ashamed when I think of what I did."

Gently lifting my chin, He continues, "You believe that because your love was weak that it was not real, but that is not true. Immaturity and weakness are not the same as rebellion. Your Shepherd responds to rebellion far differently than He does to immaturity and human weakness.

"You have nothing to fear, for you are greatly loved. Your past is over and forgotten. In your Shepherd's eyes, it is as if it never happened. You have been set free, Lovely Lady, and you are deeply loved. In the days ahead you will come to know your Beloved intimately and then you will never suffer the pain of the shame and guilt from your past again."

I take His hand. "You are so kind to me."

"I can be nothing other than that, for that is who I am. Now, may I fasten this token of Our affection on your arm?"

"Yes, my Friend," I respond, holding out my arm. "This is a gift that I will treasure forever."

I look in the mirror and am surprised at the lovely reflection staring back at me. Painfully aware of my past, I whisper, "I may be dark, but the Master Shepherd finds me lovely."[68]

Comforter responds, "You are a lily among thorns. You are beautiful and absolutely delightful."

"I pray that one day I might be made whole, for my heart has suffered great damage and I feel so very weak."

"You shall be victorious, Lovely Lady. We shall heal you, restore all that has been stolen from you and raise you up to be more than a conqueror. Now, may I have the honor and privilege of escorting you to the palace? After all, one should not keep the King waiting."

"I thought the Master Shepherd was going to introduce me to the King?"

"He will, but I am to lead you to Him."

"I am glad You are coming with me," I say taking His arm. "It feels as though I have known You my entire life."

"You have, Lovely Lady, you have."

The Affectionate Father

Chapter Nine
THE KING'S TABLE

How beautiful you are, my darling, how beautiful you are! [69]

$\mathcal{C}$omforter leads me through the massive, ornate palace doors into a room that is larger than any house I have ever seen or dreamed of. He escorts me down a long hallway, which is lined with servants dressed in white. They smile and nod in such a friendly manner that it makes me feel as if they know me.

Halfway down the hall, we pass a set of double doors behind which lively music is being played. Stopping, I ask, "Comforter, what's in that room?"

"That would be the ballroom, Lovely Lady. Would you like to go in?"

"May I?"

"One need only ask," He responds, opening the door.

Standing in the doorway, I cannot believe my eyes. This must be the largest and most glorious ballroom in the entire world! The floor appears to be made of clear glass; a river of fire appears to be flowing beneath it. The room is filled with couples spinning and twirling gracefully as heavenly music fills the air. Everyone looks like they are perfectly happy.

I have never danced and do not even know how. That is

Rhonda Calhoun

not something a shepherd girl gets to do, but I have often wondered what it would be like to dance with the one you love.

I am perfectly content to watch the dancers until I notice, on the far side of the room, a lone man pacing back and forth. His head is down and his arms are behind his back. He appears to be involved in a serious conversation with himself or perhaps he is praying, I am not sure which. I cannot make out his appearance, but there is something about this man that fascinates me. I stand on my tiptoes trying to get a better look, but a multitude of dancers continually block my view.

It is not a conscious decision, I am just so drawn to him that I find myself making my way through the sea of dancers. All the while, trying to see his face.

The closer I get, the better I can see him. He is tall and thin with nearly shoulder-length dark hair and a not-so-full beard. He is dressed in a most handsome white tuxedo with a red cummerbund. A red rose adorns his lapel. I catch only a brief glimpse of his face. I cannot say that his outward appearance is particularly handsome, but there is something about this man that is absolutely irresistible.[70]

I am standing just a few feet away when he looks my way. I cannot believe my eyes! This man, dressed in the finest apparel I have ever seen, is none other than the Master Shepherd!

Our eyes meet and, for what seems like a very long time, I do nothing but gaze into the depths of perfect Love. He takes a step toward me. I feel myself blushing and look away. My heart races. He now stands directly in front of me. Unable to look into His eyes, I stare at His feet. He gently lifts my chin and says, "You have made My heart beat faster with just one glance of your eyes."[71]

"And you have captured my affections," I respond, my voice shaking like a leaf in the wind.

I see such love in His eyes — a love that burns with intensity like coals of fire, consuming and piercing, yet gentle and ever so compassionate. It is obvious that He is captivated by my appearance, but why? Looking down, I realize that this is the first time He has ever seen me dressed in anything other than rags.

It's the dress that He finds beautiful.

Kissing the back of my hand, He addresses my unspoken thoughts saying, "The dress *is* lovely and it does look great on you, but *you* are what makes the dress beautiful, My love. *You* are the one I find captivating."

"Me?" The word is so faint that it barely makes it past my lips.

"Yes, you."

Gratitude mixed with love is greater than my fear and I exclaim, "Thank You. Thank You for everything! Thank You for this dress, the bracelet, the flowers and the cottage! Thank You for inviting me here! Thank You for introducing me to Comforter! And thank You for not rejecting me after I rejected You!" Tears of appreciation spill down my cheeks.

"It is My pleasure to love you unconditionally. I will never stop doing good to you, for you are My treasured possession."

I feel myself blushing again; I turn away. Once again, He lifts my chin and says, "How beautiful is your love!"

Not knowing how to respond and feeling extremely uncomfortable with all the attention, I change the subject. "So, who are all these people?" I ask, looking around the room.

Without taking His eyes from me, He answers, "This is the King's royal court and they are His loyal subjects."[72]

"May I be so bold as to ask why You are not dancing?"

"There are queens and maidens without number here, but they hold no attraction to Me. There is only one I desire and that is you. You are the one I love, and I have been waiting for you."[73]

"For me?"

"Yes, for you."

He bows, takes my hand, and asks, "Will you dance with Me, most beautiful among women?"

Lowering my head, I answer, "In the fields, watching my sheep, I have often dreamed of dancing with You. I even practiced, not that I ever thought it would happen. There is nothing on this earth that I would rather do, but I have this small problem." I look around and then lean close whispering, "I have never really danced before; I don't know how."

Rhonda Calhoun

I expected Him to laugh at me, but instead He leans forward and whispers in my ear, "It is not necessary for you to know how to dance when you dance with the One who loves you."

"But, how will I know what to do?"

"I will lead you and show you the way. As you follow My lead, I will cause you to shine so that others might see My beauty and glorify My Father, for that is My greatest joy."

With fear and trembling, I agree to try. He leads me to the center of the dance floor. With just one nod from Him, the music stops and the dancing couples retreat. A holy hush fills the room. My heart beats so fast and furious that I am certain He can hear it. My entire being trembles. Smiling down at me, my Beloved whispers, "Just follow Me."

I whisper a prayer of desperation, for I have no desire to look foolish. I close my eyes as He places His hand in mine. Fear fills my being so I force myself to open my eyes and lock gazes with my Beloved Shepherd.

I can't do this!

"You can if you place your feet on top of Mine," He whispers.

"What?"

"I will carry you through this life if you will just step on My feet and let Me be the One who lives My life through you," He gently reponds.

I place my feet on His and peace instantly covers me. "You don't have to walk alone, My love, for I am always here."

With a nod from Him, the music begins. I immediately recognize the tune. It is the Song of the Lamb, the song my Shepherd hummed as He held me in that dark valley amongst the lilies. It has the same peaceful effect on me now as it did then.

As I focus on Him, my heart grows calmer. I begin to dance with ease and move with amazing grace. It feels as though I am floating on air. I soon relax completely and even find myself enjoying the dance.

On the dance floor, surrounded by a room full of spectators, I discover that there is absolutely nothing on earth that remotely comes close to the joy of dancing with the One I love. I never would have dreamed, in a million years, that I would be dancing with the Master Shepherd. The impossible is coming true, and I love it!

Neither of us speak; there is no need. Looking into His eyes, I see a beauty richer and greater than anyone or anything I have ever seen. At this moment in time, held in His loving embrace, I see that He is most handsome and completely desirable. I know in the depths of my being that I can trust Him with every part of my being.

The music stops and my Beloved whispers, "You may be uncertain of the next step in life, but you can always be certain of Me. I am the Good Shepherd and My sheep know My voice and follow Me, and they will not follow another." Kissing my forehead, He continues, "I would love to stay and dance with you all night, but I must go."

"But, I thought You were going to introduce me to Your Father, the King?"

He smiles and kissing the back of my hand, replies, "And so I shall, but I must go."

Comforter is now by my side. The Master Shepherd bows and says, "Life is a dance, My love, and I will always be your Partner."

He then hurries off disappearing through a side door. Comforter offers me His arm, which I gratefully accept.

"Comforter, I have spent most of my childhood dreaming about what it would be like to dine at the King's table and now that it is about to happen, I find that I would rather stay here on this dance floor with the Master Shepherd than be anywhere else in the whole wide world. Fame and fortune no longer hold any attraction for me. I only want one thing, and that is to be in the arms of my Beloved Shepherd."

"And so you shall, Lovely Lady."

Comforter leads me across the dance floor and into the hall. As the door closes behind me, I lean against it. "Did that *really* happen, Comforter? Did I just dance with the Master Shepherd?"

"You certainly did, and what a beautiful couple you are!"

Rhonda Calhoun

"The orchestra played a song that the Master Shepherd hummed the night He found me in the valley of despair. He said it was the Song of the Lamb. It is such a captivating tune. Are there words to it, Comforter?"

"There are, but we will talk of that later. Right now, you have an appointment with the King."

Comforter and I resume our journey through this amazing palace, but my thoughts remain fixed on my Beloved Shepherd. Comforter stops before a magnificent set of double doors, which are made of the finest cedar. He does not even knock, but opens the door and, with just one glance, I am terrified. The room is astonishing, unbelievable and far too magnificent to adequately describe. The floor looks like a sea of glass.[74] In the center of the room is a golden throne with what looks like an emerald rainbow above it. Seven lamps burn before the throne. Thousands upon thousands of ministering servants wait in attendance while myriads upon myriads stand before the throne singing, "Holy, Holy, Holy, is the Lord God, the Almighty, who was and who is and who is to come."

This place is terrifying! I tighten my grip on Comforter's arm. He leans close and whispers, "You have nothing to fear, for you have been bought with a price."

"What?"

"Don't fear, for I am with you, Lovely Lady."

The moment we step across the threshold, a trumpet announces our arrival. A door opens on the far side of the room and another trumpet blast follows. My Beloved Shepherd steps into the throne room, but He looks very different. His hair is white like wool, like snow; and His eyes are like a flame of fire; and His feet are like bronze that has been caused to glow in a furnace. On His head are many crowns. He wears a golden girdle and a crimson robe with the words, "King of kings and Lord of lords" written across His thigh.[75]

He looks directly at me and smiles a thousand smiles. He speaks and His voice is like the sound of many waters. He comes toward me. I can do nothing but tremble and stare. The Master Shepherd *really* is the King and not just any king, but the King of all! I tremble before His awesome power and obvious authority.

Suddenly, as if waking from a deep sleep, everything begins to fall into place. If the Master Shepherd truly is the King, and He obviously is, then that means I was just dancing with the *King*! Me, a poor, weak shepherdess with a history of failure was just dancing with the King of kings! How can it be? Does He realize who I am, or more importantly, does He realize who I am not?

The closer He comes, the faster my heart beats. He reaches out and takes my hand in His; I faint.

I wake in His arms; the kindness I see in His eyes fills me with peace. No longer does He appear before me in His glory, but as a mere Man, as the Master Shepherd, but dressed in royal garments. He whispers, "You look beautiful, My love."

"You *really* are the King?"

"Yes, I really am the King," He responds, chuckling. "Now that this fact has finally been established, perhaps you would like to meet My Father, the Ancient of Days?"

"Can this weak heart of mine endure such an encounter?" I ask, still trembling.

"With Me by your side, you can endure anything, for I am your strength and your song," He answers.[76]

The sound of another trumpet fills the room and an attendant announces, "His Majesty — the Ancient of Days!"

Two men surrounded by light swing open a set of double doors. In walks a grand, noble looking Gentleman. His hair is white like snow, His countenance is glorious. He is not just gentle, He is gentleness. He is not just kind, He is kindness. He is purity, and His eyes are filled with fire.[77] His very presence drains my strength and I collapse, falling to my knees.

The Ancient of Days makes His way across the room, stopping to embrace several people. A small boy runs up and tugs on His robe causing an outburst of delight to explode from His Majesty. He quickly scoops the boy up into His arms and spins him around. Once He is seated on His throne, He places the boy on His knee and proceeds to give him a "pony" ride.

My Beloved Shepherd and King approaches the throne and says, "Father, I have brought someone to meet You."

Rhonda Calhoun

The Ancient of Days looks directly at me and says, "Arise, My dear child, and come to your Father."

I try to stand, but my legs are unsteady. "Your Majesty, I am afraid I cannot, for my legs have lost all strength. And I fear that my heart would surely stop beating if I were to come any closer."

Chuckling, He answers, "You do delight My heart, child. Have no fear, Little One, draw close to the One who loved you first and loves you most."

He nods at Comforter, who then lays His hand on my shoulder. Something that feels like warm oil flows through me, strengthening not just my legs, but my entire body. I am immediately revived. Comforter takes my hand and escorts me across the sea of glass. The closer we get to the throne, the more I tremble.

I kneel before His Majesty too terrified to look at anything other than the floor. Comforter is the first to speak. "This is the child—she is the one!"

My Shepherd-King turns to me and says, "Allow Me to officially introduce you to My Father, the Ancient of Days."

"Arise, Little One," the Ancient of Days says.

Once again Comforter helps me to my feet. I timidly look up and the first thing I notice is how incredibly beautiful the Ancient of Days is. His hair is whiter than the whitest snow, and His face and entire being are absolutely radiant.[78] The depth of purity and goodness in His eyes reminds me of my Beloved Shepherd.

He gazes deep into my heart,[79] then addresses His Son saying, "She is beautiful; We have chosen well."

He then stands extending His hand to me. "Come and eat from My table;[80] there we will talk of My beloved Son."[81]

With my Shepherd-King on one side, the Ancient of Days on the other and Comforter following close behind, I am escorted into the magnificent dining hall. The banquet table is beautifully decorated with snow-white lilies, tall candles and fine china. Every room in this palace is absolutely breathtaking!

Comforter holds my chair then remains behind me. My Beloved stands before the Ancient of Days and says, "Father, there is one thing I desire."

Every servant in the room stops what they are doing, for never in history had anyone ever heard the King's Son ask for anything.

My Beloved continues, "Father, I desire that My bride-to-be would love Me with the same love and in the same way that You love Me."[82]

"Your desire shall be granted. I shall present to You a bride without spot or wrinkle, a bride who loves not her life unto death," the Ancient of Days replies, nodding at Comforter who nods in agreement.

My Beloved takes His seat across from me. I stare into His kind eyes as servants place a multitude of silver bowls and platters of wonderful looking food on the table. Once again, Comforter serves me. I turn to the Ancient of Days and thank Him for our extravagant feast.

He replies, "It is My good pleasure to give you the kingdom."

Not understanding what He meant and too bashful to ask, I simply nod.

I watch my Shepherd-King and follow His lead during dinner, for I have no idea what is proper etiquette.

I cannot believe that I am sitting in the King's palace with the King Himself and His Father. All of my wildest, most extravagant childhood dreams put together do not come close to the reality of what I am experiencing.

The Ancient of Days lifts His golden goblet to His Son and says, "I offer this cup of the covenant to My only begotten Son and to His Bride who is pure, spotless and without wrinkle."[83]

My heart is pounding. He is offering the betrothal cup to His Son. My Beloved responds, "Father, not My will, but Your will be done," and He drinks the cup.

Without hesitation, my Beloved turns and offers me the cup.

What? How? The King is offering me the betrothal cup? This cannot be! He desires to make me His bride? I could never marry the King. I will never be pure, spotless and without wrinkle. I cannot

Rhonda Calhoun

accept, for I am not worthy.

I turn my face away, and my past crashes in on me like waters breaking through a dam.

Oh, why did I come here? What was I thinking? I should have just stayed with my brothers. If only I had resisted Compromise....

I want to run far, far away and hide forever.

The Ancient of Days' strong, yet gentle voice interrupts my fearful thoughts, "Child, your heart is filled with great shame, much regret and deep pain. You feel great guilt and tremendous fear in your heart. Allow this affectionate Father to speak kindly to your troubled heart and give you peace."

He takes my hand and continues, "Let me tell you about a day gone by, a day when you wandered far from the safety of My home. During that time, you failed to feed your soul from the King's garden, which caused tremendous weakness and suffocating apathy to take root in your life. Your love soon grew cold, and you turned to another lover called Compromise. You found yourself caught in a thicket, wounded and so alone. I saw you there; you were lost and without hope. I heard your cries.

"My heart reached out to you. I sent My Son to rescue you. He went willingly knowing that it would cost Him His very life. I loved you so much that I was willing to trade His life for yours, and My Son loved you so much that He was willing to suffer great abuse at the hands of men that you might be set free."[84]

I look at His wonderful Son who sits before me bathed in glorious light. Everything about this Man is perfect and good. He is incredibly beautiful and ever so kind. Tears flow down His face as He stares into the distance to some unseen time and place.

His Father continues, "Everyone, just like sheep, have gone astray.[85] A true Shepherd lays down His life for His sheep, and that is exactly what My Son did. He allowed Himself to be taken captive for your sake.[86] And His captors were anything but kind. They mocked Him, spit in His face and plucked out His beard. A vine of thorns was fashioned into a crown, which they beat into My Son's flawless head. He was whipped without mercy, then led to a hilltop where soldiers nailed His hands and feet to a tree. But, it was not the nails that held Him—there isn't a nail on earth or in hell strong enough to restrain the Son of God! No, it was your Beloved's great love that held Him there, and that same love holds you, My child.

"Your Beloved Shepherd hung on that cruel tree, battered and bloody, His parched tongue cleaving to His jaw.[87] He was thirsty so you never would be. He made it possible for you to drink from the river of Life.[88] My Son is the Tree of Life. If anyone eats from this Tree he shall live forever. His death and resurrection has already made and continues to make you perfect!"

My heart is filled with a bittersweet mixture of love and anguish as I hear the extravagant price my Shepherd paid to rescue me from death and hell. I now understand that my Beloved is so much more than a mere Man, so much more than a Shepherd, and even more than a King—He is the Savior of the world!

I can scarcely contain the swirl of emotions in my heart as the Ancient of Days continues, "The beauty of My Son's death and resurrection is the fruit that it produced. His death purchased you; His blood made you pure, spotless and without blemish. You were made perfect in His death. My child, the peace you long for is only found in My Son and what He did on the cross."[89]

Extending His hand toward His Son, He continues, "Greater love has no one than this, that one lay down his life for his friends.[90] A Lamb and a Lion, a Lover and a King, a Deliverer and a Redeemer, a Savior and a Bridegroom—this is who My Son is."

Unable to contain the love exploding in my heart any longer, I jump up and shout, "My Beloved is sweet in death and sweeter still in life! I will waste my life on You, for You have rescued me from certain death. You left everything to make me Yours, and I will do the same. I will leave everything and follow You. Everything I am and have is Yours!"

The sweet fragrance of spikenard fills the room.[91] My Beloved drinks deeply of it.[92] I hurry to His side and kneel at His feet. "You, my King, died for me. I know it is true! How good and kind and beautiful You are! From this day forth, I will remember Your death and will hold it close to my heart. You are an oasis filled with forgiveness, fragrance and beauty in the midst of a dry, barren desert.

"You are wise and all-powerful and desire only the best for me. You are to me a cluster of henna blooms, which are sweet to my senses and ever so delightful! You are a Man in whom is found everything.[93] You are not a burdensome King or a ruthless dictator. Your tenderness towards my weakness is unique, and Your lovingkindness leads me on the paths of righteousness.

"You have restored life to this poor heart and I love You for it! You are my sovereign King, my glorious Shepherd, my suffering Savior and my wonderful Redeemer. I give You my worship!"

The spikenard grows stronger. My Beloved takes my hand and says, "My darling, for you to mature in love, you must understand that I love you regardless of your actions. I love you even in your weakness, even in your immaturity. Does a loving parent despise his children or cease to love them because of immaturity or weakness? Do they turn their backs on them when they stumble and fall? Do they reject them when they choose the wrong path or make wrong decisions? Of course they do not, and neither do I; it would be impossible for Me or My Father to respond to those We love in such a destructive way.[94]

"Feasting from My table of abundant love and mercy does not produce carelessness or spiritual apathy; but rather, it produces fiery love that ascends before My Father's throne as a sweet perfume,[94a] which is exactly what has happened here this evening."

I cry out, "Keep me as the apple of Your eye; hide me in the shadow of Your wings, for I am Yours!"[95]

My Beloved King stands to His feet, nearly knocking over His chair and proclaims, "Behold, you are so beautiful to Me! Your eyes are like the dove, eyes that are filled with pure devotion. Your gaze is fixed on Me and does not wander to and fro, but is chaste and constant like the devotion of the dove. I no longer say that you *look* beautiful, My darling, but from this time forward, I declare that you *are* beautiful!"[96]

He raises me up before Him. We stand hand in hand,

face to face and heart to heart. Neither of us moves; we are barely breathing. Time stands still. Oh, how beautiful my Savior is! I am lost in His love and in the sweet fragrance that grows stronger by the minute. My Beloved whispers, "Sweeter than myrrh is the fragrance of our love."

"Myrrh is the burial spice, my Lord."

"It is indeed. Our love is unto death."

I respond, "I will love You unto death, my Lord and Savior for there is none like You. You alone satisfy my deepest desires and You are the only One who can exchange those things in my life that are ashes for true beauty."

My Beloved turns to His Father and exclaims, "Father, look at her! Look at My beautiful one — she now knows who I am! She understands what I did for her on the cross. She understands that I am not only her Shepherd and King, but I am also her Savior and Redeemer! Oh, how beautiful she is, how beautiful she is, Father!"[97]

Unable to restrain my affection, I interject, "You are the one who is beautiful, my King, and ever so delightful! You are beautiful caring for Your sheep, beautiful dying on a cross and beautiful reigning as King.[98] To You alone is due whatever beauty this poor soul may have, for You are the One who has embraced this devastated girl and called her lovely. It is in Your great love that I find rest for my soul. In You I have found life and abundant mercy and goodness.[99]

"How sweet and how strong is Your love! I rest in the abundance of Your love; my security is found in You alone.[100] The fragrance of Your love fills this castle drawing me to Your side."[101]

Comforter adds, "'Tis a love that is stronger than death."

I now turn to the Ancient of Days and say, "Oh, how wide, how high, how deep, how long is Your love! How kind, how loving, how generous You are! You loved me so much that You sent Your only begotten Son to die for *me*! You sacrificed Your greatest treasure for *me*. How can this be?"[102]

The Ancient of Days opens His arms wide, and I run into them; love floods my being. "I love you in the same measure as I love My Son. I am your Father — no one can change that fact, for

Rhonda Calhoun

I created you. The question is, will you be My daughter?"

For as long as I can remember, I have wanted a father. "I would like nothing better than to be Your child, but I am afraid."

He holds me in His safe, strong arms. Between sobs, I confess, "My father abandoned me at birth."

Holding me close, He responds, "I know child, but I will never abandon you. It is important for you to grasp both truths — you are My child and you are to be My Son's bride.

"Rest assured that We will never leave you, My child. The love I have for you will never end, for I love you with an everlasting love. Others may come and go, but I will never leave you or forsake you; My love will remain constant even if yours does not. Others may misrepresent My love, but know that My love is never based on your behavior or conduct. My love never changes. It is surer than the rising of the sun and deeper than the deepest ocean."

He tenderly kisses my forehead.

"Father, I give You my heart. Tell me what to do that I might please You."

"Child, I do not need you to *do* anything for Me. There is absolutely nothing you can do that will cause Me to love you any more than I already do. Likewise, there is nothing you will ever do that would cause Me to love you any less. I love you because I love you. I cannot help Myself; it is who I am and what I do. Can a mother forget her child? Can a father turn his back on his offspring? They might, but I never will. If your father and mother forsake you, I will take you up.

"Being a child of mine is not based on whether or not you do good or bad. I do not demand perfection. Neither is it about "getting it right." Being a child of Mine means that you are part of My family. I am your Father and you are My daughter. It is that simple. I desire a family who loves Me and each other."

I look up into the eyes of truth, eyes that watched me grow in my mother's womb, eyes that have never turned away from me and I say, "How great is the Father's love that I should be called a child of God!"[103]

Chapter Ten
THE KING'S GARDEN

Like an apple tree among the trees of the forest
so is my Beloved. [104]

My newly discovered Father wipes away my tears. I run my fingers through His extremely soft beard. "You are so good to me," I whisper.

"And I always will be. You can trust Me with your life, Little One."

Turning to His Son, He says, "Perhaps You would like to take My lovely daughter on a walk through Our garden?"

It has been such a long time since I have walked in the King's garden that I jump off His lap and ask, "Please, could we? Could we?"

My exuberant response causes Father, Comforter and my Beloved to laugh outloud. My Beloved King and Shepherd extends His arm to me saying, "Shall we?"

With great delight, I wrap my arm through His; He escorts me through a side door. The sun is low in the sky, but the air is still warm. Our short walk across the palace grounds is spent in sweet silence. It feels as though I am floating on a sea of love and I relish every minute of it. I am so glad that my Beloved

Rhonda Calhoun

found me.

I never thought I would ever walk in this place again.

We arrive at the garden and my Beloved removes the gold key from around His neck. Placing it in the lock, He turns it; my heart responds as though the key had been placed in it. *Something just happened to me; I feel free.*

My King asks, "Do you remember what you prayed just before I brought you into this garden the first time?"

"I can think of nothing at this moment, my King, for I am overwhelmed by all that has happened this day," I respond.

"Your prayer was that My Father would unlock your heart so that you could love Me without reservation or restraint.[105] And that is exactly what He has done and is doing. Truth has a way of doing that, My love."

He is right; there is a freedom in my heart that I have never felt before. I want to run and sing and shout and dance all at once.

What kind of love brings with it such joy and freedom?

He leads me through the gate. I have a feeling that, from this moment on, my life will never be the same. We step around the privacy hedge, and my eyes fill with tears of joy.

Oh, how beautiful this place is – it is even more beautiful than I remember!

We proceed slowly through one garden after another, going deeper and deeper into this exquisite paradise. My newly awakened heart eagerly drinks in its beauty and splendor.

We come to a part of the garden that I have never been before. In the center, is a beautiful fountain flowing with golden water. A stone bench is just a short distance away and beside the bench is a large, white basket filled with various kinds of fruit that I have never seen before. Pointing to the basket, I ask, "What kind of fruit is that?"

"This is the fruit of My Spirit," He answers as He leads me to it.

Sitting beside Him on the bench, He chooses a large, red piece and places it in my hand. So strange...it is in the shape of a heart. He says, "That fruit is called Unconditional Love. That green one is Joy. This yellow one is Peace. That emerald green one is Patience, and the gold one is Kindness. Goodness is this pink one, and that dark blue one is called Faithfulness. Gentleness is this lavender one, and this last one is called Self-control, which is a burnt orange color."[106]

"Wow! They all sound wonderful, and I wish I had room in my stomach for all of them, but alas I do not. Which one is the best?"

"They are all wonderful, and all of them are necessary, but the greatest of these is definitely Love."[107]

"How may I acquire this fruit?"

"No one can give you this fruit; it must be grown. If you live by the Spirit and walk by the Spirit, then you will bear much fruit."[108]

"I desire to live and walk by the Spirit," I answer, not really understanding what I am saying.

My Beloved reaches into His pouch and says, "Then, this is for you." He hands me something that looks like a plum.

"What is the name of this fruit?"

"This is not a fruit, My darling; this is a gift and it is called Grace."[109]

"What is Grace?"

"Grace is a gift that cannot be earned and is never deserved. Grace is My Father's empowering presence in your life, which enables you to do and to be all that He has called you to do and be – nothing more and nothing less. My Father pours out grace on those with a humble heart. Take and eat it," He answers.

Biting into its tender flesh, I say, "It is extremely sweet and full of flavor." Juice runs down my chin. Wiping it with the back of my hand, I giggle. Quickly remembering that I am with the King and should act like a lady, I tuck my hands behind my back.

Recognizing my embarrassment, my Shepherd and Friend responds, "You are who you are and that is good enough for Me. Do not worry about outward behavior, My love, for it is the thoughts and intentions of the heart that cause you to be lovely."

Feeling free and loved, I look up and smile.

He continues, "Always remember, Grace can never be

earned and must never be refused. Come now and let us continue on, for there is much I want to show you."

He leads me to a narrow gate near the south wall. Written on the gate are the words, *"The Path of Life."*[110]

"This is the path I desire to walk on!" I exclaim.

He pushes the gate open and responds, "Then this is the path we shall take."

We travel only a short distance when the path becomes so narrow that we must walk single file. I follow closely behind my Beloved because the foliage is so thick that it is becoming increasingly difficult to see my way. My Beloved stops beside an extremely dense vine that completely covers the tall stone wall running parallel to our path. Its leaves are a deep emerald color, and the blooms are three different colors: yellow, red and white.

I bury my face in the midst of the flowers and breathe deeply. The fragrance is intoxicating. Examining them more closely, I notice that the three flowers grow on the same stem. Fascinated, I caress the velvet-like petals asking, "What is the name of this lovely plant?"

"This is called, Everlasting Virtues. The three different colored flowers each have a different name. The white and smallest bloom is called Faith. But, do not be fooled by its size. It is extremely powerful to the point that, when applied, it can move mountains.[111] The yellow flower is called Hope. Notice that its petals are each shaped like a cross. When this flower is eaten, it restores life. Last, but certainly not least, the large, heart-shaped, red flower is called Selfless Love, which never fails to accomplish what it sets out to do. Faith, Hope and Love grow profusely in My garden and are free to all who come here."[112]

"Love appears to grow everywhere," I respond.

"That is more true than you know."

"May I have these virtues, my King?"

He breaks off a cluster and quickly weaves a crown. Placing it on my head, He says, "But now abide Faith, Hope and Love, but the greatest of these is Love."[113]

"My King, tell me more; show me more!" I cry out.

"It is My delight to reveal to you the mysteries of My kingdom."[114]

Breaking off another cluster of flowers, He continues, "If you knew all mysteries and had faith strong enough to move mountains but did not possess love, you would be nothing. If you gave all your possessions to feed the poor but did not have love then it would profit you nothing.[115] Love is the most important element in My kingdom, My darling. For Mine is a kingdom conceived, founded, established and fueled by perfect Love."

"Oh, that You would help me acquire these virtues and teach me the ways of Your kingdom!"

"Rest assured, you will learn and walk in My ways."[116]

"Tell me more!"

"Peace, righteousness and joy are the air that fills this place.[117] The soil from which every plant draws its sustenance is love.[118] I am the Light, which causes everything to grow and mature.[119] A river of living water, which flows from My Father's heart, runs through this garden bringing life to all who drink from it.," He says as He points across the way to a winding river that appears to be covered in dancing diamonds.[120]

"How glorious!" I exclaim.

Leading me onward, we come to a place where vines have formed a thick canopy over the narrow path. Strawberry-sized fruit, some blue and some pink, hang like grapes from the vines. Picking several, my Beloved says, "This fruit is called Goodness and Mercy."

"May I eat of it?" I ask.

"Certainly."

He hands me one of each color, and I quickly pop them in my mouth. I comment, "It is amazing that these grow on the same vine, yet the Mercy fruit is full of flavor and very sweet while the other has very little flavor or sweetness."

Smiling, He responds, "Never judge a fruit by its sweetness. Many things in My kingdom appear plain and simple while being highly desirable and extremely valuable."

"I know what goodness is, but what is Mercy?"

"Mercy is the tender, lovingkindness of God that takes you where you need to be and makes you who you need to be despite yourself," He answers.

Rhonda Calhoun

Spinning around, I exclaim, "This is such a wonderful place; everything I need is here!"

"All you will ever need is found in Me, My darling."

Coming around a bend, we find that vines have completely blocked our path. I push against the thick web; it is stronger than it appears. There is absolutely no way to break through; we will have to turn back. The One I love simply holds His hand up and the vines part.

How did He do that?

My Beloved takes my hand and gently leads me through the opening. Within minutes, the vines grow over the opening. I walk on but am unaware of my surroundings because I keep looking back wondering how He was able to cut through a tangled mass of vines with just a wave of His hand.

"All things are subject to My authority," He answers without my asking the question.

"No doubt," I respond.

"You shall see greater things than this as you continue walking with Me on this path."

"So, exactly where does this path lead?"

"This is the Path of Sorrow and Suffering and it leads to Death Valley, which is at the heart of My garden."

"The Path of Sorrow and Suffering! I thought we were on the Path of Life? How can the two be the same? And, what are we doing walking on the Path of Sorrow and Suffering?" I ask, horrified at the implications of this name.

"The Path of Life and the Path of Sorrow and Suffering are one and the same. Life is not void of pain or suffering. Unless a seed falls into the ground and dies, it cannot bring forth fruit. The Path of Life always leads to death, but death is really just the beginning of life."[121]

"But, I do not want to die, and I certainly do not want to go to a place called Death Valley!"

"Oh, but you do, for only after one dies does he really begin to live! Death Valley is the only place where you can find true Humility and Self-Sacrifice. These rare plants grow only under the Great Rock. Whoever eats these plants matures in love and becomes great in My kingdom. Even though many desire to be great, very few pursue this path because it is filled with purifying pain and self-sacrifice. Are you willing to go through the piercing and crushing required to gain such priceless virtues, My love?"

"I heard rumors about these plants. People say that they are costly and quite bitter to the taste but sweet once digested. They also said that if one dared to reach under the Great Rock that the Rock would fall on them, bringing certain death.[122]

"Kind Shepherd, is there not another path I could choose? Is there not a plant that would be sweet to the taste and easy in its attainment but still bring about the desired results?"

"There is another path, and it is called the Path of Least Resistance. It leads to a plant called Earthly Comforts, which unbeknownst to those who pursue it, is unattainable, for no one can ever be truly comfortable or content outside of My kingdom.

"The Path of Least Resistance is a wide path, and many walk there.[123] It circles the outside perimeter of My kingdom. One never really goes anywhere on this path except in a circle, but there is never any shortage of company along the way," He answers.

"Do You walk there, my Beloved?"

"I do, but the fellowship I have with those who walk there is very limited. For the most part, they are not interested in Me and very few are even aware of My presence. The truth is they do not think they need Me. They are consumed with indulging their fleshly appetites and pursuing momentary, fleeting comforts and pleasures."

I shiver at the thought. "I don't want to live like that! I think I would rather stay on this path even if it means pain."

"I was hoping you would say that."

We step into a small clearing where I see one of our favorite resting places, the Tree of Life. "The Path of Sorrow and Suffering leads to the Tree of Life?" I ask, quite confused.

"This path leads to many places, not just to Death Valley," He answers as He leads me under the shade of this wonderful Tree.

"Are we not going to Death Valley so I can eat of Humility and Sacrifice?"

Rhonda Calhoun

"That day will surely come, but not today, My love. You must be made ready before you can fully pursue those virtues," He responds while spreading His cloak beneath the branches of this magnificent tree. He invites me to join Him, which I eagerly do.[124]

"I will return momentarily," He says as He hurries away disappearing behind a hedge of purple and gold flowers.

Thousands upon thousands of flowers surround me. I find myself thinking about my brothers and their harsh treatment of me. I remember my compromise. I think about the dark valley filled with lilies; it was there that my Beloved Shepherd found me.

I was so very lost and completely hopeless! But, thankfully, I will never again be without hope because I now have a Savior.

My King returns with a handful of lilies. He kneels before me and says, "You, My darling, are a lily among thorns; you outshine all who do not know Me. The world appears as thorns to Me compared to your great beauty. You thrive in the hidden places, not in the hustle and bustle of the city, but in the cool countryside, in the quiet fields, in My presence.

"You are a lily, which is pure, innocent and yields a sweet perfume. You are My sole inheritance. My Father has promised you to Me. Have no concerns and no fears, for you are the one chosen for Me. I will tenderly watch over your life; you can trust Me."[125]

I take the flowers and breathe in their fragrance. Turning my face toward His, I respond, "Your love is sweet to me."[126]

"As is yours to Me," He adds.

"Is it true? Am I really like this lily?"

"It is true, My darling, for in the midst of a dark valley, you still desired Me. You looked so beautiful among the rough, unpleasant, disagreeable thorns! Suffering often reveals the beauty of a lovesick heart.

"You are a lily, which is totally dependent upon Me for everything. In the midst of this dark world, you shine and are truly outstanding among ten thousand! Do you not know that darkness only magnifies true beauty?"[127]

Unable to contain the love exploding in my heart, I take

His hand in mine and exclaim, "My Beloved, You far surpass me! I may be like this lily, which merely looks beautiful on the outside and smells sweet to the senses, but You are the Tree of Life, which gives eternal life to all who eat from Your table! You yield perfect fruit, which nourishes my soul and satisfies my hungry heart. You extend Your arms and provide shade, protecting Me from the burning rays of this world and bringing sweet rest from its cares! Your trunk is strong and broad, and I lean upon You in my weakness! Your roots are deep and firmly established; You change not! Oh, my Beloved, it is true—You are the Tree of Life and You offer life eternal!"[128]

He gently squeezes my hand; tears have formed in His eyes. Nothing more needs to be said. Closing His eyes, He leans against the tree trunk and whispers, "My love, do you hear what I hear?"

I listen closely. After a few moments, I reply, "I hear birds singing and leaves rustling. That is all; there isn't much else to hear in this place."

"In the stillness, you will know Me.[129] Listen long and listen often, and you will hear My very heartbeat."

"I want to know You more than anything, "I whisper.

I close my eyes and listen. Peace floods my soul, and everything else fades away. Suddenly and quite faintly, I hear the beat of His heart; I hear the sound of love! What grace floods my soul! Life evermore! I am lost in the reality and beauty of His eternal love! "My heart beats for you," He whispers.

For a very long time, I simply listen to the steady rhythm of His heart. I open my eyes and look at my King. Wondering if He has fallen asleep, I reach out to touch His shoulder, but before I can, He asks, "Yes, My darling?"

I nearly jump out of my skin. "How did you know I was trying to get Your attention?"

"I know everything—even with My eyes closed," He answers, smiling.

"You are amazing, and Your wonders never cease!" I exclaim.

"I believe you were about to ask Me something?"

"Oh, yeah...I was wondering. I wonder if—."

Rhonda Calhoun

"Yes?"

"I was wondering if I could—." I stop again.

How do I ask Someone who has already given His all for more?

He smiles and says, "I delight in giving good gifts, My love. So, ask whatever you will, and it is yours."[130]

"I only want one thing; there is only one thing I seek and that is to dwell in Your house and behold Your beauty all the days of my life."[131]

"Your request delights My heart, for you have asked for the best and it shall not be taken from you. The answer to a request such as this is always yes. Now close your eyes and give Me your hand, for in knowing Me more intimately you will love Me more completely."

He leads my trembling hand to His face and whispers, "Now experience the extravagance of My love for you."

All thoughts of myself fade away as my fingers touch His forehead. I follow the deep gashes made by the crown of thorns. In my mind's eye, I see Him nailed to a tree where bloody love trickles down His battered and beard-plucked face. His face is unrecognizable. Strips of skin hang from His body. I see the nails in His wrists and ankles. Tears fill my eyes and spill down my cheeks.

What kind of love willingly suffers such pain as this? What kind of God would give up a glorious crown in order to wear a crown of thorns?

I open my eyes and see tears flowing from my Beloved's closed eyes. I withdraw my hand.

For what reason does He cry?

Knowing my every thought, He answers, "For the joy set before Me, I endured the shame and agony of the cross. The joy that was ever before Me was My bride.[131a] These tears that you see are nothing but tears of great joy, for great is My love and equally great is My joy."

Driven by a hunger to know Him more fully, I resume my search. I touch this manifestation of His passionate heart— His fiery, hot tears flowing unhindered down His cheeks. They become water for my thirsty soul as I explore the depths of His sacrificial love.

His cheek is soft and smooth just as He is gentle and kind. Not once has this Shepherd-King ever treated me harshly. On the contrary, He has always been extremely gentle, loving and kind.

I trace the outline of His mouth, the same mouth that spoke creation into existence, the same mouth that speaks words of truth, hope and affirmation, even when correcting me.[132] There are no words of accusation or condemnation ever found in this King's heart.

I open my eyes and join my fingers in memorizing every detail of His face. I trace His ears—ears that eagerly listen for the sound of my voice and hear the very secrets of my heart. I look into His eyes; He returns my gaze. His eyes are like two endless wells overflowing with eternity. Wisdom and tenderness flow from them. He knows all there is to know about me, and yet He loves me—I can see it in His eyes!

With tears streaming, I say, "I am beginning to see not only who You are, but also who I am. I have eaten from Your table and found strength and life forevermore. I will never be the same."[133]

"My love, you have chosen well." Standing, He takes my hand and continues, "Come, it is getting late, and we have another stop to make before our day is finished."

Shaking the grass from His cloak, He wraps it around my shoulders. Instead of returning the way we came, He leads me deeper into this never-ending garden. We pass a large rock, which is partially covered by a massive vine of miniature red roses. From the heart of this rock flows a steady stream of crystal clear water. I stop for a closer look. "The rumors are true! There really is a rock from which water flows! Is it also true that if one drinks of this water he will live forever?"

"Everyone who drinks from the water that I give shall never thirst; the water that I give will become in them a well of water springing up to eternal life."[134]

"May I drink?"

He scoops up a handful of water and holds it to my lips. I drink deeply. It is more refreshing than anything I have ever

Rhonda Calhoun

tasted. I exclaim, "I do love this place! I wish I could stay here forever!"

"One day you shall, but right now we must hurry or we will be late for the celebration."

"We are going to a celebration?"

"We are."

"For whom?"

"For you, My darling. My Father is celebrating your safe and much longed for return."[135]

"A celebration for me! How wonderful!"

After passing through many gardens, we stop before a tall stone wall that is completely covered with ivy. Reaching into the midst of the thick vines, my Beloved lifts the well-hidden latch. The ivy mysteriously parts, the gate swings wide, and we step into the palace courtyard.

Chapter Eleven
THE BANQUETING HALL

His banner over me is love. [136]

*I*n the middle of the courtyard, a large stone statue of a Lion lying beside a Lamb greets all who enter. Just behind it, a three-tiered fountain bubbles forth its crystal clear water high into the air. The moon shines full and bright. We stroll across the courtyard toward the west wing of the palace.

"This, My love, is the Banqueting Hall. It is here Comforter trains and equips His students."[137]

Lively music and much laughter floats through every crack and crevice. "It sounds like they are having a good time," I reply.

"I am sure they are, but the real celebration begins with our arrival."

As soon as we step onto the porch, two servants quickly open the gigantic, intricately carved, cedar doors. A shofar immediately announces the arrival of the King, and everyone in the room is suddenly quiet. Every head turns and every knee bows before this King whose arm I cling to. I feel quite unworthy to be standing by His side, but I am much too afraid to let go.

Sensing my anxiety, He whispers, "You are exactly where you belong, doing exactly what I want you to do and, by the

Rhonda Calhoun

way, you are the most beautiful lady here."

"I am so afraid."

"With Me by your side, you have absolutely nothing to fear," He says as He escorts me through the sea of people. After stopping several times to speak with various ones, we arrive at the other side of the room where a beautifully decorated table awaits us. The Ancient of Days stands at its head. Behind Him hangs a large golden banner with shiny red letters that reads:

The King Loves You Even In Your Weakness

His banner over me is love![138] I look into the eyes of my Beloved who returns my gaze. I ask, "How is it that I have stumbled upon such marvelous love as this?"

"You have stumbled upon nothing, My love. I chose you while you were in your mother's womb. I have watched over you and sought you out that I might bring you to the place where you would love Me. It is not an accident that you are here with Me, for I have won your heart with My unstoppable, insurmountable, unquenchable love!"[139]

"But, why would you want me after what I have done?"

"My darling, I do not base My affections on your actions. I base My love on who I am, on My nature, My character and nothing more. I love weak and broken people!

"Look around you at this room full of people. Some are wealthy and some are so poor they do not know where they will find their next piece of bread. Some are intelligent while others cannot add two plus two. Some are successful in business while others have no employment. Some are leaders in the things of the Spirit while others are struggling to understand even the simplest concept regarding Me. Some have never walked away from Me while others have.

"But, there is one thing they all have in common and that is they all love Me and desire to know Me intimately. They have surrendered to Me and that makes them successful. Whether they appear successful in the eyes of the world or not does not affect My view of them in the least. I do not judge as the world judges, for I look at the heart. And when I look around this room, I see hearts of devotion, pure hearts."

"I long to have a pure heart, but I have so many flaws."

"A pure heart does not mean a perfect heart; do not confuse the two. Having a pure heart means that the desire of your heart is to please Me, it means that the motives of your heart are pure even if you fail to walk perfectly."

"You have brought me to Your banqueting house, and Your banner over me is love," I say, looking back at the banner.

"Exactly. The banner I have placed over your life is love. I view *everything* through that banner and everything means *every* thing—both the ugly and the lovely."

Father and Comforter join us. It is obvious they are happy to see me. My newly found Father places His arm around my shoulder and says, "This banner speaks the truth, Little One."

"I know it is true because You say so, but it is difficult for me to believe and even more difficult for me to feel," I reply.

"The day will come when you will not only believe it, but you will be an instrument whereby many others will believe as well," He answers.

With a gentle squeeze He continues, "My commitment to you is greater than your commitment to Me. It is in this reality that you can rest. And because of this truth, you can trust Me with everything—your life, your victories, your weaknesses, your pride and even the bent towards sin that is in every human heart. You can trust Me with absolutely everything."

"That is what Your Son was just saying," I reply.

My Father hugs me and says, "I have promised My Son a Bride without wrinkle or blemish. You need not fear that you would fall short of being all that I have promised Him. I have already made provision for your faults; they have already been taken care of. Do not focus on becoming perfect, but focus on becoming His.

"Be still and know that I am God.[139a] Absolutely nothing is impossible with Me. In the days ahead, I will fill you with such love that you will never again doubt that you are loved infinitely."

With a wink, my Beloved excuses Himself and leaves me to Comforter's care. He disappears with His Father through a

Rhonda Calhoun

side door. I look around the crowded room. Everyone is laughing and talking, eating and drinking. "Comforter, are all of these Your students?"

"Most are; others are here to see if they want to be," He answers as He extends His arm.

Gripping the crook of His elbow, He leads me around the room. "Why would anyone not want to be a student of Yours?" I ask, stunned at the possibility.

"Lovely Lady, not all are willing to pay the price required, for following the King is not a life of comfort or self-indulgence. It is only when one realizes that the King is worthy of all that one is and all that one has that full surrender can come. But, take it on good Authority—this King is truly worthy of your affections. His gift of eternal life may be free, but it will cost you everything. So you see, Lovely Lady, why many are not willing to subject themselves to My counsel, for they are not willing to pay the price of love."

Comforter's countenance changes; His voice softens as He says, "If only they knew the preciousness of the One they refuse."

The pain in His eyes is clearly evident as He continues, "A good father disciplines His children. His discipline is pure and good and to be desired. It may seem terrible at the time, but His discipline yields the peaceable fruit of righteousness.

"There are a few who are willing to live in Our kingdom, and those I bring to this house of wine where I give them nourishment and all they need for their spiritual growth."[140]

On the far side of the room, a group has gathered before a large framed document. "What are they looking at?" I ask.

"That, Lovely Lady, is a poem that I am sure you will find most inspiring," Comforter answers as He leads me across the room.

I read aloud:

Beautiful Man!

In the burning heat of the day
You hang before the eyes of mankind:
naked, abused, and alone,
Oh, so painfully alone!

Your beautiful brow
bleeding from the crown of thorns,
promises that I, too, shall wear a glorious crown.

Your eternal eyes,
blackened from the repeated blows,
promise that my eyes shall behold my beautiful King.

Your magnificent mouth,
bleeding and parched from lack of water,
promises that I shall drink and never again know thirst.

Your broad back,
mutilated from the lashes of a whip,
promises comfort and healing from all my diseases.

Your splendid side,
pierced through by a cruel spear,
promises me entrance into the very heart of God.

Your battered, beautiful body
racked with pain and bearing my sins,
promises me forgiveness and eternal, unspeakable joy!
Three nails held you to that cross:
Faith, Hope, and Love.

Faith that I might see,
Hope that I might believe,
and Love that I might live!

People say that love can be felt,
but cannot be seen.
But I beg to differ, just look at the cross
and tell me what you see.
Is this not true Love that you see hanging there?

Rhonda Calhoun

"Comforter, who wrote this?"

"Her name is Mary, and she lives with her sister, Martha, and brother, Lazarus. Mary was quite young when she first met the King, but she was quick and eager to return His love. This precious girl soon grew to love Him so much that she decided to give Him all that she had. A few days before your King laid down His life, He went to Martha's house to be with His dear friends. Mary came into the room and knelt before her Beloved. She surprised everyone when she poured the entire contents of a very expensive bottle of perfumed oil over His head and feet.

"Her actions caused quite a commotion among those present as they considered her extravagance wasteful. But what they failed to realize is that nothing is ever wasted when it is poured out on the One you love, on the One who deserves all that you are and all that you possess. Mary invested her all on an eternal King who records every kindness in His Book of Remembrances. Of course, the King understood the significance of Mary's actions and quieted the room, saying, 'Leave her alone for she has done a good deed to Me. She has anointed My body for burial.' This young girl's actions remain to this day as a memorial to her King."

If only I could love like that girl.

"The day will come, Lovely Lady, when you shall," He responds to my unspoken thought. "But, for now, come with Me that I might share some good news with you."

He leads me to a small, secluded table where a burning lamp casts its golden light on a golden cup. Comforter holds my chair and then sits across from me. Taking my hand in His, He says, "You have found favor with your King more than all who are in the world.[141] His every thought is about you, and He continually brings you before His Father in prayer.[142] He loves you without reservation. This King desires you; His heart burns for you. He has chosen you to be part of His bride, and I have the honor and privilege of preparing you for that day."

He picks up the cup and continues, "Lovely Lady, will you give yourself to your King? Will you live for Him alone? Will you give your heart, soul, mind, will, desires, ambitions, your everything to the Lover of your soul? Will you accept His gift and His life and offer yours in return? Will you drink this cup?"

Clutching Comforter's wrist, I respond, "There must be some mistake. Surely, the King knows that I am just a commoner. Surely, He remembers how horribly I failed Him. Comforter, I have nothing to give Him, no dowry, no land, no perfume. I have nothing of any value to offer. He certainly knows that I am not worthy, doesn't He?"

Not waiting for Him to answer, I continue, "Comforter, it is unheard of for a King to choose one who is not of royal blood to be His bride. For a King to do so is costly and very painful. I cannot drink for I am unworthy of such an honor."

"But you *are* worthy, Lovely Lady. You are worthy because His love makes you worthy. He desires you, and that makes you worthy. He has chosen you, and that makes you worthy. He paid the bridal price, which determined, once and for all time, your value and worth. Yours was the most extravagant price ever paid. That means your worth is greater than any other. Your King died for you and you are of royal blood, for His very life flows through you.

"Lovely Lady, as strange as this may sound, your decision should not be based on your worth or your ability to remain true. Your decision should be based on Him. Make your decision based on a love that is stronger and greater than yourself, a love that is stronger than your weaknesses and sins, a love that is stronger than death itself. The King's love is powerful enough to save you and powerful enough to keep you."

My fragile heart is stunned. I turn my face away; my past comes crashing in on me like waters breaking through a dam.

I could never marry the King! I am flawed and weak and common! If only I had resisted Compromise....

"Comforter, this is not possible...."

"It is more than possible, Lovely Lady, it is your destiny."

Looking into His eyes, I take a deep breath and say, "I never dared dream anything so marvelous as what You are saying could ever happen to me. Things like this only happen in fairy tales, and everyone knows that fairy tales do not happen."

"Lovely Lady, this is like a fairy tale in that it is glorious,

Rhonda Calhoun

but it is so much more than that because it is real. This is true love. You were born to be loved by the King, and you were born to love Him in return. This was His plan before this earth was ever created. The Ancient of Days' desires a family; He desires a bride for His Son. And you, Lovely Lady, are destined to rule and reign with the King as His bride.

"Your King did not regard equality with His Father as something to hold onto, but He emptied Himself and took on the form of a bondservant, a shepherd. He humbled Himself by becoming obedient unto death and not just any death, but death on a cross. He did this to win your heart and to save you from your sins.[143] In doing so, He suffered cruelties that I cannot bear to recall."

Comforter takes a moment to collect Himself and then continues, "Lovely Lady, you are a priceless treasure and were purchased at a dear price, but a price not too dear for the One who truly loves you. You are destined to be His bride, if you so desire."[144]

As if waking from a deep sleep, I express my thoughts outloud, "The King loves me even though I am immature and ever so weak? I can be His bride — if I so desire?"

"It really is true. Your King *really* loves you, Lovely Lady. He desires to make you His bride."

"I know this may seem like a strange question, but does the King *like* me?"

Gently laughing, Comforter answers, "He likes you much more than you can comprehend. He delights in you and enjoys you."

I am overcome with love, joy and excitement all at once. *Where is this One who not only loves me, but also likes me?*

Scanning the room, I cannot find Him. Comforter says, "The One you seek is with His Father in the wine cellar. Would you like Me to take you there?"

"Oh, please do!"

Comforter leads me to a side door and we quickly descend the stone steps. Just before reaching the last step, my Beloved steps out from behind a wine rack. Skipping the last two steps, I say, "I accept Your gift and Your life and I offer You mine in return."

My heart feels strangely warm. My Father looks on with eyes of love saying, "I am and will restore to you all that was lost through sin. You are whole again. You are My daughter in every way. Now receive a taste of eternal life."[147]

He blows His sweet breath over me; a wave of giddiness sweeps through me, flooding my soul with hope and joy. I drink deeply from this river of love, which causes me to feel slightly intoxicated.

"Are you really My Father?" I boldly ask.

"Yes, I am really your Father. You are bone of My bone and flesh of My flesh. I created you. I am your Father, the Ancient of Days."

Growing more intoxicated by the moment, I respond, "What a good Father You are!"

Feeling light-headed, I look at my Beloved and say, "Take hold of me and sustain me with Your intoxicating presence. Hold me close and never let me go, for I am faint with love!"[148]

In a gentle, yet strong voice, He replies, "I will never, ever leave you.[149] I shall keep you and protect you in the most wonderful way."

"Then feed me from the Tree of Life that I might grow strong and beautiful and reproduce after my kind. Surround me with all sorts of flowers that I might find beauty and rest. Flood me with Your amazing love and cover me with Your goodness, for I am truly lovesick!"[150]

Leaning heavily against my Beloved, I continue, "There is no one like You, my King. In Your presence is fullness of joy; in Your right hand, there are pleasures evermore.[151] Comfort and console me in such a way that I can see, feel and know Your wonderful presence. When You are near and I can see You, hold me close and never let me go.[152] May Your left hand defend and protect me even when I cannot see You. Work behind the scenes in my life, orchestrating and ordaining my every step, I pray."[153]

The three most important Men in my life encircle me. My giddy heart is suddenly filled with anguish as I realize I have nothing to offer Them. I have nothing to give Them when They have given Their everything to me.[154] *How can I ever repay such love?*

Kneeling before my Beloved, I say, "My Lord, there is but a tiny flame of love burning in this poor heart of mine, and I give it to You. Please, if I have found favor in Your sight, grant that this heart might be gloriously kindled with fragrant love and beautiful deeds of kindness that I might bring honor to You and glorify Your precious name."[155]

"You shall indeed glorify Me," says my Beloved.

His words cause my heart to soar!

"Come and let us join our guests," my Beloved tenderly responds.

Choosing a bottle of wine from His vast supply, He says to His Father, "We have saved the best wine for last."[156]

I follow reluctantly, for I would rather stay in this wine cellar forever drinking of His love than be anywhere else. A joy has filled my soul to the point that nothing else matters. I am weak, yet feel strangely strong; such is the power of His love.

Reentering the room, Comforter escorts me to the King's table where I recline between my Beloved and Comforter. Father reclines beside my King who immediately instructs a servant to bring me raisin cakes and apples from His garden that I might be refreshed and my strength renewed.[157]

Several people try to engage me in conversation, but I find it extremely difficult to stay focused. Every topic seems dull and lifeless compared to the words spoken by the One I love. I have tasted of something that is far beyond anything this world has to offer and now nothing else can satisfy. I have finally found my reason for living, and I long to sit at His feet and gaze on His lovely face, undistracted.

My Beloved takes my hand and addresses the room, "Ladies and gentlemen, if you would be so kind."

Waiting until everyone is silent, He continues, "My bride-to-be is resting under My wing right now. I have drawn her close because I am working in her life in such a way as to bring her into full partnership with Me. I am causing her love to mature.

"During this season, she is being strengthened and made whole. She is in a season of Divine Love and is not to be disturbed.

The day will come when I will ask her to go out and win countless souls for My kingdom, but that is not what I want her to do right now. Therefore, I charge you not to disturb her or try to recruit her for good works until this season of preparation is complete." [158]

He then turns His attention to Comforter and quietly says, "My Friend, you have done well; My bride grows increasingly lovely."

Comforter replies, "It is the love of her King that produces such beauty."

"And we both know that love never fails." The Two nod and smile at each other as if they have a wonderful secret.

My Beloved extends His arm to me and says, "It is time to escort you home, My love."

My wonderful Father kisses my forehead and softly says, "Regardless of what should come your way, We will always be here for you."

He then bids me good-night. My Beloved takes my arm and I ask, "What did Father mean by that?"

Comforter follows closely behind as we step outside.

"My love, there will be different seasons in your life just as there are different seasons in a year. Spring is the time when I plant new truths in your heart and usher you into new experiences with Me. Summer is when I water, prune and pull out the weeds that grow among the healthy things I've planted. Autumn is the season of harvest; it is when you not only see the matured fruit surrounding your life, but you also get to eat of it. Winter is the season of death. It is during this time that I prepare you for the next planting and harvesting time. Before every promotion comes a time of pruning.

"A seed must fall into the ground and die before it can bring forth fruit. Each season has a specific purpose, and each is for your good. It is important that you know the season that you are in so that you will be able to embrace what I am doing."

"I still do not understand," I respond.

"You will, My love, you will."

I look up and see Charity and three of her friends huddled around the fountain. As soon as they see us, they come running.

How will I ever endure their senseless chatter? Charity runs directly to me, grabbing my arm and saying, "I heard that you were here and just had to come and find out what it is that you have you been doing. Rumors are flying all over the village about you. I've been sitting here all evening just waiting for you to come out. I have so many questions!"

Holding up my hand, I say, "Please, Charity, perhaps another time would be better."

"Don't be silly. I don't know when I'll see you again and everybody is talking about your disappearance. Nobody seems to know exactly what happened to you. There's all this talk about you and the Master Shepherd and...." She lowers her voice, looks around to see if anyone is near and then continues, "There's even rumors that you are in love with the King. Can you believe it? You...and the King?" She laughs, long and loud.

Taking her hand in mine, I wait until she stops laughing then say, "Charity, the King and the Master Shepherd are one and the same. The King is kind and good. He loves the weak and broken and never rejects anyone who comes to Him."

With a shrug, she says, "So tell me, just when are you going to return to your family? When are you going to go back to work in the vineyards? What about the sheep, and when are you..."

My Beloved clears His throat and says, "Pardon Me, Charity, but I must interrupt."

Gently laying His hand on my shoulder, He continues, "She has just recently been through a very difficult season, and desperately needs rest. She is highly sensitive right now and easily distracted so I must ask that you not disturb her. If you will excuse us."[159]

He bids Charity and her friends good-night and then leads me on. I look back and hear Charity saying, "How rude! She just walked away without a word! What is she doing out here all by herself anyway?"

She didn't see Him! She couldn't hear Him!

"Charity couldn't see You, could she?"

"Some chose not to see."

"But, why? Why would anyone not want to see You?"

"Because they are comfortable with the ways things are and don't want to change," He answers.

"If she couldn't see You then how did she hear You?"

"I hold the hearts of kings in My hand and turn them which ever way I want."

I ponder His words all the way back to my cottage. By the time I get to my room, I am thoroughly exhausted, in a sweet way. After bidding my Beloved good-night, I quickly get ready for bed. On my pillow is a bouquet of beautiful lilies. I place them in the vase on my night table. I close my eyes and enjoy their lovely fragrance.

'Tis a strange thing — this love of mine. For unlike physical hunger, which lessens with the feeding, my hunger only grows fiercer, more demanding, when fed. I know that I will spend my life pursuing this beautiful Man. I will not be satisfied until I know Him and every facet of His being. I cannot live a life of lukewarm love — I must burn with desire for Him; anything less than that would be shameful.

My physical body is tired, but my mind is racing. I cannot sleep for thinking about my Beloved and the price He paid to make me His bride.[160]

After what seems like hours, I decide to write my Beloved a letter. I take the paper and ink on my night-stand, and after several attempts, compose this letter:

Rhonda Calhoun

To my Beloved,

I cannot sleep for thinking of You. The revelation of Your death lays heavy on my heart. How is it that You would die for me? You are so good and so perfect and I, well, I am nothing more than a peasant with nothing of value to offer One so great.

You are a rich, fertile oasis in the midst of a dry and barren land.[161] I am a lily growing among thorns.[161a]

My heart is glad that You have called me Your own, but I must admit that it is quite difficult for me to believe that You have truly chosen me. When I look into Your eyes and see the fire burning there, I can almost believe it. It is only when I fail to gaze on Your beauty that I become distracted with the things of this world. I have come to realize that there is nowhere I would rather be than with You.

I am poor, but with You by my side, I lack no good thing. I am weak, but You are strong. I am hungry and thirsty. Give me bread that I might eat and water that I might drink. Give me milk that I grow more in love with You, and give me wine that I might experience the exhilaration of knowing You intimately.

I eat from Your table, but never get enough. I am always searching, but never fully finding. I long to know You, to explore the chambers of Your heart.

Love of my life, I pray that You would come and possess me. Fill me with hunger so that I am never satisfied! May I know the sweetness of Your breath, hear the beating of Your heart, feel the touch of Your hand, taste the goodness of Your character, and see the beauty of Your face.[162] You are all I need and all I want. You are the love of my life, the reason I live. You are the light of my world, my Shepherd, my Redeemer and my King. I love You more than life!

Forever,
Your Bride-to-be

I fold the letter and then hurry down the hall. To my surprise, Comforter is still awake. Before I can ask, He holds out His hand and says, "I would be delighted to take your letter to the King."

"How did You know?"

"I know everything, Lovely Lady," He says, smiling, "I will personally deliver your letter."

"Thank You, Comforter." I kiss His cheek and then return to my room. Sleep comes quickly and easily now.

My night is filled with dreams of my Beloved riding through Hope Valley on a white horse. A large army rides with Him. Beside my Beloved is the captain of the army carrying a banner that reads:

"The Bridegroom King Loves His Princess Bride!"[163]

Rhonda Calhoun

The Sovereign King

Chapter Twelve
THE VOICE OF MY BELOVED

Behold he comes leaping upon the mountains. [164]

The days and months pass quickly. My Beloved and I walk in the garden every day. I thoroughly enjoy our times together as I am getting to know this incredible Shepherd-Savior-King. Father comes often to our little cottage and takes me on long walks. He is so kind and affectionate towards me, which is something I desperately need, having never known a father's love. He is a good Father, and I never tire of His company.

A year has passed since my Beloved brought me to this place. I can hardly believe the transformation that has taken place in my life and heart. I do not feel nearly as ashamed, my fears are subsiding and a new confidence fills me. Life has become enjoyable once again.

This morning, Comforter is teaching me how to make bread. I have learned much from my faithful Friend already. He has taught me how to run and play and dance. I am even learning how to laugh again. He has been instructing me in the ways of being a bride, giving me what He calls "Princess lessons".

Each time I express my feelings of unworthiness, which is still more often than I like, Comforter replies, "You are His bride whether you feel like it or not."

One would think that someone who was destined to rule and reign with the King would have everything she wants, that servants would wait on her hand and foot, and that she would never have to lift a finger, but that is not the way it is in this kingdom. As a matter of fact, I have learned that it is just the opposite. To reign in this kingdom, one must be a servant to all. One can do nothing from selfishness, but all is to be done with humility, regarding others as more important, always looking out for the best interest of others rather than your own.[165]

I am only just beginning to understand what it really means to be a follower and lover of the King. Often, I feel discouraged at my progress or lack thereof, but Comforter always tells me the same thing. I can hear His voice even now, "Lovely Lady, the flesh dies slowly, but it surely dies when immersed in a sacrificial life-style of unselfish love."

I look up at my dear Friend. He has already made four loaves of bread and is kneading the dough on another; I am still working on my first. "Comforter, why are we making so much bread?" I ask.

"One must always remember the poor," He answers.[166]

Pointing to the two loaves on top of the wood-burning stove, He says, "Those two are for a family whose husband is very sick and unable to work, and this one is for the widow, Anna."

"Comforter, I love everything about this place and I never, ever want to leave!" I say, clapping my hands together; a cloud of flour fills the air causing me to laugh. Comforter smiles, obviously delighted by my outburst. Just then the door opens and in walks my Beloved, who immediately starts laughing. "What's so funny?" I ask.

"You are!" He answers, "You're covered with flour from head to toe."

"Comforter is teaching me how to make bread," I say, proudly displaying my lump of dough.

"I can see that," He says, as He wipes the end of my nose with His finger.

"We will give this to the poor," I add.

"That is excellent since My Father defines pure and undefiled religion as taking care of the widows and orphans and keeping oneself unstained by the world."[166a]

Turning to Comforter I say, "Can I make bread for the poor every day?"

"As you wish, Lovely Lady."

The King takes my flour covered hand in His and says, "A sheep has wandered away and is believed to be on Mount Hermon. I must go at once to rescue it."

"Oh, no! Not Mount Hermon! You can't go there! No one has ever gone there and returned!"

"A Shepherd always goes after His sheep, regardless of where they wander or what the cost. You have nothing to fear, My love. This is not the first time I have ascended the Mountain of Myrrh, and I will most certainly return to you before night falls."

I look at Comforter, desperate for His intervention, but He simply smiles and says, "The King loves the lost more than He loves His own life, Lovely Lady."

Leaning against the doorway, I reluctantly and sadly bid my King farewell. Comforter stands behind me with His hand on my shoulder. I lean against Him as my Beloved disappears from sight. Oh, how my heart fears for His safety!

The day crawls by at a snail's pace. I wander around the yard watching for His return. Not able to eat, I sit under the old walnut tree and wait. The moon makes its appearance even though the sun has not fully set. Crickets, by the hundreds, are doing their best to sing louder than the large frog population hiding among the bulrushes.

Feeling quite restless, I remove my sandals and walk along the water's edge. I have gone only a short distance when, to my utter delight, I hear the sound of His voice.[167] I cannot understand His words, but I recognize that sweet, powerful voice piercing the approaching darkness. His song echoes off the mountains and floods the valley. "He's coming! The King is coming!" I shout.[168]

I scan the mountains until I see Him. He is leaping gracefully like a gazelle. I watch His every move. He runs like

Rhonda Calhoun

the wind. With great agility, every obstacle, every hindrance becomes nothing more than the smallest of ant hills before this awesome Man. He comes to me as a kind, gentle gazelle.

How like Him. He is kind, gentle and full of grace. A gazelle is not a predator—He is not coming to devour me.

With incredible speed, He descends the mountain. My Beloved is clothed in glory and majesty, power and authority. I stand trembling as I watch this awesome King conquering the heights and depths of this life.[169]

I run to Comforter, who watches from the cottage steps. Falling at His feet, I say, "Comforter, just who is this King that defeats every enemy and overcomes every obstacle? Just who is this King of glory?"[170]

"He, Lovely Lady, is the King of kings and the Lord of lords! To Him be the glory, honor and eternal dominion forever."[171] His words are weighty to my soul. We both look to the high places where the King continues his speedy descent.

How awesome and fearful He is!

Overwhelmed by the authority and power I see, I withdraw to the veranda and sit on a bench both to hide and to think about what I have seen.

I have never seen Him appear so powerful or mighty.

Someone knocks on the lattice door. My heart leaps. Behold, He is standing behind our wall, behind my wall of self-protection, my comfort zone. He stands behind the wall that shuts out the world with its problems and separates me from the needs of others. He is gazing at me through the lattice, standing ready for action.[172] My heart is pounding! He calls softly, "Rise up, My love, My beautiful one, and run with Me on the mountains!"[173]

Am I to run with Him on the mountains where people are devoured by wild animals and killed by thieves? Why should I leave my comfortable home? I remember all too well what it is like in the world; it is not safe. Those who should love and watch over me, rejected and used me. I love my Beloved, but I cannot go back there.[174]

I turn my face away.

He opens the latch and stands before me. "My love, it is to your advantage that you rise up and come with Me, for My kindness is unending and My jealousy is unyielding. The winter is past, and the rain is over and gone.

"Have you so quickly forgotten that I was faithful to you during the winter season when you experienced the harsh, bitter pain of rejection and compromise? I brought you through and rescued you from destruction. Therefore, you can trust Me in every season, My love.

"Spring time has come. My loving presence has brought forth great beauty and sweet virtues in you. You have truly blossomed under My tender affections. You are growing in maturity and grace. Look at your heart—your vineyard is in bloom. The time has arrived for singing.

"Come, My love, face your fears and the areas of compromise that remain in your life and run with Me. We will leap over every hindrance; We will remove every obstacle. It is indeed time to overcome those things that hinder you from complete obedience. So, leave behind your fears and come away with Me!"[175]

I am unable to respond. My Beloved kneels before me, taking my trembling hands in His strong, steady ones and says, "It is time for you to run on the mountains with Me."[176]

"But, I am afraid of heights and terrified of wild animals. I do not want to face my fears; I cannot go with You! Please don't ask me to."

I begin to weep.

Stroking my hair, He says, "Listen, My love. Can you hear the voice of the turtledove, which signifies the soon coming harvest?"[177]

He points to the cottage roof where two doves sit snuggled together. Their gentle cooing fills the air. He says, "The dove is pure, innocent and loyal to its mate. The dove has no peripheral vision and can only see straight ahead. You have eyes like the dove; stay focused, My dove, and arise.

"My darling, My beautiful one, come along, for this is not the time to draw back in fear, but to step out in faith trusting in My unfailing goodness. Come with Me to the harvest fields, to your friends and family and to the Mountain of Myrrh. You have nothing to fear, for I will take care of you just as I care for the lilies of the field."

He looks directly into my eyes, gently but firmly saying, "I did not bring you to this place so you could spend the rest of your life hiding under My wing. I brought you here to win your heart and capture your affections so you would follow Me wherever I might lead. With an unveiled face you will see My glory, which will transform you,[178] for I desire a partner who will go where I go and will rule and reign over the nations with Me."[179]

Ever so slightly He tugs on my hand. "Rise up, My love, My beautiful one. Take up your cross that you might wear a crown."[180]

My heart longs to obey; I desire to go, but fear paralyzes me. The King knows me even better than I know myself. Sitting beside me, He says, "My dove, you are so pure and true and loyal. I know you are afraid. Run to My side and hide yourself in what I did for you on the cross. Trust in Me. I will protect and sustain you. The question is, 'Will you obey Me even if you're afraid? Will you face your fears and allow Me to deliver you from them?'"[181]

I hear the tender love in His voice. I look away. I cannot go.

Placing His hand under my chin, He gently turns my face toward Him. "Do not turn away from Me, My love. I want to see your face, for it is lovely. Let Me hear your voice for your voice is sweet. During a time of crisis, do not turn away from Me, but cry out to Me. Tell Me what you are feeling, and allow Me to help you. Lift your voice and sing, daughter, sing."[182]

I respond, "My Beloved King, You have captured my heart. Now, capture the foxes in my life. I know how to catch the foxes that threaten the safety of my sheep, and I know how to catch the foxes that ruin the grapes, but I am unable to capture those things that spoil my growth and fruitfulness. I am unable to overcome those things that create fear in my heart. I am unable to overcome the areas of my life where I am guilty of compromise. Deliver me from them that I might be completely Yours. I have made progress and I see much improvement, but I cannot say yes to Your invitation."

Daring to look into His painfully pure eyes, I continue, "I thoroughly enjoy eating from Your garden and drinking from Your fountain. I love my comfortable cottage and the solitude that comes with it. But, I realize I am not really concerned about the harvest or my neighbors, and I certainly have no interest in conquering the Mountain of Myrrh. I can see there are still areas in my life that are not completely submitted to You, things that are still hidden. So, turn away from me and catch the foxes that are ruining our vineyards and deliver me from compromise and fear, for I cannot come with You as I am."[183]

"So be it," He responds.

My heart is gripped with searing pain as He turns and slowly walks away. Torn, I follow at a distance; my eyes fixed on the ground.

My Beloved speaks briefly with Comforter who hands Him His rod and staff. He is but a short distance away when, no longer able to contain the pain in my heart, I cry out, "I love You even though I have turned You away! I realize that You desire to feed me, not in a place of compromise, but among the lilies, among those who sincerely seek to walk in purity and innocence. So go, my Beloved, until the dawn breaks and the darkness in my life is consumed and conquered by Your unfailing love. Return to me when I am able to follow You wherever You go!"

My Beloved looks back; His look is one of great tenderness. He responds with a nod and then continues on His way. I shout, "My Beloved is mine and I am His!"[184]

Comforter draws near. In His tender way He says, "Lovely Lady, it may seem that your Beloved is forsaking you, but the truth is, He is embracing you all the more. The true Friend, the One who sincerely loves and cares for another, must bring discipline when the occasion demands it. Your Beloved is more concerned with you becoming all that you were created to be than He is in winning a popularity contest.

"The wounds that come from a friend are more faithful than the countless kisses of an enemy. How unfortunate that so many prefer the latter to the former. Your King must wound you that He might heal you. As strange as this sounds, His discipline truly is His most loving and most intimate kiss. He

Rhonda Calhoun

loves you way too much to leave you in a condition that will be and is detrimental to your well-being."

"Comforter, is there no other way?"

"There is only one way for the believer, and that is the way of the cross. You must understand that human devices are of no avail in a spiritual battle. Your battle is against the inclination within you to be your own god, to walk in your own strength and to make your own decisions. It is the way of the unredeemed, human heart.

"Lovely Lady, the King withdraws His presence to kindle an even greater fire in your heart. He is not angry with you, but desires that you fear no one or nothing. He desires that you allow nothing or no one to hinder you from walking in holiness and wholehearted obedience.

"Draw near to Him and He will draw near to you. For the King shares the intimate things of His heart with those who are wholly His, with those who lay their heads on His chest and listen to the sound of His heart and are willing to follow Him wherever He goes."[185]

"Comforter, I cannot go with Him. I am much too weak, and my heart is not fully His; I see that now. My beautiful Shepherd must leave. He must go so that my love will become greater than my fear."[186]

"Perfect love casts out all fear," Comforter adds.

I shout into the darkness, "Go, my Beloved, and run on the mountains. Run like the graceful gazelle, like a young stag on the mountains that separate us and overcome the obstacles that keep me from following You!"[187]

Chapter Thirteen
I MUST ARISE

On my bed, night after night I sought him. [188]

$\mathcal{I}$ watch for the One I love, but He does not come. I look for Him in all of our old meeting places, but He is not there. On my bed, night after night I try to figure out where He might be. Great is the pain and longing that fills my heart! [189]

Five very long weeks later, I realize that there is nothing I can do to make my Beloved return, even with all my prayers, all my worship, and all my searching. My heart is sick with grief. I never thought it was possible for a heart to long for another so deeply.

I spend this day, just like every other one, searching the grounds and calling to my Beloved, but He does not answer. Unable to eat dinner, I sit by the stream, staring at the Lebanon Mountains.

Is that where my Beloved has gone, or does He run on the dreadful Mountain of Myrrh?

"Just one moment in my Beloved's presence is better than a thousand elsewhere," I whisper. [190]

Comforter slowly approaches. "May I join you, Lovely Lady?"

"Certainly, my Friend."

"Your King loves you with a great tenderness, Lovely Lady. His absence is making you even more beautiful and glorious. I know that it seems like He has forgotten you, but the opposite is true. His eyes remain fixed on you, and He watches over you with great care. You will come through this test with a love in your heart that will sustain you through future storms and numerous trials of this life."

"Comforter, if the heavens were to open before me and I was able to see the angels in all their splendor, it would not satisfy this heart of mine, neither would it alleviate my longing for just one glimpse of my Beloved's beautiful face. There is no one or nothing that moves my heart like He does."

"Your King cares, Lovely Lady," He responds laying His hand on my arm.

"I know it is true. I know that He loves me and that He cares, but I long to hear His voice. How much longer before I can feast on His love and feel His kind touch again?" Looking toward the mountains, I whisper, "Return to me, my Beloved!"

Excusing myself, I stroll over to the King's garden and lean against the locked gate. Peering through the bars, I think back to the first time my Beloved brought me here. What a wonderful day that was!

I cannot see past the tall hedges, but I know what wonders and delights are hidden behind them. I whisper, "I long to walk through this garden and taste of Your goodness and mercy. But the truth is, without Your presence, even this perfectly delightful garden would not satisfy my heart."

I look at my lovely cottage, which overlooks Hope Valley. What was once my haven, my treasure, my delight now holds no attraction or comfort for me. It, too, has become empty.

I run to the sheep pen, hoping to find a little comfort among the sheep, but they have nothing to offer me. My heart finds no comfort or delight here either.

Everything I once loved and held dear no longer comforts me. Food has lost its flavor, beauty is empty and vain, pleasures offer no joy and rest is nowhere to be found. Without my Beloved by my side, there is no enjoyment or peace for me in this valley or in my heart.

I find Comforter waiting by the stream and join him. "Comforter, I seek solace but can find none. If all of nature were to join together to entertain me, I could not feel it nor receive it, for there is only One who can fill the void in my desperate heart. I must be with Him, whatever the cost."

"It is true—there is no other love that can satisfy your heart nor will there ever be. He alone truly satisfies."

"When will He come to me?" I ask.

"Do not wait for Him to come; go where He is. Leave behind your old, comfortable ways and pursue your Beloved, for there is no fear in love."

"I would if I knew where to look. I have prayed more than ever and still He hides His face from me. I have sung songs of love to Him and still He is silent. I have meditated on His words of life and still He withholds His presence. Comforter, if You know where He is, please do not withhold His location from me any longer."

"Lovely Lady, you know the answer, He has already told you," He says taking my hand in His. "Love has not been perfected in the one who allows fear to rule his heart."

I know He speaks truth. He always speaks the truth, but that is not what I want to hear. I am not interested in perfecting love; I simply want to know where to find my Beloved.

It is late, so I bid Comforter good-night and retire to my room. Falling across the bed, I see the dried lilies on the mantle— gifts from my Beloved, tokens of His love.

Oh, how I long to find Him!

Comforter's words come back to me.

Is He saying that fear rules my heart? Is that what keeps my Beloved from coming to me? Fear? Fear of what?

Suddenly, I understand. Fear has become an idol in my life. I have allowed it a place in my heart and given it permission to influence my decisions. Looking back over my life, I see that I have made fear a friend.

A still, small voice whispers in my ear, "Never make a decision based on fear, Lovely Lady."

With many tears, I cry out for help, repenting of my sin and asking for perfect love to fill me. Exhausted, I soon fall asleep

Rhonda Calhoun

and dream that I am a beautiful mare drinking from a river.

Over the sound of rushing water and rustling leaves, I hear His voice. Leaving my thirst behind, I gallop to the base of Mount Hermon where I see my King gracefully leaping over every obstacle, both small and large.[191]

My breath catches in my throat—what a striking King He is! We now stand face to face, heart to heart, eye to eye.[192] It seems as though He is peering into the very depths of my soul.

"Arise and come away with Me, for the time has come for us to run together on the high places. We will leap on the mountains and run on the hills. We will overcome every obstacle and climb to the highest heights. I will hide you in the clefts of the rocks, the shadow of My cross. In the safety of that place, you can tell me all that is on your heart."[193]

I look back at the green pasture with all its comforts. How can I leave my home? I want to say yes, but fear tugs on my bridle. The King sees and responds, "You have nothing to fear. The winter is behind you and the spring has come. The sun is shining, and the birds are singing. The grass is green, and the trees have all budded. The time has come for singing.

"Come with Me and run on the mountains. Together, we will leap over every hindrance and remove every obstacle. It is indeed time to overcome those things that hinder you from perfect obedience. So, leave behind your fears and come away with Me!"[194]

He reaches for my reins, but I draw back in fear. Reaching out again, He whispers, "You can trust Me."[195]

"My King, I love You—I am Yours! Only I cannot go with you. I want to, but I am too afraid. Please turn away from me; I cannot go."[196]

Stroking my neck, He replies, "You are My favorite mare. I have adorned you with splendid jewels and golden tassels. You are most elegant and strong."[197]

He then turns and walks away. He is nearly out of sight when He turns and shouts, "If you do not know where I feed My flock, then follow the trail of the flock and pasture your goats by the tents of the shepherds—there you will find Me."[198]

I wake with a start. I now know where He is! I will find

Him in the one place I refused to go—in the village with my brothers and the other shepherds. I will arise and leave behind my place of comfort, my place of safety. I must return to the village and find the shepherds![199]

Grabbing my shawl, I race through the cottage and out the door. Running through the darkness, I call out to the One I love. I run through the lush pastures, the frightening wilderness, and on to the village. I run without fear, without hesitation, for zeal consumes me.

Morning finds me running through the streets asking friends and even strangers if they have seen my Beloved; no one has. My intense longing to be with the One I love overcomes all my inhibitions and fears.[200]

It is lunch time, and the shepherds will be gathering around the village well; I hurry there. If anyone knows where the Master Shepherd is, it should be them. To my surprise, I learn that they have not seen Him in an even longer time than I.

Charity and several of her friends sit on the steps of the meeting hall, eating. I hurry to them asking, "Have you seen the One my soul loves?"[201]

Charity turns to her friends and exclaims, "What a silly girl she is to love so passionately!"

Her statement has no impact on my love-starved heart; I resume my search. I am resolute in my decision to seek Him with all my heart, my soul, my strength and with everything that is within me. I will not quit until I find my Beloved.

I have gone through every street in the village and have no idea where else to look when someone calls my name. I turn to see several shepherds making their way toward me.[202] I am flooded with relief when I see my old friend, David, among the shepherds.

He will certainly know where I can find Him.

With renewed energy, I run to them. "Have you seen Him whom my soul loves?"[203]

David eagerly responds, "We have been looking for you, my lady."[204]

"Please tell me you know where my Beloved is."

"Have no fear, we have only just left Him—He is in the

121 Rhonda Calhoun

garden gathering lilies."

"Lilies? Did you say lilies?"

"Yes, He is gathering lilies," David answers.

"Oh, how good He is! Once more He reminds me that I am His first love and I can trust Him, for He is all I need!" Without wasting another moment, I run to the village gardens. Scarcely had I left the shepherds, when I found the One my soul loves![206]

My Beloved Shepherd is feeding a newborn lamb from a bottle beneath the shade of the Tree of Life. A group of men, women and children listen intently as He shares the good news of His kingdom. A freshly picked bundle of snow-white lilies lay at His feet.

Seeing me, He smiles. No longer concerned with what people think of me, I run into the midst of them and fall at His feet weeping. "Whom have I on earth but You? Besides You, I desire nothing. My flesh and my heart may fail, but You are the strength of my life and my portion forever! I have made You my refuge. I will spend the rest of my life telling others of all Your works.[207] You have captured my heart and I will never, ever send You away again. You are all I want and all I need. I will never let You go!"[208]

"I have missed you, too," my dear Friend responds, softly chuckling.

Clinging to His ankle, I continue, "Come, my Beloved, and go with me to my mother's house[209] and to the house of my friends that they might know You as I have come to know You."[210]

My Beloved hands the lamb to a shepherd. He allows Himself to be captured by a mere human being. I lead Him through the streets to the outskirts of the village. Running inside my mother's house, I exclaim, "Mother, look Who has come!"

She looks up from her mending and replies, "So, you decided to come home, did you?"

"Mother, I have brought Someone to meet you."

Ignoring what I'm saying, she asks, "Where have you been, child? You abandoned your brothers in their work with no thought to our needs. And rumor has it that the King took you in, but that can't be true because you are nothing more than the fatherless daughter of a poor woman."

"But mother, it is true. The King did take me in and He loves me just as He loves you. Look, I have brought Him here even now."

"What are you talking about? There's no one here but you and me."

What is she saying? The King stands by my side, and I am holding His hand.

"Mother, He is right beside me. The Master Shepherd is really the Bridegroom King and He is right here."

My mother stands with her hands on her hips. "The Master Shepherd I know, but someone like me could never know the King. As for the Master Shepherd being the King, everyone knows that isn't true. Now stop this ridiculous ranting and come with me."

I follow, leading my Beloved into her bedroom. It seems strange to be back in this house. Everything looks so drab and is a bit disorderly; I never noticed that before. I see my rod and staff propped in a corner and my shawl hangs from a wooden peg.

Mother runs her hand over the shawl, saying, "I kept this, knowing that the day would come when you would come to your senses and once again return to us and to your sheep."

The front door opens and my two brothers enter, followed by several friends.[211] As soon as they see me, their expressions change from joy to obvious displeasure. Undaunted, I hurry to them, saying, "Look Who I have brought—."

"What are you doing here? Where have you been?" my eldest brother asks.

"I have been with the Master Shepherd, who is really the King. I have brought Him with me so you can meet Him."

"What are you talking about? There's no one with you but Mother," my younger brother answers.

"But He is standing right here beside me. Don't you see Him?" I ask.

They look at each other and shrug their shoulders. My oldest brother says, "Why don't you stay here with us? It is time you accepted the fact that you are a commoner and that is all

Rhonda Calhoun

you will ever be. You can help with the sheep, or, if you would prefer, you can work in the vineyard. Either way, it is better than living in a world of fantasy. And you never know, if you work really hard you might one day have a flock of your own."

"No, thank you. I will not make that mistake again. I will not ever leave my King—not for money, or fame, or pleasure, not even to gain your approval or acceptance."

I lean back against my Beloved and then continue, "Nothing will ever again be more important to me than my relationship with Him."

My King whispers in my ear, "I live to make intercession for you, My bride. You are always in My thoughts and I hold you in the hollow of My hand."[212]

"Mother, did you hear Him?" I ask.

"Child, you have become fanatical. Stay here with me and I will help you forget this nonsense."

"Mother, if you could only see the beauty of the King. If only you knew how much He longs to embrace you."

"Child, I do not believe for one minute that the King would have time for insignificant, poor people like us," she replies.

"But, mother, I understand because that is how I felt until I gave Him a chance. He proved it to me. It really is true! He desires to have an intimate relationship with you. He longs for that."

My youngest brother walks up and angrily says, "Don't you know that your very own father didn't want you? The day you were born he took off, and no one has seen him since. He abandoned us. And now you think the greatest King who ever lived wants to have a personal relationship with us? You are crazy!"

He storms outside.

My Beloved leans forward. "Come, My love, it is time to go," He says, gently squeezing my hand.

I bid my mother and brother farewell. If only they could see Him; if only they could know Him as I know Him.

"Where are you going?" my mother asks, her hands on her hips.

"Mother, I know that you don't understand, but I must

go with Him, I must follow where ever He leads."

"Then go, child, and don't ever come back."

We walk through the village in silence. I am thinking about my family.

I wonder if the reason my father left was because of me.

My Beloved whispers, "It was not your fault. You are not the reason your father left. Your father loved the trinkets that Compromise offered him more than he loved righteousness."

"I always wondered if it was my fault," I say as a mixture of relief and sadness floods my soul.

"Your father made a choice, and sadly, his decision adversely affected you and many others, but that does not mean the ones affected are to blame. Such is the nature of sin. But, you are not to blame, you are innocent, My love."

"Why didn't You intervene? What didn't you stop him? You are certainly powerful enough," I ask.

"Man was created with a free will. Neither Myself, Comforter or My Father will ever go against your will. Your father chose his path. We pursued him and did everything we could to get him to repent, but he would not. We shed many tears over the pain his decision caused in the life of your family. It was not what We would have chosen for you. We choose life every time; We choose righteousness.

"We did not forget you or your family; We kept you. We drew you. We watched over you. Do not think that because you suffered loss that We were not there. Pain is a part of this fallen world, but it won't always be this way. There is a day coming when I will ride in on My white horse and make wrong things right. I will gather together all who know Me and make them My bride. But I will judge the earth and will cast out all who have rejected Me. And what a terrible day that will be! Woe to My enemy on My wedding day!"

I am overwhelmed by this revelation.

Am I to be part of this bride? Is that what Comforter is preparing me for?

Approaching the village well, I see a small crowd gathered around Charity. Martha, one of Charity's friends, is the first to see me and immediately she pushes her way through the crowd to my side. Charity and the others follow. Martha lays her hand on my shoulder; I shudder for some reason. My Beloved gives my hand a reassuring squeeze.

Charity leans close and whispers, "I see that you found the Master Shepherd!"

"I found my Beloved King."

"I see no king, only a Shepherd," Charity responds.

I am beginning to understand that some people are limited in their ability to see my Beloved because they see Him through their own beliefs or lack thereof.

Martha addresses my Beloved, "Shouldn't she be tending sheep? And what about the vineyards? They need pruning. She has been tucked away with You for such a long time, and everyone knows that there is much work to be done in *Your* fields. As for me, I could certainly use some help with my work."[213]

I cling to my Beloved's arm, telling myself that I will go wherever He sends me and do whatever He says to do.

Reaching out, He gently removes Martha's hand from my shoulder, saying, "Martha, Martha, you are worried about so many things. There is really only one thing that is necessary and My darling, My beautiful one, has chosen it and it will not be taken from her."[214]

My Beloved then turns and addresses the crowd, "I charge you not to disturb My love until she is ready, for she remains under My care where I continue to strengthen her and make her whole. Make no mistake about it, the day will come when she will work in My vineyards. She will again shepherd My sheep, but it will not be until I say she is ready."[215]

Having delivered His message, He leads me away from the crowd, through the streets and out of the village. I take a deep breath. I am relieved that He did not send me back. It is so good to be alone with Him again. I walk in silence enjoying His closeness.

How do I communicate my affection to the King of kings? How can mere words flowing from some inner place of imperfection adequately express love to the One who loves so perfectly and so completely?

I stop and face this beautiful Man. Taking His hands in

mine, I say, "Good King, Safe Savior, I know that I will never, on this earth, while in this body, be able to honor you rightly. My words are such fragile, empty things compared to the greatness that I see in You."[216]

I look deep into the eyes of One who did not complain when demonstrating His love for me on a cross.

If only I could live my life the way my Beloved lives His. Is it possible for a heart like mine, so weak and prone to sin, to lay my life down for another, for Him? Can I learn to love unto death? I do not know the answer, but looking at my Beloved, I believe it just might be possible.

I say, "My Beloved, I will love You with all my heart and soul, with all that is within me. I will follow wherever You lead. I will walk the same path that You tread. I will deny myself, pick up my cross and follow You.[217] I will never send You away again. So, lead me on, my King. I will follow You anywhere!"

Rhonda Calhoun

The
Safe Savior

Chapter Fourteen
HOW BEAUTIFUL YOU ARE

Who is this coming up from the wilderness?[218]

*J*ust as we crest the hill overlooking Hope Valley, I see Father and Comforter standing beneath the old walnut tree. I glance at my Beloved and He nods. Needing no further encouragement, I run like a gazelle shouting, "Comforter! Father! I found my Beloved!"

I throw myself into my Father's arms. Spinning around, He says, "Welcome home, child. We have been waiting and watching for your return."

He sets me down. Dizzy, I stagger, nearly falling over while giggling like a young child. Comforter comes to my rescue and steadies me. "It is so good to see you, Lovely Lady," Comforter says.

I whisper, "It was just like You said—perfect love does cast out all fear."

"Indeed it does," He replies, tweaking the end of my nose.

Father takes my hands in His and looks deeply into my eyes. I feel such love for this affectionate Father; He is very good to me. Very tenderly and gently, He says, "Your father and mother have forsaken you, but I have taken you up. I will always love you, Little One."[219]

Rhonda Calhoun

Once more I fall into His wonderful arms and allow His love to wash over me filling me with peace. I then run a short distance away and spin around announcing to the world, "I am not fatherless anymore! I not only have a Father, but I have the kindest, most wonderful, loving Father in the whole wide world!"

My Father joins me. He kisses my forehead and says, "Allow Me to wipe your tears away, My dear child."[220]

I thought I knew what love was like, but I have found that the love expressed by these Three is far greater than anything I have ever experienced or dreamed possible. Joy floods my being and I begin to laugh. Running to my Beloved King, I exclaim, "Father loves me; He *really* loves me!"

"Much more than you know," He replies.

We cross the stream and I skip ahead, eager to be home. I stop just long enough to pick a handful of wildflowers. Running into my wonderful cottage, I see that the table is set with silver dishes filled with delicious looking food.

"There's no place like home," I whisper to myself.

In this place, the months pass quickly and soon winter arrives. I spend nearly every evening in front of the fireplace talking with Comforter, Father and my Beloved. I never grow weary of Their presence or Their words. Comforter speaks often about the importance of guarding my heart and my time because He says that I will become like the things that I focus on, the things that I give myself to. My heart is filled with hope each time I hear this because I am spending my days gazing on my Beloved and my nights dreaming of His goodness.

This evening, my Beloved and I walk arm in arm under a brilliant, star-filled sky. The snow has melted from the valley floor but still covers the surrounding mountain tops. As we enjoy the beauty surrounding us, my Beloved asks, "Do you know why I built you a cottage, My love?"

"So I would have a place to live?"

"That is true, but not entirely. The real reason is because I long for you to be a lovesick worshipper. I desire for you to live your life before an audience of One. In order for that to happen, you must know Me and the only way to know Me is to spend time with Me."

Taking my hand in His, He continues, "May I ask you a question, My love?"

"Of course."

"Are you in this relationship for Me or for yourself? Are you a follower of Mine because of what I do for you, what I give you?"

His question catches me by surprise. I want to answer that I am here solely for Him, but I know that is not the whole truth.

"What if I were to remove My presence for a moment?" He asks, "Would you still trust Me? If I removed the comforts and blessings that come as a result of your relationship with Me, would you remain true? If you lost everything, would you still love Me, would you still trust Me?"

My emotions are running rampant and out of control. I know what it is like to be alone. I know how much I enjoy all the fringe benefits of abiding in His presence.

After a long silence, I answer, "I honestly cannot say that I know the answer to Your questions. I know that I love You, but I also know that my heart is prone to selfishness. I fear that there is a part of me that revels in the glory of my position. I also know that being comfortable is important to me. So, I ask You to purify my heart and cause me to live for You and You alone."

"I shall, My dove, I shall."

"Why do You call me 'dove'?"

"Because, like the dove, you have eyes for only Me. Doves mate for life. They have no peripheral vision and can only see straight ahead; they aren't easily distracted. I am working to transform your life so that you will be like the dove."

We continue our walk in silence. My heart is heavy with the truth that His questions exposed.

I long to mature in purity and devotion for my King! How I long to be like the dove.

Spring comes quickly and with it the beauty of new life. The birds are singing, the trees are budding, flowers are breaking through the ground and the grass is bright green.

This morning, Comforter announces that I am to begin singing lessons. I almost laughed in His face because I am the most unlikely candidate for singing lessons. "Are you sure you've got the right girl?" I ask.

"Nothing is impossible with God, Lovely Lady."

So, with a blanket tucked under His arm, a basket filled with lunch and flute in hand, we head to my favorite tree by the stream. The warm sun feels so good on my face. All around robins diligently gather materials for their nests. Brightly colored tulips and daffodils grow in mass along the river bank. As far as I can see, flowers of every sort and color fill this valley with incredible beauty.

Comforter gives me my first singing lesson, which I find to be so delightful that, when He tells me it is time to stop for lunch, I beg Him to continue. He laughs and replies, "I thought you were the least likely candidate?"

"Like You said, 'Nothing is impossible with God.' "

While I eat, He plays the Song of the Lamb on His flute. Again the music so deeply touches me that I lay my bread down and lean my head against the tree, closing my eyes. As the last note fades, I can barely speak.

"Comforter, what is it about that song that renders me helpless?"

"It is a song that flows directly from the heart."

"It is so beautiful, much more beautiful than anything I have ever heard. Will you teach me the words?" I ask.

"This is a song which cannot be taught; it must flow out of your experience. You will hear it again and when the time is right, you will know the words."

Laying down His flute, He continues, "Do you remember the account of how your King died for you?"

"How could I ever forget something as painful and beautiful as that, Comforter?"

"Good. It is most important that one never forget, but allow me to tell you what happened after His death."

Turning to face me, He continues, "When your Beloved died, they laid Him in a tomb hewn out of a rock. On the third day resurrection power surged through His body, raising Him from the dead. All heaven watched as He descended into hell, took the keys of death and Hades from Satan and then sat down on His throne at the right hand of His Father."[221]

Comforter pauses; He scans the horizon then continues, "It is important that you know that the King you love is not only a God of love, but is also more powerful than anyone or anything in existence. He will protect your heart and keep you from harm. He knows everything there is to know about you; therefore, He knows how to lead you and keep you. You can trust Him. He is more powerful than death and the grave, more awesome than anything this world has to offer."

Suddenly, the ground begins to quake beneath me and a distant roar fills the air. Clutching Comforter's arm, I look up. A great cloud of dust fills the horizon. I jump to my feet. As the cloud grows closer, I can see that there are riders on horseback. "Who is this coming up from the wilderness surrounded with columns of smoke?" I ask.[222]

"That, Lovely Lady, is the King and His sixty valiant warriors. What you are looking at is a picture of your King's victory over sin and death. In a Garden called Gethsemane, your Beloved wrestled with the fact that He was to be crucified.[223] Three times He cried out to His Father, 'Let this cup pass from Me, I pray! Nevertheless, not My will, but Your will be done.' His agony was so intense that His sweat became mixed with drops of blood.

"In that Garden, He was crushed like an olive, and fragrant oil poured forth. He may have given His life on the cross, but the decision was made and sealed in the Garden when He surrendered to His Father's will and drank the cup, which was the price of your betrothal. But death could not hold Him. He rose from the grave just as you see Him today—clothed in great power, fragrant with the scented powders of One who purchases valuable treasures and surrounded by an angelic host.[224] How awesome in beauty and mighty in power is your King!"[225]

"I long to know Him in His fullness," I whisper.

"And so you shall, Lovely Lady, so you shall. But look, your Beloved brings His palanquin."[226]

"What's a palanquin?" I ask, straining to locate my Beloved in the midst of the thick cloud.

"A palanquin is a traveling couch. Your King is not

Rhonda Calhoun

content to have another make your couch. He made this one with His very own hands. It is how He brings His bride safely through the dangers of this life and to His eternal home."

My heart races as they draw closer. I see my Beloved and my heart leaps! Even after all this time, I still have the same reaction to His presence.

Comforter continues, "Lovely Lady, the King is not content that He and I be your sole defender, but He has brought an extravagant number of His strongest and most loyal servants to guard you.[227] They are all native born, which means that they are not hired hands, but they will lay down their lives to protect you. They are valiant soldiers who are experts with the sword.

"Notice that they are dressed in armor and each has a sword at his side—they will guard you against the terrors of the night and the powers of darkness. Your Beloved is extravagant in His protection over you! He wants you to know that He is more than able to keep you safe, even in the midst of great persecution and danger."[228]

My Beloved dismounts by the river's edge, hands the reins to one of His guards then walks toward me. I do not wait for Him to reach me, but run to Him with Comforter close behind. I bow low before my King; He takes my hand and raises me up saying, "Come, My darling, and see what I have made for you."

We wait for the dust to settle, then begin our walk to meet those who carry the palanquin. We have gone but a few steps when the sweetest, most delightful perfume fills the air. Turning to Comforter, I whisper, "Is that myrrh and frankincense I smell?"

"Yes, Lovely Lady, it is. Your Beloved has just come from the Mountain of Myrrh and the Hill of Frankincense."

"Myrrh is a burial spice and frankincense is used by priests when offering up prayers," I say.

"That is true. The King intercedes for you day and night, thus the frankincense. As for the myrrh, His death and resurrection were bathed in its sweet fragrance, which He still wears."[229]

We walk in silence. The two fragrances mingled together are intoxicating and grow stronger the closer we come to the palanquin, which eight royal attendants carry on their shoulders.

The men lower the palanquin and Comforter pulls back the curtain, revealing the couch's magnificent interior. With a wave of His arm, He says, "Your King has made this couch for you with cedar from Lebanon. Cedar never rots. It is a fragrant, costly and rare wood.

"The supporting pillars are made of silver, which represents your redemption. Its chair is of solid gold, which speaks of the divine character that is being formed in you. The cushioned seat is made of purple fabric, which is the color reserved for royalty.

"Lovely Lady, your Bridegroom has used only the finest of materials to build this for you and has filled it with love. Silver is better than cedar, gold is better than silver, but love is better than gold, better than them all. You will be filled and saturated with love, for nothing is better than that." Turning to face me, He adds, "This palanquin also represents you."[230]

I cannot believe my eyes. This couch is extremely luxurious and ever so beautiful.

My Beloved walks up, I say, "I have never dreamed of anything this beautiful in my entire life. To think that You are comparing it to me is more than I can imagine. And to think that You made it just for me is even more amazing," I say to my Savior-King.

"Yes, My beautiful one, I made this just for you. As you travel through the wilderness of this life, with all its dangers and turmoils, you will be carried safely through in this couch."[231]

I step inside and run my hand over the rich fabric. I am in awe of His extravagance. He continues, "I withhold no good thing from you. Your heart has been infused with My strength and virtues. I have filled you with charity and peace and beautified you by My death. I have placed My very own life within you and made you Mine. I have given you eternal life and adorned you with My righteousness."

I quietly whisper, "Oh, how magnificent and how costly is this couch that You have made for me!"

Hearing someone call my name, I turn to see that a group of young people from the village have followed my Beloved.

Rhonda Calhoun

Every eye is fixed on the King and me. Charity is among those who stand watching. An intense desire for them to know the Master Shepherd as their Bridegroom floods my heart. My Beloved leans over and whispers, "Go and tell them."

Without hesitation, I obey.

With surprising confidence, I say, "Charity, Martha, friends, I now know the secret of living a life filled with joy and peace. It is a simple thing really. The key is to pour out all that you are and all that you have on the only One who is worthy of such adoration and affection. As you do, you crown Him with a glorious crown, a crown of voluntary love, which is much better than crowning Him with a crown of thorns."

Martha interrupts, "What are you talking about? The King would never wear a crown of thorns! It's really true what people are saying about you — you've lost your senses! You *are* crazy!"

"Martha, have you never noticed the crown of scars He wears? Draw close to Him and you will see not only them, but you will also see other evidences of His great love for you."

How I long for her to see His beauty and know His goodness, but my words appear to be ineffective.

Charity draws closer and so do a few others, but Martha and several others step away. Undaunted, I continue, "My Beloved has loved me enough to grant that I, too, might have the honor of having, in a small way, fellowship in His sufferings and it is sweet to my soul. I encourage you to go forth and gaze on this Man. Allow your heart to be captured by His affections because His love is beyond anything this world has to offer. Leave behind your comforts, fears, imperfections and selfish ways and dedicate your heart to Him.

"Go forth, daughters, and gaze on your King. As you do, you will crown Him with a most beautiful crown. He will betroth Himself to you and that will be the day of His gladness of heart, for truly He desires to make you His Bride. As a Bridegroom rejoices over his bride, so your King will rejoice over you. He is a safe Shepherd, but He is also a magnificent Bridegroom King."[232]

Charity's eyes are filled with tears. Taking her hand in mine, I lovingly say, "It is true, Charity. You can know Him as the Bridegroom King, too."

"But I do know Him," she replies.

"You know Him, but only as the Master Shepherd. You need to know Him as your Bridegroom King. He is so much more than a Shepherd; He is so much more than a kind Father; He is so much more than a Savior. You need to know Him in His fullness, for He longs for that more than anything," I answer.

For a moment, it appears that she is going to turn to Him, but instead she covers her ears and runs away. My heart is sad; I remember a day when I did the same thing.

Suddenly, my Beloved looks directly at me and shouts, "How beautiful you are, My darling, how beautiful you are!"[233]

I run to my Beloved. We stand face to face, heart to heart looking into each other's eyes. I love this Master Shepherd, this glorious King! Every voice is silent and every eye is now fixed on us.

My King takes my hands in His and continues, "You have grown in grace and beauty, My love. Your eyes now see clearly and you look at Me with devotion and purity, just like the dove.[234] Your dedication, which before was vain and disorderly like goats scattered over the mountains, is now extravagant, orderly, pure and submissive.[235] You have learned well, My love, for you have received My word and allowed it to cleanse you from that which was impure and unbalanced. Your diligence has been rewarded. You are and will be quite fruitful, My love."[236]

Laying His finger on my lips, He traces the outline of my mouth saying, "Your lips are like a scarlet thread and your mouth is absolutely lovely. Your speech is filled with grace and purity...like the daughter of a King. Our relationship is intimate and full of grace."[237]

Brushing the hair back from my face, He whispers, "You blush at My words, My love. Oh, how sweet your emotions are to Me! Your heart is so tender and genuine...you have surrendered all to Me. Your thoughts are continually focused on Me. You listen as I speak and meditate on My words allowing them to transform your life.[238]

"You could have chosen another, but you have chosen Me. You have set your affections on My purposes. Your will is like a strong fortress resisting everyone and anything that hinders

Rhonda Calhoun

My purposes.[239]

"You have matured. Now you have the ability to love and nurture others and you do so with a delighted heart. You have fed on the truth, on the pure food from My garden. Now you have much to give to others, for a vessel cannot give what it does not contain. You have done well, My love."[240]

I kneel before Him and respond, "My Beloved, if this is really who I am, then I say 'yes' to You now. I refused to go with You before because of fear,[241] but now I will go my way to the Mountain of Myrrh and to the Hill of Frankincense that I might overcome the obstacles that hinder me from following and loving You completely.

"I realize that I am not fully mature and still have areas in my heart that need correcting, but I will go with You anywhere. I will go to the Mountain of Myrrh. I will fully abandon myself to You and Your purposes. I still feel weak and broken, but I realize now that it is not about feeling qualified. It is about me trusting in You and Your ability to keep and empower me. All the days of my life I will seek Your face and love You with all that I have and all that I am."[242]

My Beloved responds, "I will allure you. I will bring you into the wilderness and speak kindly to you. I will give you vineyards and you will be fruitful. But, for your sake, I must also allow seasons of difficulty and suffering. In the midst of suffering, you will sing as you did in your childhood.

"And it will come about in that day that you will call Me 'Husband' and will no longer call Me 'Master'. And I will betroth you to Me forever. Yes, I will betroth you to Me in righteousness and in justice, in lovingkindness and in compassion. And I will betroth you to Me in faithfulness, then you will truly know Me intimately."[243]

Chapter Fifteen
THE MOUNTAIN OF MYRRH

I will go my way to the mountain of myrrh and to the hill of frankincense. [244]

$\mathcal{B}$idding my Beloved farewell, I hurry to Comforter's side and say, "I understand that every person has a God-ordained path to walk. This is not a random path, but one that is carefully chosen by the King. Therefore, I must go my way to the Mountain of Myrrh and the Hill of Frankincense. I need to do this so that I might overcome my fears. and learn what it means to be a priest in the house of God. I must embrace my cross and follow the Path of Life.[245]

"Comforter, I must never refuse my Beloved again. I must overcome my greatest fear, for only then will I be truly free to follow wherever He should lead. And for me, that means I must climb the heights of the dreadful Mountain of Myrrh. I shall depart straightaway, before fear overcomes me and I change my mind."

"I shall accompany you," my dear Friend replies.

"Oh, thank You, Comforter," I exclaim throwing my arms around His neck, "I was hoping you'd say that."

After packing the necessary provisions, we set out. Comforter leads the way. I have a feeling this is going to be very difficult, but I refuse to dwell on the hardships that I am certain lie ahead. Instead, I set my heart on obeying my Beloved and think of Him only.

After several days, we finally arrive at the base of the Mountain. I am filled with fear, fear of heights and the fear of becoming a meal for some wild animal. I am seriously thinking of returning to my comfortable cottage when I see a solitary lily growing through a small crack in the rocks. This small flower has pushed its way through impossible circumstances in order to stand tall and bloom. I remember my Beloved's words, "You are a lily among thorns."

How my heart is encouraged at this reminder — my Beloved finds me lovely just like this determined lily, and He will cause me to bloom even in this treacherous, barren place. I turn to Comforter and say, "I will lift up my eyes to the mountains, but where shall my help come from?"

Comforter responds, "You tell Me...where shall your help come from?"

I continue, "My help comes from my Beloved who made heaven and earth. He will not allow my foot to slip, and He who keeps me will neither slumber nor sleep."[246]

"You speak truth, Lovely Lady," Comforter says.

"And the truth will set me free," I say as I begin the arduous climb.[246a]

Because of the extremely rugged terrain, it takes several days to make it to the top. This mountain is desolate and absolutely undesirable. There is nothing here except a large variety of wild animals, barren land, razor-sharp rocks, and, at the top, snow drifts higher than my head.

Comforter searches until He finds a small cave. Digging out the opening, He announces this will be our new home. Using a broken branch, I brush the snow out of the mouth of the cave while Comforter scours the surrounding area for firewood.

As the sun sets, I light the fire while Comforter drags a log inside so that we will have a place to sit. Enjoying a meal of dried meat, bread and pomegranates, I have very little to say.

Feeling exhausted, both physically and emotionally, I bid Comforter good-night and spread my blanket as close to the back of the cave as possible. Lying with my back to the opening, I close my eyes. I feel so vulnerable; this mountain is infested with lions, leopards and other animals seeking anyone or anything to devour. And I know they are really hungry right now.

An owl continually asks, "Whoooo? Whoooo?" Growing more irritated by each hoot, I imagine myself running out and shouting, "Me, that's who!" It isn't very long before a pack of wolves adds their howling to the various other frightening sounds on this mountaintop.

No one ever returns from these mountains; no one ever lives to tell of this place. I will die here, I am sure of it. Fear knots its fist in my stomach, but to leave now would accomplish nothing. I must overcome my fears even if it means my death.

Fear has convinced me that a lion or a leopard is lurking just outside the cave waiting for me to fall asleep so that I can be its midnight snack. Everything in me wants to quit, give up and run down the mountain back to the safety and comfort of my cottage. I am terrified.

With every ounce of courage I can muster, I turn over facing Comforter who has made His bed near the mouth of the cave. His back is toward me. My voice trembles as I quietly call His name. He does not answer. I call louder. He still does not respond. After the third time, I decide He must be asleep. Closing my eyes, I cry out, "Kind Father, I am so afraid. Please fill me with Your perfect love and chase away all my fears. Surround me with Your mighty angels and protect me from my enemies, for this child is in need of Your protection."

I open my eyes. I still hear twigs cracking and wolves howling. My heart is still racing. Not knowing what else to do, I sing. My song echoes throughout the cave, drowning out the voices of my enemies. I sing myself to sleep.

The morning sun rises over the mountain range. Its long arms of light reach into my place of refuge and rest on my face, waking me. I see that Comforter has a fire burning; the wonderful aroma of sizzling meat fills the air. He smiles and says, "Good morning, Lovely Lady. I trust you slept well?"

Rhonda Calhoun

Pulling my shawl tightly around my shoulders, I join My Friend on the log. "Not exactly. I was quite frightened, so I sang myself to sleep."

"I heard your worship; it was beautiful. It seems your singing lessons did some good," Comforter says trying to cheer me up. He hands me some bread and cheese.

"Then, You were awake?"

"Yes."

"Then why didn't You answer when I called?"

"Sometimes it is best not to rescue, Lovely Lady."

Taking a bite of cheese, I think about His response.

"Comforter, why am I really here?"

"You are here because you desire to be."

"I had no idea the Mountain of Myrrh would be like this. I did not know that it would be this frightening, this cold and this challenging. How long must I stay here?"

"You can leave now, Lovely Lady. No one holds you here."

"But that wouldn't accomplish anything, would it?"

"Lovely Lady, you are here to die to your selfish desires and impure motives so that you might live wholly devoted to your King. As for how long you will be here — you alone hold the answer to that question."

"But Comforter, I am eager to return to my Beloved. I miss Him already and I miss my warm, comfortable cottage and the apples and raisin cakes. I miss the stream and the beauty that surrounds my cottage. Perhaps, it would be best for me to go now?"

Comforter replies, "As I said, you may if that is what you want. The King does not demand your love. The love you possess is the one thing you can give Him that no one else can give. It is your choice to be here just as it is your choice as to when you leave. If you choose to stay, you will be anointed with myrrh, which is the oil used to symbolize obedience unto death. But, Lovely Lady, you must understand that you cannot really live until you die to your selfish desires and ambitions. If you choose to leave before you have fully surrendered your will and your life, then you will miss out on the fullness of what Your King has planned for you. And if you do so, We will still love you...that will never change."

"Comforter, I want to die to myself more than I want to feel safe and comfortable. Please, tell me, what must I do to please my Beloved."

"This is not about doing something to please the King; you already please Him. This season in your life is meant to cause your love to mature. Like I've said before and will probably say a hundred more times, there is nothing you can do to cause your King to love you any more than He already does. Likewise, there is nothing you can do to cause Him to love you any less.

"Life is not primarily about doing; it is about being a lover of God and a lover of men. It is impossible to work your way into the image of your King, Lovely Lady. On this mountain, you will learn what it is to deny yourself, pick up your cross and follow the path that your Beloved walked. You will learn how to live and love as He lived and loved."

"That is my greatest desire."

"Then stay here where your Beloved embraced death. He lay in the tomb until resurrection power surged through His body. Myrrh must be crushed and pierced before its fragrance is released. It is quite fearful and most difficult to yield to the crushing and piercing process, but it is truly rewarding, since it yields the peaceable fruit of righteousness."

Seeing my obvious distress, Comforter takes my hand and continues, "Lovely Lady, nothing is more desirable than the surpassing value of knowing your Beloved Bridegroom King intimately. Whatever price you are called to pay, it is worth it. The slain Lamb must have a slain bride, for He will not be unequally yoked."

"Comforter, I choose to stay. I position myself to receive all that my Beloved has for me. I will stay here and die to my selfish desires and ambitions. I will face my fears. I will endure discomfort and hardship if it means that I will become more like my Beloved."

Taking my hand in His, He says, "You are a wise maiden. Now, allow Me to anoint you with the oil of myrrh."

I stare into the fire. I have so many questions.

Rhonda Calhoun

I look into Comforter's kind eyes; He is such a good Friend and I trust Him. "I don't understand this kingdom, but what I do know is that I was so afraid of leaving my comfort zone that I refused to go with my Beloved. I turned Him away. I don't ever want to do that again. So, do what You need to do to purify my heart that I might live my life in one hundred percent obedience following my Beloved anywhere He should lead. You have my permission to anoint me with the oil of myrrh."

I kneel before Him. Comforter crushes the myrrh and places a small amount on my tongue. It is extremely bitter. He then removes the cork from a horn of oil. The extremely fragrant myrrh floods the cave. "Lovely Lady, with this oil, I anoint you for service to your King."

A shiver runs through my body as the oil runs over my head. "May I live only for my King. Crucify my flesh and cause me to overflow with the oil of His love that I might be a light in the midst of a dark world. May I look like Him, smell like Him and carry my heart like He does from this day forward. I pray that I would shine with the light of His love all the days of my life."[247]

"And so it shall be," Comforter adds.

I spend the day perched on a large rock near the edge of the mountain, wrapped in a blanket, reflecting on my life and meditating on my Beloved. I retire early and, unlike last night, sleep ever so peacefully.

I wake to the sound of Comforter singing as He prepares breakfast. I hurry to join Him. After eating, we step outside and sit together on the rock. The sun is just coming up over the distant mountains. In a matter of minutes, its glorious light drives away the darkness and paints the surrounding mountain range and valley with vivid red and gold colors. The whole scene is absolutely breathtaking.

Comforter says, "There is an aspect to the Mountain of Myrrh that is most important and extremely valuable to your growth, Lovely Lady."

"I thought this place was a place to die, not grow," I say.

"Except a seed fall into the ground and die, it cannot bring forth fruit."[248]

One must die in order to live — what a strange concept - but so many things Comforter has taught me are quite contrary to the ways of the world.

"So tell me, Comforter, what else is there for me to know about this place of death and dying? Whatever it is, I will do it."

"I am glad to hear you say that. The gift I have to offer you is the gift of fasting," He states.

"Fasting! You can't be serious! Are you suggesting that I go without food?"

"Only if you want to."

"But, I'll be hungry!"

He softly laughs and replies, "Yes, you will be hungry."

"I don't see what's so funny. I can't live without food! How can I go without food?"

"Lovely Lady, you are indeed a delight. As for being hungry, you will certainly feel hungry, but you will find that fasting accelerates the movement of your heart unlike anything else. Fasting is a gift from your Father and something that is greatly to be desired."

I look away not really wanting to hear more. I find myself thinking of the times my Beloved King fasted. Before I met Him, I heard that He fasted forty days. One day I asked Him why others did not fast, and He answered, "While the Bridegroom is with you, the attendants do not fast, do they? But the time will come when I will be taken away from you, and then you will fast."[249]

I have often wondered what He meant. I turn back to Comforter and say, "I'll think about it, but I'm not promising anything."

Did I just say what I think I said?

"Instead of just thinking about it, why don't you talk to your Beloved about it? See what He has to say."

I walk a short distance away and pray for the grace that will be necessary for me to deny my appetite.

The first few days are very difficult. Every time I am tempted, which is often, I say to myself, "I love my Beloved more than I love food."

I am extremely hungry, but I finally get to a place of joy

Rhonda Calhoun

and even exhilaration; my flesh is certainly being crucified.

Each morning, Comforter anoints me with the fragrant oil of myrrh. I am learning to embrace those things that feed my spirit and to refuse those things that feed my flesh. I am learning the importance of doing what the King desires, rather than what I desire. I am learning to love more and complain less. I am learning that there is value in self-denial and suffering.

Comforter was right; fasting does cause my heart to soar! I love my Beloved more than I love indulging my fleshly appetites.

Six long months pass during which time I fast one day a week. I have learned what it is to live a sacrificial lifestyle. I have suffered much loss, but it all seems so insignificant in comparison to the price my Beloved paid for me. Much has been given; therefore, much is required. There have been many things that I have surrendered – things which I dare not mention, especially when I measure them by the sufferings my Beloved endured for my sake.

Today was an especially long day, and I am thrilled when it is finally over. I lie down on the hard ground to sleep and picture my Beloved's face. I have grown even more fascinated with His beauty in this place where beauty is nowhere to be found.

I am surprised when, instead of spreading His pallet by the mouth of the cave, Comforter places it beside me. Lying down, He says, "Lovely Lady, it is time."

"Time? Time for what?"

"It is time to leave this place of myrrh and travel to the Hill of Frankincense where you will be anointed with fragrant perfume."250

Can it be true? Am I to leave this barren, desolate place where predators lurk in the dark, watching and waiting for me to stumble or grow careless?

"Are You sure, Comforter? Am I truly ready? I don't want to leave a moment too soon."

"Lovely Lady, I am sure, for you have learned the value of dying to self. You have learned to love even in the midst of great hardship. In the morning, we shall begin our descent," He answers.

With a happy heart, I fall asleep and dream of my Beloved. I wake before the sun. Comforter sits just outside the cave softly playing His flute. Closing my eyes, I listen as He plays the Song of the Lamb. My heart longs for the day when I will know the words to that song.

Eager to face the day, I join Him. Together we watch the rising sun once again chase away the darkness and flood the valley with its glorious light.

"You have grown in grace and beauty," Comforter says.

"Thank You, Comforter, for You have made me thus. You have created in me a desire to live my life in such a way that I might be consumed, just like the darkness, so that my Beloved can shine through me, just like the sun shines.[251] I hope and pray that my life will be pleasing to my Beloved."

"It already is, and so it shall be, Lovely Lady. You have grown in great grace and beauty like the dawn. You have become as beautiful as the full moon, as pure as the sun. Now, come and let us prepare to leave that we might journey to the Hill of Frankincense."[252]

Rhonda Calhoun

Chapter Sixteen
THE HILL OF FRANKINCENSE

I will go my way to the hill of frankincense. [253]

*C*omforter and I carefully make our way down the treacherous mountain. It is much easier descending than it was ascending. Several leopards follow close behind, but I feel no fear, which amazes me.

We arrive in the Valley of Decision, which is not nearly as beautiful or fertile as Hope Valley, but it certainly looks inviting after being on that barren mountain for so long. I consider staying here for awhile because it would be so easy, but that thought quickly leaves as I look at Comforter's kind face. At my bidding, we continue on.

My family's village is not too far from here; I can almost see the rock wall surrounding it. *I wonder what my friends and family are doing right now. I'm sure they're not suffering like I am.*

In an effort to reign in my wandering thoughts, I ask, "Where is this Hill of Frankincense?"

"It is one of the rich, fertile mountains in the Lebanon mountain range."

"It is near Father's palace and my cottage then?" I excitedly ask.

"It is not far from your home, Lovely Lady."

Rhonda Calhoun

My heart soars! *At least I will be a little closer to my Beloved and the beautiful Hope Valley.*

The following evening, we arrive at the base of the Lebanon mountains. Comforter points out a small mountain and identifies it as the Hill of Frankincense. Looking at its lush vegetation and gentle slopes, I am relieved. This place looks so much more inviting than the Mountain of Myrrh. "Comforter, what a wonderful place this is!"

"Indeed it is, for this is the hill where your Bridegroom died."[254]

Filled with mixed emotions, I ask, "This is the place?"

Comforter startles me as He suddenly cries out, "Who may ascend the hill of the Lord? And who may stand in His holy place?"[255]

His voice echoes off the mountain and into the valley. Holy fear fills me and I fall to the ground. An unseen, Divine presence surrounds me; I dare not look up, but bury my face in the grass. I lay there trembling. When the glorious presence lifts, I cautiously look up and ask, "Who may ascend this holy hill, Comforter?"

"The one who has clean hands and a pure heart, who has not lifted up his soul to falsehood and has not sworn deceitfully."[256]

Lifting my eyes to heaven, I pray, "Father, I can never achieve this myself. Will You purify my heart and cleanse my hands that I might ascend Your holy hill?"

Comforter answers, "The Father will pour out the spirit of grace and intercession on you in this place."[257]

He reaches out and taking my hand, beckons, "Come, let us begin our journey."

I hesitate. "Comforter, I know my heart; it is weak and prone to wander. Who am I to ascend this holy hill?"

"Who are you? Let me tell you who you are. You are the blood-bought daughter of the Ancient of Days and you have been chosen by the King of kings to be His bride, His eternal partner! You are the love of His life and the one He longs for! You are flesh of His flesh and bone of His bone! You are His most prized possession, the soon to be treasure of heaven! You are beautiful and ever so delightful! You are destined to rule and reign with the King of kings for all eternity! You are whiter than snow, brighter than the noonday sun! You are His chosen one, His disciple, His bond-servant, His friend, His sister, His daughter and you will be His bride for all eternity! *This* is who you are."

"But, I fear this holy place," I respond.

"Be strong and courageous! Do not tremble or be dismayed, for I am with you wherever you go."

I grip His hand. "Stay close, Comforter. Please don't leave me or let me go."

Climbing this hill requires such little effort compared to the Mountain of Myrrh. I am surrounded by such beauty that I soon forget my fears and, after a short time, even hurry ahead of Comforter but never very far.

We make it to the top before sunset and I am finally able to relax. The view is amazing; I can see for miles. I can see the distant Mountain of Myrrh, my family's village and the wilderness. Turning to my right, my heart leaps, for I have a splendid view of Hope Valley. Somewhere nearby is my Beloved and my Father. I miss Them very much and long for the day when I will be with Them again.

"It is magnificent, is it not?" Comforter asks.

"It is indeed! I think I am going to like it here."

"I know you will, but not for the reasons you think," Comforter answers as He walks away.

Hurrying after Him, I ask, "Now, what did You mean by that? On second thought, perhaps, I shouldn't ask. Is this something I want to know, Comforter?"

He spreads out a blanket and hands me some fruit, bread and cheese, saying, "I only meant that there is more to this place than meets the eye, if you have eyes to see and ears to hear. But, we will talk of this later."

Somewhat nervous, I break off a piece of bread.

Whatever He is talking about cannot be as difficult as the Mountain of Myrrh.

I decide to ignore His comments and change the subject. "Comforter, I am so glad to be in this place. There are no lions or leopards lurking around, waiting to devour me. The weather is

Rhonda Calhoun

warm, the sun is shining and everything is lush and green. I am surrounded by beauty."

"This is a good place, Lovely Lady, but not only because of the reasons you stated. This place is good because here is where you will find your voice."

"Find my voice? I didn't know I lost it."

Chuckling, He replies, "You cannot lose something you never had."

"Comforter, why must You talk in riddles? Please speak plainly."

"So be it. In this place, you will find the voice of your heart. Here I will teach you to pray. Here you will intercede on behalf of those who are lost in the Valley of Hopelessness and the Valley of Despair. You will cry out for the broken and the poor of the earth. The spirit of prayer will come upon you and lives will be changed and souls saved as a result of your intercession."

I sit in silence as His answer fights its way from my head into my heart.

This seems like a good thing and quite painless, so why does Comforter sound like I'm not going to like it? Am I missing something?

Curious, I ask, "So, unlike the Mountain of Myrrh, I get to actually *do* something here?"

"Yes, Lovely Lady, you get to do something here. But, remember your King has countless angels around His throne— He doesn't need anymore servants. He can have anything He wants, yet He craves your affection."

"Like I said, I think I'm going to like this place."

I bite into the sweet flesh of my peach; the juice runs down my arm, making me laugh.

The sun sets as Comforter leads me to a tent hidden under the boughs of an enormous weeping willow tree. Inside, I find a feather mattress, an oil lamp along with several flasks of oil, and writing utensils.[258] Lying on top of the mattress is a bouquet of snow-white lilies.

Where did they come from? Could it be that my Beloved was here?

I hurry outside, but before I can ask, Comforter says, "He has left, Lovely Lady, but He does come here often."

Going back into my tent, I pick up the flowers. *He was here and left me a token of His affection. How good and kind He is!*

Inhaling the sweet fragrance, I picture His face, His eyes, His mouth. *I long to complete this season of preparation so I can return to my Beloved!*

I quickly fall asleep and dream of my wedding day, which takes place in a beautiful garden filled with lilies. I awake well before dawn to the sound of a shofar. Hurrying out, I find Comforter standing on a rock wall, in the dark, with shofar in hand. "Comforter, what has happened?"

"I sounded the alarm because there is a crisis in the village.[259] A lion has made its way down from the Mountain of Myrrh and prowls the streets somewhere within the village walls."

My heart sinks. "Surely there is someone who can find the beast and destroy it?"

"You are that someone," He answers, looking directly at me.

"Me? How can I do that? I am on the top of this mountain and it would take many hours for me to reach the village."

"You can intercede, which is far more effective than anything you could possibly do in your own strength. Intercession is simply positioning yourself before your Father and petitioning Him to intervene on behalf of another."

"That's something I can certainly do."

I hurry back to the tent and fall on my knees. The minutes turn into hours. Suddenly, I am filled with perfect peace. I have no more tears and no more words.

Stepping outside, I realize it is past noon. I shade my eyes. Comforter is still on the wall. He turns around and says, "The lion has just been found. All is well in the village. A tragedy has just been averted."

My legs start shaking violently. Comforter hurries to my side and puts His arm around me. "You have labored well on behalf of your King, Lovely Lady."

"What? How have I labored for the King? All I did was pray for the safety of the people in my village, not for my King," Ir reply.

Rhonda Calhoun

"When you labor for those in His kingdom, you labor for the King. When you give water to a stranger, you give water to the King. When you share what you have with another, you give to the King Himself.

"The King loves the people in His kingdom so much that He feels everything they feel.[260] And so it is that today your prayers have served to bring about the will of the King, rescuing someone from the mouth of a lion."

I am overwhelmed with this revelation and spend the rest of the day and late into the night pondering and praying about Comforter's words.

The next morning, I find a basket filled with a variety of spices just outside the door of my tent. Seeing Comforter on the wall, watching over the kingdom, I hurry over and ask, "Comforter, do You know where this basket came from?"

"I do indeed, Lovely Lady. I placed it there Myself."

"What a delightful gift! Thank You, dear Friend."

"Do you understand the significance and purpose of these fragrant ointments, Lovely Lady?" He asks, reaching for the basket.

"I do not. Would You please tell me?"

He beckons me to sit with Him and I quickly join him. He says, "These spices represent your service to the King, which is multi-faceted and will be most fruitful.[261] During your time on this hill, you will be anointed with these fragrant spices, which will help transform your soul."

Holding up the first pouch, He says, " Each spice has a distinct and specific purpose. Saffron is the spice that represents faith; it is very expensive and literally worth its weight in gold."[262]

He places the saffron in my lap and holds up another. "This is henna, which represents forgiveness. This spice is very special as it stains the skin red, representing the salvation of sinners through the shed blood of your King. It is also used the night before the betrothal ceremony to anoint the bride's feet and hands, clearly marking her as one who belongs to another."[263]

Handing me the henna, He picks up the next, "This is spikenard, which is also very precious. It speaks of light, and there is no light brighter than that of your Beloved."[264]

I add it to my growing stack. "And this one is calamus, which represents doing what is right in God's sight. This one is cinnamon, which points to holiness of heart."[265]

Placing them in my lap, He holds up a pouch, the scent of which I immediately recognize. "This one you know well."

"I do indeed," I reply. "That is myrrh; it symbolizes obedience unto death."

"You are correct. It represents the bitter sufferings your King endured as a Man. Even the King learned obedience through the things He suffered.[266]

"And this is aloe. Aloe represents intimacy and healing. Last, but not least, we have frankincense. Frankincense grows well on this hill, as you can see."

He points to a group of trees growing nearby as He continues, "Frankincense represents the purity of prayer and intercession."[267]

Laying the empty basket beside me, He adds, "You will leave this place quite fragrant, Lovely Lady."[268]

"That is my desire, Comforter," I say, placing the spices back in my basket.

The following morning Comforter crushes the spices. He then carefully measures each one and places them in a tiny flask of oil.

From that day forth, every morning and every evening, He anoints me with the fragrant oil saying, "The King's daughter is all glorious within. You are dressed in the garments of the King, which are woven with golden threads representing the Divine character that is being worked in you. You will be led to the King in garments that are stunning. Your service to the King glorifies Him.

"Those with a pure heart whom the King will give you charge over will follow you and they, too, will be brought into the King's presence. They will enter the chambers of the King and they will be led forth with gladness and rejoicing."

The incredible fragrance of the spices permeates my flesh and my senses all day long and throughout the night. I cannot escape its effects, but then I would not want to.

Time passes quickly on this hill; I spend most of my days

Rhonda Calhoun

and nights alone in my tent meditating on the beauty of my Bridegroom King and praying for His perfect will to be done in my life and on the earth. I fast regularly, not because I have to, but because I want to. I love the way fasting tenderizes my heart.

There are many nights when the shofar blows, and I hurry out to find Comforter standing on the wall. He instructs me as to any prayer needs that have arisen. I join Him in prayer until He directs me otherwise. Not every situation turns out the way I desire or the way I think it should, but Comforter constantly assures me that the King always causes things to work together for good, even tragedies.[269]

This morning, while sitting on the wall meditating on the things I am learning, an eagle soars across the valley directly in front of me. I watch this beautiful creature and wonder what it would be like to fly above the earth allowing the wind to carry me wherever it desired. Something within me cries out to know freedom such as this, to live unhindered, to be filled with grace and beauty and to fly away on the wings of God into the highest heavens.

The sweetest breeze whispers past me. I look up and see that Comforter stands behind me. "Those who follow the King are like the wind—no one knows where they came from and neither do they know where they are going," He whispers.

"How is it possible to be like the wind?"

"When one follows the Wind they become like the Wind."

Deep in thought, I watch this magnificent bird as it effortlessly rides the wind, dipping and soaring, thoroughly enjoying the adventure. "Comforter, I want to be free like that. I want to follow my Beloved King wherever He leads and I want to do so with complete abandonment."

The eagle suddenly dives into the forest below but only for a moment. It quickly rises with its magnificent wings gracefully reaching for the highest heights. It is obvious that this majestic bird requires very little effort to rise above the earth; it simply rides the currents that are there, adjusting its wings from time to time. Just as quickly as it appeared, it catches a strong, upward current and with no perceivable effort at all is carried over the mountaintop and out of sight.

"What a magnificent creature!" I exclaim.

"Indeed," He responds. "Lovely Lady, you cannot keep an eagle in a forest. You can tempt it with every temptation, but it will always fly away, returning to its lofty home among the highest of rocks.

"You, like that eagle, have spread your wings and, with your eyes on your eternal, lofty destination, are soaring upward. You have learned to rise above the difficulties of this life, to face your fears and run anyway. You are no longer fascinated with the things that captivate those whose eyes and hearts are fixed on the fleeting pleasures of this earth.

"Lovely Lady, you have grown in grace and beauty on this hilltop. You have continually crucified your fleshly desires and, as a result, your spirit soars on the wings of love."

"It is only because of who You are that I am who I am."

"That is true," He responds as He points to a cleft in the rocks on a nearby mountain. My breath catches in my throat – the King is standing in the mouth of a cave shining like the sun. My Beloved waves at me. Just as I raise my hand to respond, He disappears into the cave.

Turning to Comforter, I ask, "What does my King desire most of all?"

"A bride that is fascinated by Him," He answers.

Oh, that I could be one who is fascinated!

"Fascinate my heart, Comforter. Make me hungry, make me lovesick, make me thirsty for the King! My home is God, and I will remain hidden in Him. So make me dead to everything that hinders love. Fascinate me with who You are so that nothing else will have any hold on me, I pray!"

"You have found your voice, Lovely Lady."

"I have?"

"You have. This is why your Beloved led you here."

I remain on the wall praying for wings to fly above apathy and complacency that I might have a fascinated, passionate heart for my Beloved King and Friend.

Rhonda Calhoun

Chapter Seventeen
THE BRIDAL PROPOSAL

Come with me from Lebanon, my bride! [270]

It has been just over six months since I came to the Hill of Frankincense. I discovered my flesh and my will die slowly, but they certainly die when perfect Love is pursued.

Comforter and I spend the entire day praying on the stone wall together. The sun is setting as He says, "The motives of your heart have become extremely fragrant, Lovely Lady."

"You are the One who anointed me with the oil of myrrh and the precious spices, Comforter. Any good thing I possess is a result of the love that has been poured into me. Overcoming my imperfections has not happened through the frailty of my human will or the strength of my flesh, but rather because of my Beloved's great care and diligence. His loving sacrifice adorns me with grace, gifts and virtues. His love overcomes the faults that so easily distract and threaten to steal the affections of my heart that should be reserved for the King. Perfect love is transforming me."

"Speaking of your Beloved," Comforter says, looking over my shoulder.

Standing just in front of the willow tree is my beautiful wonderful King! It has been so very long since I have seen Him. "Run to the One you love, My Lady," Comforter says.

Leaping off the wall, I run like the wind and hold Him until my arms ache. "I am so very happy to see You!" I exclaim.

"How fragrant you are!" He says, burying His face in my hair.[271]

"Comforter saturates me daily with the oil of myrrh and with all kinds of precious spices. His love and devotion adorns me and it's all for You, my King!"

"Your dedication is extremely fragrant and quite intoxicating."

"I am Yours, my King."[272]

"You are altogether beautiful, My darling! There is no blemish in you!"[273]

Altogether beautiful, no blemish in me? I cannot comprehend such matchless love and grace. I am well aware of my many faults to fullly believe His statements.

He gently squeezes my hand and smiles. Reaching down, He picks a flower from the multitude of flowers. "What do you see?" He asks, holding it before me.

"Well, I see a pretty flower, a daisy to be exact."

"Look closer, My darling," He says, handing it to me.

I take the lovely little thing. It's white petal are less than perfect, a couple are slightly bent and curled. The center of the daisy is a deep yellow color. Something moves, something tiny and red and—. "Aaaah! There are bugs on it!" I shriek, throwing it on the ground.

My Beloved quickly rescues the rejected flower. He lovingly smooths its bent petals. Only then does He address me saying, "I know that there are bugs on this flower, but that is not what I see. When I look at it, I see a lovely flower filled with sweet fragrance and elegant beauty—a glorious creation meant to be enjoyed and delighted in.

"The same is true when I look at you—I see a lovely creation, filled with sweet fragrance and elegant beauty, whom I thoroughly enjoy and take great delight in.

"I do not focus on the things in your life that are flawed and less than perfect. I know they are there and I will heal and deliver you from them as we walk through this life together. But those flaws are not who you are, neither are they what determines your value."

Once again, He offers me the daisy. This time I hold it—bugs and all. He continues, "I desire for you to see others the same way I see you. When you encounter people who 'bug' you, do not focus on their weaknesses or imperfections, but rather see beyond their flaws and look for the beauty hidden within.

"My desire is for you to learn how to love others the same way I have loved you."

Twirling the daisy in my hand, I whisper, "Little flower, you may be flawed, but you certainly are lovely, just like me."

My Beloved takes my hand and says, "Come with Me, My bride, to the Mountain of Myrrh that you might view this life from My perspective.[275] Let us look down from the dens of lions and from the mountains of leopards that you might know that I am able to keep you in the midst of life and all its dangers. Come and see the world from heaven's point of view."[276]

"I will follow You anywhere...even the mountain of myrrh," I reply without fear or hesitation.[277]

"You have captured My heart, My sister, My bride! Just one of your virtues is enough to capture My attention, but you have grown so much that I am overwhelmed. Rest assured I would have loved you had you possessed none of your glorious qualities, but how lovely you are adorned with submission and wholehearted devotion!"[278]

"My Lord, I have eaten from Your abundant goodness and lovingkindness and I am satisfied. I need nothing but You."

As Comforter joins us, My Beloved says, "It is time."

With great joy, I gather my few belongings. We begin our descent. I enjoyed my time on the Hill of Frankincense. And, as strange as this may sound, I even find myself looking forward to returning to the Mountain of Myrrh—not because my time there was pleasant, but because my time there produced a willing and abandoned heart. Who knows what great virtues await me there now that my Beloved is by my side.

After two days, we arrive in Hope Valley; the wilderness lies before us. Without delay, my Beloved leads me into this dark, dangerous place. But, it does not seem as dark or as frightening when the One I love is by my side. In what seems like a very short time, we are standing at the base of Mount Hermon, the Mountain of Myrrh. Without hesitation, my King leads me upward. "We must travel to the highest peak to give you the best perspective of My kingdom," my Beloved says.

By the third day, I am quite weary. I have heard and seen several predators lurking along the path just waiting for me to slip, fall or lag behind. I know how these creatures work; they pick off the weak, sick and careless ones. I stay close by my Beloved's side and dare not venture away even for a moment.

It is noon when we finally arrive at the summit. My King escorts me to a large rock at the edge of the mountain. Comforter jumps up on the rock and offers me His hand. My King joins us. The view is absolutely breathtaking; we can see into eternity! A sudden gust of wind causes me to lose my footing. I quickly lock arms with Comforter and my Beloved; they are my Anchors and keep me steady.

Overlooking the Valley of Decision, I stand secure, even on this high, treacherous mountain, even with the wind coming against me. "It is good to be here," I whisper.

"Look over there, My love," My King says pointing across the valley to a rich, fertile land. "That is your final destination."

"My final destination?" I ask, feeling quite bewildered.

"Yes, My love, that is where you will live with Me forever."

A low, guttural growl coming from behind me causes me to shiver from head to toe. I slowly look over my shoulder. A muffled cry fills my throat. "There...there...are lions...behind us," I whisper.

Eight lions are slowly approaching. With the cliff behind us and the lions before us, we have no way of escape. "Shouldn't we do something?" I whisper, frozen in place.

My Beloved responds, "I am with you...have no fear. It is important for you to learn the importance of seeing everything from My perspective.

"Resist the enemy and he will flee from you.[279] Watch and learn, My love."

He lifts his eyes to heaven and says, "Father, I thank You that You have heard Me. You have given Your angels charge over Me; on their hands they will bear Me up, lest I strike My foot against a stone."[280]

A sudden movement in the trees startles me. Peering into the darkness, I am relieved to see the Captain and his men with their swords drawn. I had no idea they followed us.

My Beloved looks back at the stalking lions and says, "I will not bow down to you, for it is written, 'Worship the Lord and serve Him only.' "

His words create instant terror in the lions and they scatter, running into and leaping over each other in their haste to get away. My legs grow weak, for I, too, am terrified — terrified because we could have been torn to pieces, and terrified because of the incredible authority and power I just witnessed. Who is this Man who is powerful enough to frighten the king of beasts?

I collapse. My Beloved kneels before me, taking my trembling hands in His steady ones. Turning them up, He kisses my palms. Love and strength pour into me. I look into His eyes, but say nothing.

Who am I to speak to One who wields such power and authority, to One who is so awesome and fearless?

My Beloved whispers into the silence, "My love, I have brought you to this place to enter into an everlasting covenant with you, for I desire to make you My bride.

"I offer you My life as your bridal price; it is the greatest price I could pay and the only thing that adequately represents your incredible value and worth. If you accept My proposal, I will be your everything. I will lavish you with unconditional love and constantly watch over you. I will never leave you nor forsake you. You can count of Me to remain by your side regardless of what comes your way.

"I will love you in the midst of your weakness and immaturity. When you slip and fall, I will help you up, wash you off and hold you close while speaking words of love and encouragement. If your love should grow cold, Mine will only burn brighter.

"I will mold you and transform you into My image. I will deliver you from evil and keep you from temptation. I will watch over you as a jealous husband watches over his precious wife, as

Rhonda Calhoun

a loving father watches over his children. I will withhold no good thing from you. Everything I allow to touch your life must pass through My hands of love. All that I allow to touch you will only be what is best for you.

"Will you accept My bridal price and say 'yes' to My proposal? Will you enter into covenant with Me?"

Brushing a curl from my face, He continues, "Before you answer, it is only right that you know what will be required. You will have to leave behind your old ways of doing things and live only for Me. You must be willing to follow Me wherever I go, for I desire a partner who will rule and reign with Me."

"You will not always reside in comfort and pleasure, for you will be called to carry your cross as you conquer the heights and depths of life. Comforter will lead you to the Mountain of Myrrh and the Hill of Frankincense many times, for it is there that the greatest transformations can happen.

"Know that My enemy will be your enemy; My friends will be your friends. You must not be afraid, but continually look with eyes of faith, for it is important that you view life from My perspective at all times. I will give you authority over the enemy of your soul so he will have no power over you.

"My love, there is a time coming on the earth when tragedy and terror will surround you; the world will reel from its impact. Lawlessness will increase. There will be wars and rumors of wars, earthquakes and famines. Disease will be rampant upon the earth. You will be hated by all the nations because of Me. And in that hour, most people's love will grow cold, but the one who endures to the end, shall be saved.[280a]

"Even during this difficult time, you will continue to grow in grace and beauty. I will cause you to become a leaning, limping, loving bride. You will be leaning because I will be your only focus and I will be your only source of strength and supply. You will learn to rest in My embrace. You will be limping because you will realize your strength is found in My commitment to you not your commitment to Me. You will be a loving bride because you will understand what it is to lay down your life for the sake of love.

"Even during the time when the world is confused and

filled with anguish, have no fear, for I will never leave you, neither will I forsake you. I will see you safely through the wilderness and through the fire."

Looking into the depths of my soul, He lowers His voice to a whisper, "But, you must love Me with all your heart, with all your strength and with all your soul. You must never have any other lovers before Me, in any form, for I am a jealous God."[281]

The intensity of His words causes me to tremble. I reply, "My Beloved, it is You who has stolen my heart. I belong to You alone, for You are the One I love. You are the love of my life!

"My answer is 'yes' to Your invitation. You are my King and I will follow You anywhere. I will travel on the path You travel, wherever that path might lead, regardless of the cost. I will look to You to be my source of strength and my provision. You are my everything. I am a lily growing in the midst of a valley that needs Your constant affection and protection. I will live my life in preparation of becoming Your bride. I ask You this day to grant me the grace to walk this path with a pure heart, my Lord."

Comforter steps forward and hands me a piece of bread and a golden cup, which I gladly receive. My Beloved says, "Eat this bread and drink this cup, which seals this covenant we have entered into this day."

I eat the bread, which represents His death. Holding up the cup, which represents His covenant. I say, "I accept Your gift and Your life and I offer You mine in return." I drink all of it.

I hand the cup to my Beloved. Without refilling it, He hands it to Comforter. "Are You going to drink?" I ask.

He scans the horizon and responds, "I drank this cup many years ago in a garden called Gethsemane. It was there I said 'yes' to My Father's will over My own. I will drink this cup again, but not until I drink it with you on our wedding day."

I cry out, "You have searched me and You know me. You know when I sit down and when I rise up. Even from afar, You know what I am thinking. I am never out of Your sight. You know everything I am going to say even before I speak. I look behind me and You are there. I look to the future and You are already there. I look around and You surround me. Is there any

Rhonda Calhoun

place I could go where You are not? If I ascend to the highest heavens, You are there. If I were to descend to deepest part of the earth, You are there, too. If I flew on the wings of the morning if I dwelt in the remotest part of the sea, even there Your hand would lead me, and Your right hand would lay hold of me.

"Darkness is not dark to You; night and day, they are alike to You. You formed me in my mother's womb. You know me through and through, inside and out. You know my every failure, my every sin, my every weakness and You still love me!

"You have watched over my life since conception; all my life is spread out before You. Before I was even born, You knew all the days of my life and You recorded them in Your book.

"I will give thanks to You, for I am fearfully and wonderfully made! How precious are Your thoughts about me! How vast is the sum of them! If I should count them, they would outnumber the sand on the seashore. I cannot imagine it, but it is true; Your thoughts are continually on me!

"O, my King, search me and know may heart. Try me and know my anxious thoughts. See if there is any hurtful way in me and lead me on the path to eternal life."[282]

"And so I shall, My love."

The
Bridegroom King

Chapter Eighteen
A LOCKED GARDEN

How beautiful is your love my sister, my bride![285]

*T*hree days later, we leave the Mountain of Myrrh headed for home. The closer we come to Hope Valley, the faster I walk. Cresting the final hill, I see a small group of people sitting beneath the walnut tree.

"Who are they? Why are they here?" I ask as I quicken my pace.

"They are friends of the King."

The King? He is here? Searching the crowd, I see the one my soul loves! The crowd sees Him too, and they run to Him. I recognize a few of the people, but most are strangers. Saul and his friends stand on the outer fringes of the crowd with their arms folded tightly across their chests.

My Beloved eagerly and affectionately greets each by name. Suddenly, a woman from my village, famous for her immoral lifestyle, pushes her way to the forefront on the group. She falls at my Beloved's feet and washes them with her tears. Unbraiding her long, black hair she uses it to dry His feet. I watch in amazement as she, still sobbing, covers His feet with kisses.

My Beloved's eyes are closed; tears glisten on His lashes. Comforter kneels beside her and places His hand tenderly on the woman's shoulder. Sitting up, she removes a flask from her pouch and then falls before Him again, pouring her fragrant, costly perfume all over His ankles and feet.

I am surprised to see that Saul has now come forward and is standing by this woman's side. It is clear that he is displeased, to put it mildly. My Beloved turns to him and says, "Saul, there is much about this life that you need to know. When a person is forgiven much, they love much."

"And Your point is?" he asks.

"Do you see this woman?"

"I see her," he replies.

My Beloved kneels beside her and continues, "She knows Me intimately. And because she knows Me, she understands that I am loving, compassionate, full of mercy and eager to forgive. She came to Me believing that I would embrace her, not reject her."

Saul clears his throat and steps back, kicking the dirt with his sandal; a dust cloud flies in my Beloved face. Without so much as a grimace, He lays His hand on the woman's shoulder. As she looks into His eyes of love, the delightful fragrance of her perfume floods my senses. He takes her hand and raises her up saying, "Woman, your sins are forgiven."

Burying her face on His shoulder, she sobs deeply. The King speaks ever so quietly to her until her tears finally cease. It is obvious that Saul and his friends are highly offended. My Beloved, while looking directly at Saul, says, "Woman, because you have believed, your sins are forgiven."

With a loud groan, Saul storms off; his followers are right behind him. *They must truly be hardhearted not to rejoice with this woman. After all, she just experienced true love, probably for the first time in her life. Saul's behavior is a mystery clothed in sadness.*

My Beloved places His arm around the woman's shoulders and leads her to my wonderful Father, who had been watching from underneath a great Weeping Willow tree. Father embraces her right away.

I stand patiently nearby praying. Comforter is soon introduced to her. He leads her to a large rock by the stream where they sit together. My heart is thrilled because I know that her life will never be the same.

Eager to share my news with Father, I run into His waiting arms. He exclaims, "Little One, look at how you have grown and how lovely you have become!"

Unable to restrain myself any longer, I shout, "Oh, my dear, dear Father, I am in love with Your wonderful Son!" Lowering my voice to a whisper, I continue, "And, can You believe it—He asked me to be His bride."

"And what was your answer, Little One?"

"I said 'yes.' This time I said 'yes!'"[284]

Laughing heartily, my Father responds, "This is indeed good news."

"Father, I will give anything, I will go anywhere my Beloved desires, for I long to know Him as I am known."

The One I love makes His way toward us; I cannot help but smile. Standing before His Father, but looking directly at me, He says, "Father, look at her, is she not lovely?"

"Indeed, she is, Son."

"Father, have You noticed how her love for Me has grown and matured? Tell Me, Father, is she now able to hear of the depth of My great love for her? Now may I tell her?"

"Son, You may now tell her about the furnace of love that has burned in Your heart even before time existed." My Father looks deeply into my eyes, then continues, "She will never turn away from You again and neither will she turn You away again."[285]

Oh, how grateful I am to this King who loved me first—even when I left Him!

My Beloved takes my hands, which are trembling with excitement. Looking into His eyes of love, I wonder how I ever came to be so greatly treasured and so deeply loved.

He smiles. I smile back as He says, "My love, I have waited so long to tell you how precious you are to Me. I love you more than life itself. My love for you is greater than the largest ocean and deeper than the deepest sea; the extent of it is far beyond human comprehension. You, My bride, have consumed Me. My thoughts are continually on you; they outnumber the sand in the sea. I watch over you with the greatest of attention and the

Rhonda Calhoun

utmost of care."

For the briefest moment, He looks away. I am barely breathing. When He looks back, His eyes are filled with tears. I swim in the love I find there. He speaks, but not with words. His eyes speak so clearly that words would be a distraction. We stand together, face to face, in love with each other, spirit to Spirit.

"This love is so far beyond anything on this earth. This love that I now possess is other than," I whisper.

"This love we feel for each other is eternal—nothing this earth has to offer is eternal. You have responded wisely, My fair one."

I respond, "You mean everything to me and I love You more than I ever thought possible."

He replies, "With a single glance of your eyes, with a single act of your will, you have made My heart beat faster, My sister, My bride. Your voluntary love has overwhelmed Me."

"You call me Your *sister*? How am I Your sister?"

"We have the same Father, do we not?"

I look at my precious, dear Father and nod.

"You are My bride *and* you are My sister. A bride is chosen," He continues, "but a sister is born into the family wihtout being chosen. A brother and sister have the same blood flowing through in their veins. You are both My chosen bride and My blood-bought sister.[286] When you looked upon Me with eyes full of abandonment and reached out to Me with myrrh-covered hands, you wounded My heart, thus capturing the heart of a King that no power on earth or in hell could conquer.[287] There is nothing as powerful as unselfish love.

"How beautiful is your love, My sister, My bride![288] You once said that My love is better than wine,[289] but I say that your love is better than wine; it is better than anything in this life.

"In order to capture your heart, I drank the cup of suffering in a garden called Gethsemane, for your love was worth it—every part of it![290]

"You said that My name is like fragrant, purified oil,[291] oil that has been poured from one vessel into another. I say that you, too, are rich in purified oil, for you have poured your love into Me! Oh, My love, the fragrance of your oil is better than all kinds of rich spices!

"Your thoughts are sincere, and the desire to love Me fills your heart. Oh, My beautiful one, your love is much better than all that this world has to offer![292]

"All of the pleasures that are at My disposal, and they are innumerable, are not sweeter nor more desirable than you, My dove. I am undone by the sweet fragrance of your devotion and your willingness to sacrifice for My sake.[293]

"You have gone to the Mountain of Myrrh and to the Hill of Frankincense. There you were saturated in My oil and spices; you now look and smell like Me. Out of death comes life, My love.

"When you speak, your words are sweet and timely, filled with richness and prosperity and delighting the hearts of those who listen.[294] The fragrance of your garments, your deeds of lovingkindness, are like the fragrance of Lebanon, which is My magnificent abiding place."[295]

Feeling quite overwhelmed, I look away only to look into the eyes of Comforter who whispers, "What He says is true, Lovely Lady."

My Father nods in agreement. My Bridegroom King continues, "Your life belongs to Me, for My good pleasure. You are an enclosed, locked garden, a garden that is set apart for Me alone, and filled with all kinds of brilliantly colored, sweet-smelling flowers and rich fruit.[296] I will never tire of gazing on your beauty.[297]

"I have chosen you from among the others and you have chosen Me above all else, sealing off your life from every other affection, from everything that would distract you.[298]

"The fruit from your life is like an orchard of pomegranates, which is much more than a mere garden that is nice to look at and fragrant to the senses. The most humble pomegranate orchard is fruitful, strong and able to be seen by others from afar. Your flesh is covered by My blood just as the flesh of a pomegranate is red.[299]

"Henna, nard, saffron, calamus, cinnamon, frankincense, myrrh, and aloes—you possess them all. Your ministry to others is sweet to Me and also to those you serve. Forgiveness flows

Rhonda Calhoun

from you. You walk in My light and have learned to do what is right not for the sake of doing good, but as a result of the love that you feel for Me.

"Your heart has been consecrated to Me and is continually being sanctified, and your intimacy with Me is precious. The purity of your intercession is delightful and ever so refreshing.[300]

"Comforter has done well, for He has produced precious fruit in your life, which has filled you with beautiful virtues and great graces. You have learned to run to Me and not from Me, laying your petitions down before your King. You have learned well the way of the cross.

"You continually drink from the living water that flows from the Rock, which has become an inward source of life for you.[301] You have stored up much and have much to share with those who are thirsty and weary.[302] You have a rich history in Me, a testimony to freely share with others. You now know that you have no strength apart from Me, for I am the strength of your life. Your life is filled with a delightful fragrance, My love."[303]

His devotion for me seals my future. I am loved by the King and it makes my heart sing. For the remainder of my life, I will be a lover of God; I will live for Him and Him alone! I will spend my life gazing on His beauty, seeking His face and living in His presence! I now know that He loves me, not because of anything I do or do not do, but simply because of who He is. His commitment to me, and not my commitment to Him, will keep me close to His heart.

I feel as though my heart will burst from the tremendous joy I feel. I exclaim, "Awake, north winds—winds of adversity and hardship blow on my garden! Spread this fragrance abroad that others might become intoxicated by the goodness of my King.[304]

"South winds, winds of blessing and favor, come and make my garden spread forth sweet fragrance. Let its spices spread the fragrance of My King abroad to others that He may be glorified![305]

"Wound this heart in its deepest parts that Your love might permeate me through and through. For I desire to bring You pleasure and glory. I say 'yes' to suffering and to blessings.[306]

I need them both and trust You to bring the exact measure of each into my life.

"Empower me and fill my garden with humility, grace, charity and devotion. Fill me with everything that is lovely and fragrant. Come and take complete possession of my garden, which is my life, for I desire to live for You alone."

Bowing before Him, I continue, "Everything belongs to You — my past, my present and my future. I have experienced Your unconditional love and have seen Your face. Therefore, I gladly give myself and all that I have to You![307] Come, my Beloved, into *Your* garden and eat from its choice fruits. I acknowledge that whatever good You see in me, it is because of Your tender, loving care and it is for Your good pleasure."[308]

My Beloved looks into my eyes and responds, "I gladly take possession of you. I come into *My* garden, *My* sister, *My* Bride. I have found you to be a locked garden, closed to all others. You are a garden adorned with all kinds of beautiful, sweet-smelling flowers — flowers of self-denial, flowers of suffering and flowers of grace; all for My good pleasure.[309]

"I have removed from you those things which were harmful to you and those things that hindered you from fully obeying Me. Your life is filled with many fragrant spices, which I so enjoy.[310] I have tasted the sweetness of your love and seen your submission; you warm and delight My heart.[311] Not only are you Mine, but all that you have and all that you ever will be is now Mine."

He turns His attention to the watching crowd and says, "Come, friends, and see the beauty of My bride. Eat from her table and be nourished; learn from her. Those of you who desire to fully love Me, drink and partake deeply of the power and favor that is now part of her life."[312]

Charity is the first of several to surround me. With great excitement, I share about my journey with the Master Shepherd. They listen with interest until I talk of the difficulties encountered on the Mountain of Myrrh. Then, one by one, they slowly walk away until I am left alone. I am overcome with sadness, for I understand the importance of living a life of extravagant devotion to the King and that only comes through dying to self.

177

Rhonda Calhoun

I look up into the eyes of my Bridegroom King. He is smiling; His hand extended to me. I waste no time placing my small hand in His great, big one. There is no place I would rather be than by His side, gazing on His beauty. My joy quickly returns.

Father joins us. Embracing me, He says, "You have made this Father's heart glad, Little One. I am so very proud of you, for you have learned to love!"

The three of us walk hand in hand to the cottage where Comforter quickly prepares a grand meal for us. I have yet to understand how He does all that He does. He is always ready with exactly what is needed and always knows exactly what to say. He is most humble and never draws attention to Himself, but always, in every situation, directs all the attention to my Beloved who, in turn, glorifies His Father. It is so beautiful to see the way They love each other! Never have I known or seen such unity in a relationship. They always esteem each Other as being greater than Themselves. What a beautiful example, one that I long to follow.

We spend the evening sitting on the porch, watching the stars and sharing our hearts with each other. It is so wonderful to be home, sitting beside the Three who love so much and Who love me infinitely.

It is with a peaceful heart that I watch my Beloved and Father once more cross the grounds to the palace. Comforter puts His arm around me and says, "Most people believe that Jesus will only love them as long as they are good, faithful and remain true to Him. They live their lives as though they need to earn His affection when, in reality, they should simply live because He already loves them. They work so hard to be good that they often forget that they are God's. Just because something appears to be good does not mean that it is God. A heathen can do good, but it profits him nothing. In Our kingdom, good is determined by God alone. Man's soul alone cannot determine what is good. Only God has that right."

"Then how am I to know what is good and what is not?"

He answers, "Everything that proceeds from the Father is good, Lovely lady."

"That goes against all that we have been taught or

experienced in this life. Most often, our acceptance and self-image is based on our ability to determine what is good and then do it."

"Lovely Lady, that is the way Satan would have you live, but that is not the way of your King. Adam and Eve ate from the tree of the knowledge of *good* and *evil*. In doing so, the result was that man would be driven to determine for himself what was good and what was evil. Only God has the right to say what is good and what is evil. Man wanted to decide for himself what was good and what was evil. Before they ate, they depended on God to tell them whether or not something was good or not."

"But..."

"God has told you what is good...to love mercy, to do justice and to walk humbly with you God. That is His definition of good...no more and no less. Concerning your acceptance, that is based on His performance and He 'performed' once and for all on the cross and, Lovely Lady, that was a performance no one can ever equal."

"That is true, Comforter, and because of His love, I am free from my sins, a fact for which I am ever so grateful."

"Your Beloved's death accomplished so much more than your freedom from sin. His death gave you life—eternal life, resurrection life. His death opened the windows of heaven that you might have access to the very throne of God, both now and forever. His death changed everything!"

With much to meditate on, we bid each other good-night and I happily retire to my room. Opening my door, I cannot believe my eyes! My room is filled with every kind of flower imaginable! The fragrance takes my breath away!

I love my extravagant, affectionate Bridegroom!

I fall asleep realizing that there is only one Hero in my life and it is not me. I am finally free to love and be loved!

Rhonda Calhoun

The
Suffering Servant

Chapter Nineteen
LOVING OTHERS

Eat friends, drink and imbibe deeply. [515]

The following morning, I wake to the sound of singing. Hurrying to my window, I throw back the curtains. Standing several yards away is Comforter and a dozen or so guards. Comforter plays a harp while the guards sing. They sound absolutely angelic. I strain to understand the words, but cannot.

I quickly dress and splash water on my face. Grabbing a towel, I dry my face as I hurry out the door. It is a beautiful day, the sun is shining and birds are singing. I race around the corner of my cottage, nearly tripping over my feet. Their singing abruptly comes to a halt. The men stand as if at attention. The Captain hurries to my side. "Is all well, my lady?"

"Yes, kind sir, all is well. I heard your singing and came to listen. What was that song that you were singing?"

"That song was written many years ago by a man named Moses, my lady."

I look at Comforter who laid aside His harp. "Please, Comforter, will You play it again?"

"For you, I will do almost anything," He answers. The Captain and his men quickly resume their positions. Comforter strums his harp as they sing:

Rhonda Calhoun

I will sing to the King, for He is highly exalted.
The King is my strength and song,
And He has become my salvation.
This is my King and I will praise Him.
The King is a warrior; the Lord is His name.
Thy right hand, oh, King, is majestic in power,
Thy right hand, oh, King, shatters the enemy.
The King shall reign forever and ever.[314]

Clapping, I exclaim, "What a wonderful, wonderful song! Comforter, would You please teach it to me?"

"I will indeed."

Amazed at how quickly I learn the words, I clap my hands in delight.

"Come, Lovely Lady, breakfast is ready and waiting," Comforter says, holding out His hand.

"Thank you, Captain, and thank you all...your song is truly inspiring!"

"Begging your pardon, but that was not our song," the Captain responds

"Oh, I forgot. Well, it was beautiful!"

After breakfast, my Beloved arrives and we go for our morning walk through His garden. As we do so, I sing the song of Moses. He is delighted and tells me so.

Just before noon, the King leaves me with Comforter, Who waits beneath the walnut tree. Sitting with Comforter under this tree has become my favorite place to be—other than the King's garden, that is.

We begin with my singing lessons and then move on to princess lessons. Just as I finish my last paper, Comforter hands me a box tied with a blue ribbon and says, "This is a special gift from Us."

"Thank you, Comforter," I say while excitedly untying the ribbon. I lift the lid and discover a book. As I take it out, Comforter says, "This is the Book of Remembrances, which I wrote.[315] It contains the history of mankind and the story of the Lamb and His bride. It is the New Covenant, which states the bridal price, the terms of your marriage to the King and Our promise to take care of you and protect you. It also clearly describes the nature and character of the Three Who love you more than anyone.

"This is the most important book you will ever read and one that you should read over and over. You will find much wisdom hidden within its pages. It will be an anchor for your soul and a weapon in your hand. With it, you will be able to defeat any enemy who dares come your way. As you read, listen for My voice; I will instruct you through its pages."

I open the cover and run my hand over its thin pages. "Comforter, how will I ever keep my part of the Covenant? Just look at how thick this book is."

"Your King entered into covenant with you knowing that you would not and could not keep your end of the contract. He understands that you cannot be perfect. That is why He gave His life in exchange for yours. He already paid the penalty for your sins and once a debt is paid there is no longer any debt, now is there? Once punishment for a crime has been carried out, there is no longer any punishment, is there?"

"I suppose not."

"Lovely Lady, you are forgiven and your debts have been paid; your punishment was taken by Another. He became a criminal that you might be set free...free to be loved and to love without fear. Your Bridegroom became sin for you and gave you His righteousness. This book is Our love letter to you — it is the history of Our unending, unrelenting love for mankind!"

"I am free! I am loved! What incredible love my King bestows upon me!" I exclaim. Embracing my new book, I continue, "Comforter, thank You ever so much! I will cherish this book always."

"A book of this magnitude should be cherished, Lovely Lady, for it contains revelation upon revelation concerning your King and His kingdom.

"As you read, remember that I am with you, and I will grant you insight and understanding. All you have to do is ask."

Leaning against the tree trunk, I read the first section called Genesis. Strange name, but it is a fascinating story about a man being made from dirt. I am amazed to learn that God created the earth, the heavens and the plant life with His spoken word. But man was lovingly fashioned with God's very own hands, and woman was brought forth out of Adam's side by the very hand of God, which makes us unique, setting us apart from all others.

I soon lose all track of time. It is not until the sunlight fades and I can no longer see that I look up. Comforter is watching me. He smiles and says, "Come, Lovely Lady, it is late, and your King awaits our arrival."

"Thank You again, dear Friend, for this wonderful book. The stories are simply fascinating. I can hardly wait to read more."

"I am pleased, Lovely Lady," He replies as we gather our belongings.

We hurry to the cottage where my Beloved King and kind Father wait before the fireplace. When I enter, They stand. With my priceless book in hand, I quickly join Them, saying, "Look what Comforter has given me!"

My Father smiles. I hug Him, saying, "Father, I have already started reading and I find it absolutely fascinating!"

"Remember that this book is more than fascinating stories—it is a love letter from your Bridegroom, Comforter and Myself. Hidden within the stories are words of wisdom and direction," my Father says.

"I can hardly wait to read more. Perhaps, I could read instead of eating dinner tonight?" I ask expectantly.

"You are such a delight to this Father's heart, child. Come and dine; there will be time for reading later."

We have a lovely dinner and afterwards sit in front of the fireplace. I watch the flames consume the dry wood and think of how the love of Father, my Beloved and Comforter consumes me. I talk about the different stories I read in the Book of Remembrances. Several times, the Three of Them erupt in laughter. Obviously, I got some things mixed up.

The evening comes to a close as Father and my Beloved say good-night. I stand in the doorway watching Them cross the palace grounds and disappear into the night. Turning to Comforter, I ask, "Would You sit with me just a little while longer? I would love to read just one more chapter."

Smiling tenderly, He answers, "I would be glad to. It is

such a delight to see you enjoying My gift."

Instead of one chapter, I read five and would have kept reading except for the fact that I could not keep my eyes open any longer. The next morning, I wake earlier than usual and hurriedly dress so I can read before breakfast.

Mornings are reserved for my Beloved. Most mornings, we explore the depths of His magnificent garden. He has taught me much about gardening. He reminds me over and over that the garden of life is not just about working the soil, planting seeds, watering, fertilizing or pruning. Gardening is about so much more than that. It is about loving each individual plant as if it is the only one of its kind and discovering the many wonders and delights hidden within each plant. In our time together, my Beloved has taught me to love and appreciate all the plants in the same way He loves them, even those with bugs, prickles and thorns.

My afternoons are spent with Comforter, Who continues to teach me how to be a princess bride. At the end of each lesson, I devour the Book of Remembrances.

Each evening my Father joins us for dinner. What a wonderful time the three of us always have! There is nothing to compare with the joy of sitting with them, even if I say nothing. Just gazing on Their kind, wonderful faces is enough for me.

Spring turns into summer and summer into fall, but I barely notice, for I am in love with my amazing Family.

Comforter sits beside me under a massive maple tree while I devour the last chapter of the Book. A red and gold leaf floats from above and lands on my lap. I look up; the tree is ablaze with red, orange and yellow colors. "Comforter, when did summer end and autumn arrive?" I ask in disbelief.

He chuckles. "Lovely Lady, fall arrived several weeks ago."

"I cannot believe it; I never even noticed."

I close my Book of Remembrances and run my hand over its cover. "Comforter, this is the best, most intriguing book I have ever read. I am ready to start reading it all over again."

"And so you shall, Lovely Lady. But, for now, I believe Someone is waiting for you."

Rhonda Calhoun

He points to the garden where My Beloved stands with His hand on its gate, smiling. I remember a day nearly four years ago when I saw the Master Shepherd standing in front of this same gate. His presence has the same effect on my heart today as it did then. "Comforter, He is so wonderful and I love Him so!"

"You are being rooted and grounded in love that you might experience the width, length, height and depth of the King's great affections for you."[316]

Comforter looks back at my King and continues, "Now run to the One Who loved you first and loves you most. Run to your first Love!"

I waste no time obeying. My Bridegroom enthusiastically greets me, spinning me around the way I like. Taking my hand, He leads me to the west wall of the garden. Pushing back some vines, He reaches in and opens a hidden door. "After you, My bride."

Stepping through, I ask, "Just how many doors are there to this garden?"

"There is only one."

"But, I do not understand. There is this one and there is the front gate and there is...."

"I am the way, the truth and the life; no one comes to the Father except through Me. I am the only door," He answers.

"There are so many mysteries surrounding You. Will I ever know all there is to know about You?"

"You could spend all eternity searching and would never come to the end of Who I am, for I have no beginning and no end."[317]

We walk through a part of the garden that I have never seen before. "And what of this garden? Does it ever end?"

"There is no end to Me or My kingdom."[318]

"How can that be?" I ask, more to myself than to Him.

"How can there be a beginning and an ending to something that has always been? I have always existed and always will. I am inside of everything and everything is inside of Me—nothing exists outside of Me. I am an All-consuming God and absolutely nothing is impossible for Me."[319]

I ponder this mystery as we pass through an enormous herb garden, each plant different and just as lovely as the previous ones. Just when I think this garden will go on forever, He leads me through a narrow passageway into a clearing. On the far side of the clearing is a vineyard. My flesh recoils. It seems so long ago, yet the memory of my time in the vineyard being mistreated by my brothers is still very painful. It was there that my heart grew cold, which enabled Compromise to devastate my life. I lost all hope of ever returning to my Beloved.

My Beloved says, "I know that was a very painful time. I know that you were mistreated and overworked. Your pain is still great, but there is a way to be free from it, My love."

"How?" I weakly ask.

"Come with Me." He leads me into the vineyard. As we walk between the grape vines, my Beloved picks a cluster. Handing me a grape, He says, "My love, forgiving those who have wounded you is not optional. If you forgive others your Father will also forgive you. If you do not forgive them, then your Father will not forgive your transgressions."[320]

"How can I forgive them when my pain is still so great?"

"Forgiveness is an act of your will; it is a decision, not a feeling. Make the decision to forgive and continue forgiving every time the pain and memories come to the surface, every time you think of them. Then, one day, you will be amazed to find that the pain is gone and the wound has been healed. Forgiveness and healing go hand in hand. My bride, I will give you the grace to forgive and to love them again, if you ask."

We continue on until we come to a field of corn. Walking around its perimeter, we travel quite a distance when I notice that the surrounding hills look extremely familiar. "You have brought me to my family's vineyard." I say, as a sick feeling settles in the pit of my stomach.

"I have. This is the vineyard your mother and brother call their own, but in reality, it is Mine. I own everything that exists. I give people stewardship over properties and businesses, but I remain the Owner and watch closely to see how each person will steward what I give them. It is a great test, difficult for many, but for others it is nothing at all."[321]

Rhonda Calhoun

"For what reason have You brought me here?"

"So that you might forgive your family and find the healing and freedom you so desperately need. Look, there they are now," He says pointing to my mother and brothers who are busy tying up vines.

Anger suddenly comes to the surface as pain floods my heart; I look away and into the eyes of my Beloved. The radiance from His face convicts me.

"My love, I gave you a gift you didn't deserve and could never earn. Will you do the same for your family? Will you forgive them?" He asks.

My unruly emotions, like a sudden summer storm, fade away. *How can I accuse them when my Beloved has acquitted me of so much?*

I make myself look back. My brothers are drenched in sweat. I think of my Beloved sweating in the garden of Gethsemane. I think of what He endured for me and for them, and my heart softens.

Turning to my Beloved, I say, "My King, You have forgiven me for greater sins than they ever committed against me. I can no longer hold this offense in my heart. I choose to forgive them and ask You to forgive me for the bitterness I have held towards them."

Running the back of His hand across my cheek, He says, "Your love is so beautiful to Me! And, by the way, I forgave you a long, long time ago."

I look again at my family. "They have no idea that You own all of this. They think that what they possess and what they have accomplished is theirs and a result of their own efforts."

My King responds, "The truth is, all that they have is Mine, with one exception, and that is their affections. I never demand nor force anyone to give Me their hearts, for love that is not freely given is no love at all."

Tears fill His eyes.

"What causes Your pain?" I ask.

"My heart grieves because I know the price they will pay if they choose to remain outside of My love and mercy."

"You love them even when they do not return Your

affections. You give Yourself to broken people, people who reject You over and over, unfaithful people. What a kind and good King You are!"

His eyes are filled with passion. Taking my hand, He says, "Will you go to the lost, My love? Will you go into the village? Will you go to your family? Will you show them what My love can do to the human heart?"[322]

The old fears rise up, making my head swim and my stomach feel sick. I reach into my pouch and pull out the Book of Remembrances. Running my hand over its cover, I whisper, "I can do all things through Christ who strengthens me."[323]

I answer, "I will go wherever You send me and do whatever You ask."

He responds, "Oh, how beautiful you are, indeed!"

We turn toward home. My Beloved shares the pain He feels over those who have never met Him and those who know Him but still reject Him. My heart is stirred; In an effort to help ease His burden, I say, "By the grace of God, I will do whatever You ask me to do. You asked me to reach out to my family and to those in my village. I am now ready. My love outweighs my fear. When may I go, my King?"

"Tomorrow, My love. Comforter will go with you. Speaking of Comforter—," He says, looking over His shoulder.

I look behind me and hurrying down the road towards us is my dear, dear Friend.

What did I ever do to deserve such a wonderful Family?

"You did nothing," He answers.

Laughing, I respond, "Not even my thoughts are safe with You."

"On the contrary. Your thoughts are safest with Me."

Comforter joins us and I waste no time telling Him about how I have forgiven my family and how my Beloved said we could go to the village on the morrow. He smiles and replies, "Unconditional love is the greatest gift one can give to another."

"I suppose that is true, but what does love really look like, Comforter?"

"Love looks like your Bridegroom King," He answers, laying His hand on my Beloved's shoulder. "Love is patient; love

Rhonda Calhoun

is kind. Love is not jealous or boastful; it is not arrogant or rude. Love is not interested only in itself. Love is even-tempered and does not hold grudges. Love is not happy when someone does wrong. Love never quits, always trusts, always hopes for the best and always keeps going and giving."[324]

"Comforter, that is the perfect description of Yourself, my Father and my King," I say.

Comforter smiles and adds, "If you should search the entire universe, Lovely Lady, you would never find a more merciful Father or a more gracious King. They live to lavish Their love on you."

"I long to be like Them, Comforter."

"You will be, Lovely Lady; you are already well on your way."

Chapter Twenty
RETURN TO THE VINEYARDS

You are a garden spring, a well of fresh water. [525]

I wake to the sound of horses neighing and people scurrying about. Throwing on my clothes, I hurry down the hall. Comforter directs me to the breakfast table where my plate is filled and waiting. I am so eager to get started that I have a difficult time eating. Unable to wait any longer, I grab my bread, thank Comforter for the great breakfast, then hurry outside. Comforter follows close behind with a large knapsack flung over His shoulder.

The Captain greets me, "Good morning, my lady. I trust that you slept well?"

"I did indeed, kind sir. But I am eager to start my day and pray that our efforts will be fruitful," I respond, admiring the fine looking horse standing beside him.

"May the Good King grant us favor, my lady," he says, offering me his hand.

"What? Am I to ride this beauty?" I ask, running my hand over her hindquarters.

"You are indeed."

She is as white as snow. Her form is perfect; she has been meticulously groomed. She is adorned with many multicolored

Rhonda Calhoun

jewels and golden tassels. Her reins are golden. Her tail is braided with strands of gold and silver threads. I run my hand along her sleek neck. Her mane is also braided with gold and silver strands. I have never seen a horse as fine as this one.[326]

My brothers have always loved horses, so I grew up learning all about them. This horse is an Arabian, which is one of the finest breeds in existence. *Someone takes really good care of her.* Running my hand along her face, I say, "You are a beautiful lady."

The Captain replies, "Indeed, she is, my lady. The King Himself chose this one from Pharaoh's finest stock. He paid a dear price for her. He brought her to me just this morning and said, 'This is My prize mare. Take her to My bride, for I give her only My very best.'"

I remember the day my Beloved compared me to this beauty. Now, I not only get to see her but also ride her.[327] He does not miss a thing, this King of mine.

The Captain helps me in the saddle. The King's mare responds to my slightest movements as she trots to the clearing in front of the palace. There, on the balcony, stands my Beloved. He waves, and I smile. Great joy floods my heart at the prospect of serving Him. Comforter and the Captain join me while the guards bring up the rear.

"He is a good King, deserving of my very best. I will never again allow fear to keep me from serving my Bridegroom," I say.

"Your love is becoming greater than your fear, Lovely Lady," Comforter responds.

"Only because I was first loved, Comforter. Shall we go now?" I ask.

The Captain raises a flag and shouts, "For the King and for His kingdom!"

His men echo, "For the King and for His kingdom!" A shofar sounds. I wave farewell to the One I love.

We ride hard and furiously to the village. The Captain and ten guards lead the way while a dozen or more surround me on all sides.

It is nearly noon when we arrive. I know that many of the shepherds, watchmen and villagers eat their lunch at the old meeting hall in the center of town. I hope to speak with them before going to my family's vineyard. As we turn the corner, I see Charity, Martha and several other young women sitting near the village well, which is a stone's throw away from the steps of the meeting hall.

As I dismount, I am filled with a mixture of joy and nervousness. I take a deep breath and join them, finding a seat on the bottom step; Comforter is right beside me. As I look into the faces of these precious young women, I am filled with an intense love for each of them. I open my Book of Remembrances and turn to Luke chapter ten. As I read aloud the story of Mary and her sister, Martha, everyone is quiet. I finish reading and close my book. "What do I do now?" I whisper to Comforter.

"Simply speak from your heart, Lovely Lady."

Taking a deep breath, I tell them how devastated I was by sin and compromise and how the Master Shepherd found me and loved me. I tell them about His garden and the many mysteries found there. I tell them about love and truth, mercy and grace. Lastly, I tell them about the cross where a lovesick King died for each of them.

I see that several of the young women are crying. Charity buries her face in her hands and rocks back and forth. I hurry to her side. She says, "Your words stir my heart, yet fear consumes me."

"I understand, Charity. I know exactly how you feel, but I have learned that there is no fear in love; perfect love casts out all fear.[328] Just take the first step and say 'yes' to this glorious King and He will cause your love to grow to a point that is much greater than any fears you might have."

David, the shepherd who cared for my sheep when I first went into the King's garden, is suddenly by my side. He joins me in praying for Charity and then moves on to another. We spend several hours ministering. After everyone leaves, David walks up and says, "Look at you—you have been transformed! I am not surprised though. Anyone who spends time with our King is changed in amazing ways."

"You have changed, too. The way you were praying and speaking with such wisdom was truly inspiring. What are you

Rhonda Calhoun

doing here, anyway? Why aren't you tending sheep?"

"The King has asked me to be a shepherd of different sorts. I now watch over the souls of men rather than the welfare of sheep. It is a wonderful opportunity, and I find great delight in serving my King by serving others."

"I know you will be a good shepherd of souls, for you are a great lover of the King." Laying my hand on his shoulder, I continue, "I hate to rush off, but I must go, for I am off to see my family and work in their vineyard."

"May God grant you favor and peace," David replies.

"And to you, dear shepherd," I respond.

Arriving at my family's vineyard, I am filled with both fear and joy. It will be good to see them, but I fear their response. "Comforter, I hope and pray they will see the beauty of my Bridegroom in me."[329]

At that moment, my mother looks up from the vine that she was pruning and shouts, "Could this possibly be my long lost daughter?'

I run to her saying, "Mother, I have come to work in the vineyard with you."

My mother wipes the sweat from her brow. Shading her eyes from the sun, she asks, "What is this talk, child? We heard rumors that you believe the Master Shepherd is the King and He wants to marry you. Is this true? Do you really believe that?"

"It is true. If you would only listen."

"I told you before that I don't believe in fairy tales. I have way too much work to do to stop and listen to your senseless chatter. Just go back to your hideout and leave us in peace," she says, turning her back to me.

I cannot leave; I love them too much.

What should I do?

Comforter whispers in my ear, "Love never fails."

That's it — I will simply love them and serve them the way Comforter and my Beloved King and Father has loved and served me.

I begin working near my mother. She won't talk to me, so after several attempts, I decide to sing. About an hour passes before my mother finally speaks. "What a lovely voice you have!

I never knew you could sing."

My eldest brother has now made his way close enough to hear our conversation. He interrupts, "Just why are you here? You don't belong with us common people—everyone knows that you think you're too good for us."

I reply, "Please listen. I am not the same person I used to be. The Book of Remembrances says that if anyone wants to be great, then he should become a servant.[330] I am not interested in ruling over you, but in serving you, for I have found One who is worth wasting my life on. I desire to serve Him for the rest of my life. Whatever He desires, that I will do. He sent me here to tell you that He loves you. You, too, can know the love, joy and peace that I know. All you need to do is say, 'yes' to His love. It really is that simple."

My brother, angrier than ever, marches toward me. In a flash, the Captain steps in front of me. My brother abruptly stops when he bounces off the Captain. Quite perplexed, he asks, "What was that?"

Can he not see the Captain? I know he cannot see the King, but surely he can see the Captain?

Curious, I say, "I would like to introduce you to the Captain of the King's guard and also to my Friend, Comforter."

Both of my brothers shake their heads and look at mother. "Mother, there she goes again talking about people who are not there."

Turning his back to me, my youngest brother walks away. My oldest says, "Leave us, girl! We don't want to hear anymore of your nonsense. Just go back to your life of comfort and ease and leave us to our work!"

They really cannot see Him! I look at Comforter, who only smiles. Ignoring my brother, I go back to work. My mother slowly works her way to my side. She whispers, "Charity's been telling me stories of the Bridegroom King. Is it really true, child? Is the Master Shepherd really the King?"

"Mother, it is true! The King loves you just as much as He loves me. He loves each one the same. He longs to have an intimate, personal relationship with you. He sent me here to tell you that."

Rhonda Calhoun

"How wonderful it would be if it were only true."

"But it is true and I am living proof of it," I answer with tears flowing down my face.

"You cry. For what reason?"

"I cry for you, Mother. The King's mercies are great and His love is deeper than any ocean, but you must reach out and receive Him, otherwise His love will have no transforming effect on your life. You must voluntarily give Him your heart and your love. It is worth whatever price you must pay. Believe me, I know."

Standing upright and stretching her back, she says, "You have become ever so lovely, daughter. You are kind and loving and so beautiful. You have certainly changed. I will meditate on the things you have said."

She walks away and my heart soars! With a joyful heart, I resume my worship staying as close to my mother as possible. It isn't long before she begins to hum along with me. At one point she whispers, "What is the name of this lovely tune, child?"

"It is called the Song of the Lamb, Mother. I do not know the words, only the tune, for it is a song that cannot be taught or learned; it must flow freely from the heart."

"'That is a song I should like to know," she responds.

"As you pursue the King, you will learn the words," I respond.

I look at Comforter, who remains close by my side, and we exchange smiles. The Captain, who stands guard over me, nods.

"The sun will be setting soon, Lovely Lady. We should be on our way," Comforter says.

I bid my mother good-day and then walk over to my brothers, who turn their backs to me. No longer fearful, no longer intimidated, I say, "I must go now, but I will return tomorrow. Good-day, dear brothers!"

I walk a short distance away, then stop. Speaking loud enough for my family to hear, I exclaim, "And I love you all!"

Once we are beyond their hearing, I ask, "Comforter, why can't they see You and the Captain?"

"Envy and jealousy hardens the human heart and blinds

the eye, Lovely Lady."

"What will soften a hard heart and open a blind eye?"

"There is only one thing and that is unconditional love," Comforter answers.

I reply, "And I know what love is. Love is patient, love is kind and is not jealous. Love never quits, always trusts, always hopes for the best and always keeps going. And, most importantly, love never fails."[331]

Looking over my shoulder, I continue, "Comforter, I have much to learn."

"You have learned much already, Lovely Lady."

I grab my Friend's hand and say, "That is only because You are the best Teacher in the whole wide world!"

"The best Teacher in the world is the King," He replies.

"And He would say that the best Teacher in the world is His Father. I have never seen anything like the way You continually point to Jesus and He points to the Father."

"Esteem others as greater than yourself, Lovely Lady."

We hurry through the streets, stopping briefly to greet a few old friends. I am surprised by a powerful desire in my heart to share the truth of my newly found love with everyone I see.

Just past the meeting hall, in an alley, we pass by an elderly man dressed in rags, slumped against the side of a building. My heart aches for him. He appears to be in great need. I turn to Comforter and say, "In the Book of Remembrances, it says that if anyone has this world's goods and sees his brother in need and closes his heart against him, the love of God does not abide in him."[332]

"That is true, Lovely Lady."

Laying my hand on the satchel hanging from His shoulder, I continue, "Comforter, may I have the food you packed for my evening meal?"

Without the slightest hesitation, He hands me the bag and I hurry to the man.

The Captain and several of the guards go with me. As I draw near, I see that the man's face and arms are covered with oozing sores. His body is emaciated to the point that I am amazed he is still alive. Stooping down beside him, I say, "Good day, kind sir. I have food and some cool water. Would you allow me to share it with you?"

"I am too hungry to be proud. I would be most grateful for anything that you would give this old man."

Wasting no time, I open the satchel and hand him a banana. His eyes light up. He takes a bite and, with his mouth full, says, "Thank you."

Sitting beside him, I listen as he describes what it is like to be homeless, without a family and without anyone who cares.

"May I pray for you?" I ask.

"You can if you'd like, but God stopped caring about me many years ago. He probably doesn't even remember my name."

"What is your name, sir?"

"Stephen," the old gentleman answers.

"Stephen, I can guarantee you that our Father remembers your name." Holding up the Book of Remembrances, I continue, "This Book says that it is impossible for the Father to forget His children."[333]

"I hope you are right," he responds and bows his head.

Laying my hand on his shoulder, I pray asking God to give Stephen a home where he will be loved and accepted. I am surprised to see that Stephen has tears in his eyes.

Without me asking, he tells me the story of his life. With Comforter by my side, I listen in amazement, for this man has experienced so much tragedy that it is a miracle he is alive and sane.

When he finishes, I tell him about the Bridegroom King. He listens quietly, but does not respond. Comforter whispers that it is time for us to leave. I bid Stephen farewell, saying, "Tomorrow, about this same time, I will return with more food, some clothing and medicine for you, my friend."

"Why would you bother with someone like me?" he asks.

"Because I care and because the King cares. At the foot of His cross, we all look the same, my friend." I answer.

"Thank you," he says, "I will be watching for you."

The Captain and Comforter follow close by my side as we leave the alley. "If I might be so bold as to ask you a question, my lady?" the Captain asks.

"Ask what you will, dear Captain."

"I am in awe of this affection that grows in your heart. You not only love the King, but it appears that you also love that homeless man."

"This is true, Captain. I love him with the love that fills my heart."

"I am amazed as I watch you. This is a rare and precious love that you walk in," he responds.[334]

"'Tis a love that flows from my Beloved," I reply as tears fill my eyes.

Comforter takes my hand and says, "Your heart is filled with compassion, Lovely Lady, which is a wonderful thing and brings great delight to your Bridegroom King and Father. Your worship is a sweet fragrance."

"My worship? I do not understand."

"Worship is much more than singing. Worship occurs every time you do what the King has asked you to do. It matters not if it is in the giving of something as simple as a glass of water to a stranger, or whether you sit at your Beloved's feet, gazing into His marvelous eyes of love. Both are worship, both are adoration, for you serve a King who feels what His people feel. When they suffer, He suffers. When they rejoice, He rejoices. When they are hungry, He is hungry. He is not distant, but remains closer than a brother, closer than a mother and a father to His people."

"Comforter, I was thrilled to share my food and the good news about my Bridegroom King with Stephen today. As much as I enjoy telling others about Him, I still long and pray for the day when I will be with my Beloved all the time, when I will never be separated from Him."

"The truth is, you are never separated from Him. He is with you all the time, everywhere you go, even when you cannot see Him. He lives within you and He surrounds you." He points across the street and says, "Look over there." My Beloved is passing out bread to the hungry. He looks up, nods His head, and smiles at me. Comforter continues, "He said He would never leave you, nor forsake you. He is a Man of His word; it is impossible for Him to lie.[335] Now, run to the One who loves you most."

That is exactly what I do—I run and fall into His outstretched arms. There are no words to adequately express the joy of being held by this wonderful Bridegroom King. Snuggled in His loving arms, I whisper, "The more I seek You...the more I find You. The more I find You...the more I love You. For the rest of my life, I want to sit at Your feet, drink from the river of life and lean against You. This love I feel is so deep—it's more than I can stand. I melt in the presence of Your peace, for it's overwhelming!"

"I have felt the wind blow...whispering your name. I have seen your tears fall...as I watched the rain. I have felt the beat of your heart...when you looked at Me. I have seen your love for the hurting...when you fed the poor. I receive your love...so deep...and it's more than I can stand. I melt in your love, for it's overwhelming!" He responds.

"I want to know You, my Lord and King. I want to touch Your heart...all the days of my life. I want to know Your ways...all the days of my life. I want to know what makes You cry. I want to share in Your sorrows and dance with the joy You feel inside. I want to live my life by Your side. Lord, what are You thinking? What are You feeling? What does it take to make You cry?"

"Love is the answer to all three of your questions. Love moves my heart like nothing else," He answers.

Chapter Twenty-one
MY GARDEN

Make my garden breathe out fragrance. [556]

*E*ach morning, Comforter, the Captain, his guards and I go to the Village Square where we meet with others to hear David teach from the Book of Remembrances. David is an excellent teacher and such a wise young man. He has a deep love for people and for the King. He loves in much the same way my Bridegroom loves, without condition or restraint. I look forward to our times together, for I am learning so much from this kindhearted shepherd.

After David's teaching, Comforter and I hurry to my family's vineyard. Of course, the Captain and his men follow; they never leave my side.

I long for my family to experience the incredible love of the King, but sometimes I wonder if they ever will. My mother is like a reed blowing in the wind; one day she seems interested, and the next day she won't even allow me to speak of Him.

Winter hits fast and hard, but love for David's 'flock' has grown to such a point that I do not mind making the trip to the village each morning and would never for a moment consider not going.

This morning is especially cold; the ground is covered with

a thick blanket of snow. Comforter waits for me while I bundle up. As usual, the Captain and his guards wait with the horses saddled and ready. They follow especially close as Comforter and I enter the wilderness, for they are well aware of the dangers lurking in the shadows and keep a close watch for predators, both man and beast.

We meet inside the village hall huddled around an old coal stove. Many of the watchmen and most of the shepherds now attend the meetings. One of the shepherds named Saul continually tries to engage David in debates concerning the laws of the kingdom. David speaks the truth, but refuses to "strain at a gnat and swallow a camel", as he puts it.

Approximately fifty people pack into a room that was built to hold forty. Martha attends only occasionally, but Charity never misses a meeting. Several widows come with knitting in hand; they are making hats and scarves for the poor.

Stephen, the former homeless man, has become one of the favorites among our group. From the first time I met Stephen, I visited him daily, each time encouraging him to come home with me. I constantly assured him that my Father would certainly find a place for him to live, if he would only ask. Finally, and to my utter delight, Stephen agreed. Comforter and I led him home to the Father.

While we were still a long way off, my Father saw us coming. He jumped off the porch, leaped over the gate and raced down the path to meet us. He ran right up to Stephen and, without saying a word, threw His arms around his neck and smothered him with kisses. Having extravagantly welcomed him, my Father said, "Welcome home, son. I have been watching and waiting for your return."

Stepping back, Stephen replied, "You call me 'son', but I am no longer worthy of that title. I return to you as a humble servant."

Without even acknowledging his statement, Father turned to His servants and said, "Hurry inside and bring out My best robe and put it on My son. Put My ring on his hand and sandals on his feet so that no one will mistake him for a servant. Bring the fattened calf, kill it and let us eat and be merry; for this son of

Mine was dead and has come to life again; he was lost, but now is found!"[337]

"But I'm not worthy," Stephen responded.

"My Son's death has made you worthy and that settles it. Nothing more needs to be said. Now, come and let us celebrate."

Stephen fell into Father's arms, sobbing while He assured Stephen of His love and forgiveness. Wiping his face on his dirty sleeve, Father led Stephen into His palace. The following day, eager to partner with his loving Father, Stephen went to work in the King's gardens. He soon became one of His best gardeners. When Stephen learned of my daily trips to the village, he asked the King for permission to join me, which was granted. The poverty that Stephen saw among many in the village broke his heart. He asked the King for permission to bring fruits and vegetables from the garden so that he could share with those in need. My Beloved smiled and replied, "This is the way it is to be in My kingdom, My friend. Go, with My blessing, and do all that is in your heart to do."

I have so enjoyed watching Stephen grow more and more in love with Father, Comforter and the King.

I have come to learn that my Father, Comforter and the King feel a special love for orphans, widows and the poor.[338] They never miss an opportunity to reach out to them with practical deeds of kindness. They value compassion so much that they issued a decree that every person in the kingdom *must* love their neighbors *and* their enemies.

Because of the love that continues to grow within me, I find myself moved with compassion anytime I see someone in need, regardless of what that need might be. It has become impossible for me to turn my head or pass them by without at least praying for them.

Since Stephen began bringing food to those in need, others have joined him; many bring bread and food each morning to give away. Some have even sold their property and possessions in order to help others.[339] The sharing of our belongings has caused us to become closer and has also caused others to inquire about our King. It is amazing to think that Stephen, who was

Rhonda Calhoun

once rejected by the villagers, is the very one who caused our hearts to be awakened to the needs of those around us. He is now deeply loved and appreciated by all. The one who was rejected has become accepted.

Each evening, upon returning from the village, Stephen dines at the table with us, enjoying the fellowship of his new family. Afterward, he hurries to the garden where he works well into the night. I say night, but it actually never grows dark in the King's garden. When the sun goes down, a glorious light fills the place. I once asked my Beloved about the source of this light and He answered, "I am the light of the world; those who follow Me shall not walk in darkness."[340] Another one of those mysteries surrounding my Beloved King.

Even during the winter season, the King's garden continues to produce fruits and vegetables in large amounts. It is truly a mystery, one that I have yet to understand and don't know that I ever will. How can a plant grow and produce when the ground around it is frozen? How can one survive when surrounded by bitter, harsh winds and snow? It seems that one should die, but somehow, by the grace of God, the roots are driven deeper and life goes on.

Stephen continues to join Comforter and me on our daily visits to my family. My brothers are not very interested in talking with me, but they really enjoy Stephen, who often talks to them about the Bridegroom King. I believe that their hearts are beginning to soften. Just this morning my mother came to one of our meetings. Afterwards, she and David had a long talk. I sat in the corner praying that the eyes of her heart would be enlightened so that she can see the King in His fullness.

This evening as the sun sets and we make our way home, I ask Comforter, "Will the day ever come when my mother and brothers accept my Beloved for who He really is?"

"That day will surely come, for your Father has promised His Son a bride who loves Him fully and knows Him intimately. They will know Him as the Bridegroom King, Lovely Lady."

Joy floods my being. "It is worth it all," I whisper.

Spring is just around the corner, and hope fills the air.

Chapter Twenty-two
OPEN TO ME

I opened to my Beloved, but my Beloved had turned away. [541]

$\mathcal{T}$he morning is unusually warm for the first day of spring, but I barely notice in my haste to get to the village meeting. I continue to cherish the Book of Remembrances, for it has been vital to my growth and helpful in my understanding of the King and His kingdom.

After our study, all of us gather at the river bank to watch and celebrate the baptism of three men. As the last man comes up out of the water, the sweetest fragrance fills the air. *There is only One whose presence ushers in such a heavenly scent.*

I scan the crowd searching for the One who is outstanding among ten thousand. He is always easy to locate even in a crowd, but only if one is looking. I quickly find Him leaning against a sycamore tree watching and praying. His eyes are filled with love. Knowing every movement of my heart and mind, He looks directly at me and I am overwhelmed. I turn to join Him, but He motions for me to remain.

With the gentleness of a whisper, He moves among the congregation, touching this one, embracing that one and speaking to another. For the most part, He goes unnoticed. There are some who are aware of His presence—David, Stephen and most of the children. He makes His way to Charity; she looks directly at His face, but quickly turns away. I hurry to her side and whisper, "You saw the Master Shepherd in His royal attire, didn't you? You saw the Bridegroom King, didn't you?"

"I saw nothing, and what I thought I saw was just a result of my overactive imagination," she answers.

"O Charity, you don't understand; He really is the Bridegroom King and He has come to reveal Himself to you!"

With tightly clenched teeth, she replies, "I am having a very difficult time believing that the Master Shepherd is really the King. Until I clearly see Him for myself, I refuse to believe that He is who you say He is."

I look to my Beloved, who now sits on the steps surrounded by children. I whisper, "Blessed are those who do not see and believe."[341a]

If only Charity and the others knew how wonderful He is and how much He longs to be with them and how much He loves them, then they would run to Him and never let Him go.

My Beloved motions for us to follow. Stephen, Comforter and I quickly respond. As we leave the village, headed for my family's vineyard, I pour out the grief I feel over Charity's unwillingness to embrace Him as her King. My Beloved patiently listens. With His large hand gently squeezing my small one, He says, "Whoever gives something as simple as a cup of cold water to one of the least in My kingdom, truly I say to you, they will not lose their reward."

With a slight bow, He bids me farewell and heads back to the village. I turn to Comforter and see that tears flow unhindered down His beautiful face. He meets my gaze and quickly comes to my side. Together, arm in arm, we walk on in silence.

Arriving at the vineyard, we find my family in a foul mood. They refuse to tell me what has gone wrong and are barely civil to Stephen, which is quite strange because they like him. Unable to tolerate their attitudes, I do only the work that is necessary and then bid them farewell.

Our trip home seems much longer than usual. I am unusually exhausted and feel quite discouraged so I walk in silence.

Stephen joins us for dinner. He and I share the events of the day with our wonderful Father, who listens with great interest and compassion. Once we have nothing more to say, Father leans forward, takes my hand in His and says, "Except a seed falls into the ground and dies, it remains by itself alone, but if it dies, it bears much fruit."[342]

"What does that mean, Father?"

"One must die, if he is to live. Do you love My Son enough to die, Little One?"

Do I love Him enough to die?

I do not know the answer to that question. I want to ask, but I am afraid of the answer, for my Father knows and sees all things with perfect clarity. I decide to say nothing and quickly busy myself with clearing the table. Father speaks with Stephen yet watches me; His eyes are filled with loving adoration even though He knows I just avoided His question. When the table is nearly clear, unable to resist His look of love, I acknowledge His gaze with a smile. He opens His arms wide and I run into them. I will never get enough of His love, His affection or His affirmation! 'Tis a unique Love that can adore me so completely, so consistently that when I forget who I am and, more importantly, who He is, He still loves me!

With the day coming to a close, Stephen excuses himself. Father, Comforter, the King and I sit on the front steps. It is such a lovely night; the stars are bright against the dark sky. A nightingale sings his praises to the King, as a multitude of crickets and frogs provide backup. In a nearby pasture, a shepherd watches over his sleeping flock. It is a perfect night. I am surrounded by love and peace, but my heart feels unusually heavy.

I continue to wrestle with my Father's question. It is not long before my Father and my Beloved bid us good-night. They make Their way across the courtyard heading to their palace. They have gone only a short distance when my Beloved turns and shouts, "My bride, remember that true love is formed in the wilderness; it is formed in the place of testing. Will you love Me even in the wilderness? Will you love Me if you lose everything?"

Without waiting for a response, He turns and disappears

Rhonda Calhoun

into the dark night. Troubled by His words, I walk to the back of the cottage and climb into the hammock.

What was He talking about? What is this talk of the wilderness? Surely, He won't make me go there...or will He?

The stars dance before me and the sounds of the night once again comfort my anxious thoughts. My cozy "nest" is so peaceful that I soon forget my Beloved's unsettling questions.

Before I came to know my Beloved, loneliness and fear were my constant companions, but now I walk in great peace and safety. My Father, Comforter and Bridegroom King are extravagant with Their love and affirmation. The Ancient of Days lavishes me with His Fatherly affections; I have discovered that there are no limits to His love. The King is my dear Friend and Partner. Comforter remains my constant Companion and Teacher, even though David does a large part of my training now.

When I asked Comforter why, He replied, "That is the way of My kingdom—the shepherd cares for the sheep. It is important for you to be properly submitted to David's authority and leadership."[343]

Several months ago, David invited me to help him care for his "flock". After asking my Beloved for permission, I agreed. And I have thoroughly enjoyed ministering to the villagers; I am learning much and growing more like the King every day. The two things I asked for have now come true—I have an intimate relationship with my Shepherd and I am His partner in ministry. My life is perfect; I have all I need and feel fully satisfied.

I announce to God, "I'm the happiest girl in the entire world! I don't ever want to leave this place!"

Some time later, I fall asleep, but my heart is awake, for love is alive within me.[344] I dream of a garden filled with enormous fruits and vegetables. In the middle of this garden is a dark valley filled with loud crying and groaning. I look for my Beloved, but cannot find Him. Running into the wilderness, I embrace a large cross. A bitter taste fills my mouth; my heart is filled with fiery love. I turn to see a crack of light appear in the thick darkness. My Beloved suddenly steps through it! I hear His voice calling me.

I wake with a start!

Was that the voice of my Beloved?

I was dreaming, I think. I listen, but all I hear is the pounding of my heart. Closing my eyes again, I hear the words my Beloved last said to me, "My bride, remember that true love is formed in the wilderness, in the place of testing. Will you love Me even there? Will you still love Me if you lose everything?"

Why would He ask me that?

My thoughts are suddenly interrupted by a knock on the gate, immediately followed by the sound of His voice.[345] My heart leaps![346]

Bolting upright, I look around. The blazing torch near the lattice door pierces the thick darkness. I see movement. Peering through the lattice, I see my Beloved. Our eyes meet as He cries out, "Open for Me, My sister, My love, My dove, My perfect one!"[347]

I lean forward; my hammock swings wildly. He continues, "I call you 'sister' because we have the same Father. I call you 'love' because you are devoted to Me and to My people. I call you 'dove' because of your gentle, guileless nature and your wholehearted devotion. And I call you 'perfect one' because you have become one who walks in obedience, not one who walks in compromise. I have purified your heart and caused your love to mature."[348]

He presses His face against the lattice and continues, "Do not be content to remain in your place of comfort, My love. But rather, open to Me that we might go into the fields and do good to souls, extending mercy to them. It is not enough for you to enjoy My presence in solitude; you must also reach out to those who are lost and show them the way."

The fear that I thought had been conquered suddenly makes its presence painfully known. My Beloved continues, "My dove, I have come from the garden of Gethsemane where I suffered to the point of My sweat becoming saturated with blood. The dark night of the soul, that is where I have been. My head is drenched with dew as a result."[349]

His face is etched with pain, and His eyes are heavy from lack of sleep. He extends His hand through the opening. My heart

Rhonda Calhoun

is moved; it burns for Him.[350]   He continues, "Will you come with Me to the garden of Gethsemane? Will you embrace the cross? Will you open your heart fully to Me, My bride?

"I am inviting you into the fellowship of My sufferings. I understand that, in doing so, there is the possibility that you will turn away from Me and that would bring Me great sorrow. But there is no other way to purify a heart except through the fire of My all-consuming love."[351]

The last time He invited me to run with Him; I refused because I did not want to face my fears. I did not trust Him enough to leave my comfort zone. But I am not the same person I was then. I have taken off my old clothes and have washed my feet; I cannot go back to my old ways.[352] I will not allow fear or compromise to keep me from following Him ever again.

I answer, "I am now dressed in Your garments of righteousness and have been cleansed by Your blood. I live my life according to Your will and under Your authority. I choose to walk with You clean and undefiled."[352]

He extends His hand through the opening in the door; His hand is on the bolt.[353] The very depths of my being tremble as I swing my legs over the side of the hammock and hurry to the gate.[354] I take hold of the bolt, but what is this--my hands drip with myrrh![353] The latch is covered with the oil of myrrh, the most expensive kind of myrrh there is! The sweet fragrance of my suffering Savior fills the air.

Has He just anointed me for burial?[354]

His wonderful, empowering grace suddenly pierces my heart. *O, how my heart yearns to be more like Him, to love like Him and to live like Him!*[355]

I cry out, "Give me nothing but love and the cross! I will embrace all that You have for me. I give myself to You without reservation! I will suffer whatever is necessary that I might be wholly Yours, for You are the One who gives life to this poor heart!"[356]

I throw open the gate, but do not see Him.[357] My Beloved has gone.[358] Peering into the darkness, I see nothing but emptiness. I hear nothing but the frantic beating of my heart. I run around the corner of the house; the Captain steps out of the shadows. I ask, "Have you seen the One I love?"

"No, my lady, I have not," he answers.

I turn to run into the darkness, but he restrains me saying, "The King has ordered me to protect you, my lady. Therefore, I cannot let you go."

"But, I must go!"

"You would not be safe out there, my lady!"

"But...."

"You would not be safe," he repeats, more tenderly this time.

Relenting, I look toward the hills and cry out, "Oh, my Beloved, I cannot see You or feel Your presence! Where have You gone? You invited me to run with You, so why have You left without me? I've done nothing wrong this time! I got up when You called; I opened the door and ran after You, but You have hidden Yourself from me. For what reason? Unto what end?"[359]

The only response I hear is the sound of my voice echoing off the surrounding mountains. Tears stream down my face. With a confused and heavy heart, I resign myself to the fact that my Beloved is not going to answer. I slowly make my way inside the cottage where I find Comforter asleep in front of the fireplace.

I try to rouse Him, but He does not respond.

With an even heavier heart, I retire to my room. Looking in the mirror, I tell myself, "I will take the path of suffering; I will endure this dark night of the soul while trusting in His love. Even though it appears that He has abandoned me, I will remember that He is always with me and He is always good."

The fragrance of my worship fills my room and I am lost in love!

Chapter Twenty-three
DARK NIGHT OF THE SOUL

I am sick with love. [360]

Several hours pass before I finally fall asleep. My night is filled with dreams of me running with My Beloved on the mountains, leaping over the hills.

I rise before the sun and hurry to see if perhaps He has returned. Racing past Comforter, who is still asleep, I fling wide the front door. A thick fog lies like a heavy blanket over the dew-drenched ground. The Captain greets me.

Forgetting formalities, I respond, "Tell me, dear Captain, have you seen the King this morning?"

"I am sorry to report that I have not, my lady," he answers.

"It has only been a few hours since He left, but it feels as though it has been months. I must find my Beloved. When the fog lifts, I will seek Him."

"We are here to serve and protect you, my lady," he responds.

With a heavy heart, I go back inside. Comforter is still asleep, so I return to my room and open the Book of Remembrances. I turn to John 16:22 and read, "You now have sorrow; but I will see you again. On that day, your heart will rejoice and no one will be able to take your joy away from you."

Rhonda Calhoun

I remember well the day my Beloved read this passage to me not many days past; we were sitting under the Tree of Life. After reading this, He took my hand, looked directly in my eyes and said, "When in the garden of suffering remember this truth, My love."

At the time, I wondered what He was talking about. Not understanding, I simply dismissed it. After all, I was perfectly happy; my world was filled with peace, joy and every good thing. Sorrow and suffering was the last thing on my mind. Now I understand that He was preparing me for this day. [361]

Stepping to my window, I throw back the curtains. The fog is still so thick that I cannot see a thing. I whisper, "You will return to me; I will see You again and my heart will surely rejoice, but when will that day be? How long must I wait?"

Wrapping my shawl around my shoulders, I hurry out. Comforter is gone and the kitchen is empty, but a plate of bread, fruit and cheese has been left for me. I have no desire for food; there is only one "thing" I am hungry for and He is nowhere to be found.

Perhaps my Beloved is at the palace; if not, then my Father will certainly know where I can find Him. The Captain and his men surround me as I hurry across the grounds. We have gone but a short distance when the Captain says, "My lady, it is beginning to rain. Perhaps you should return to the cottage?"

"We are almost there," I respond, oblivious to my physical comfort.

By the time I reach the huge palace doors, I am thoroughly soaked and trembling from head to toe. Before I can knock, a servant opens the door and informs me that the Ancient of Days is away on an extended trip, then proceeds to close the door. I quickly put my hand up, stopping the door from closing and ask, "But what about the King? Is He here?"

"I am sorry, but He, too, has gone."

"And when will He return?"

"He did not say, and we do not know. Is there anything else I can help you with?"

"I don't suppose you know where Comforter is?"

"He resides within you," the servant answers.

What kind of answer is that?

"Will there be anything more, my lady?" he asks ever so kindly.

"Not unless you can heal a broken heart," I reply.

"I am nothing more than a ministering servant, my lady. I do not have the power to heal," he answers.

Bidding him good-day, I leave. "Captain, my Beloved's words have pierced my heart like a two-edged sword. Nothing is as painful as this love that grips my heart. My Beloved's absence only causes it to grow in strength and intensity. It is a bittersweet thing to love so much that being separated from the Source of that love causes such agony! But, I suppose having a love of any less degree would be even more painful."

"I am in awe of your love, my lady," the Captain responds.

I look into the distance as my tears join the rain, and voice my thoughts, "I suspect that one must endure great testing for the sake of pure love."[362]

"I must admit that I cannot understand this love that you feel, never having experienced it, but I am fascinated and amazed by it," the Captain responds.

"My love is not what is amazing; I love only because I am loved. It is the love of my King that is amazing, for He loves me even in my weakness and even though I am completely and totally undeserving of His affections. He loves both His friends and His enemies. He loves the rich and the poor, the old and the young, the lovely and the ugly. He loves those who mistreat Him and abuse Him and even kill Him. Now, that is amazing love, is it not?"

"I truly marvel at His love and your love," he replies, shaking his head.

A huge bolt of lightning pierces the sky and the following thunder shakes the ground beneath my feet. "Perhaps, you should return to the cottage?" the Captain asks as he places his hand on my elbow.

"How can I, when my heart aches to find my Bridegroom? There is no place I would rather be than by His side, beholding His beauty, for I cannot live without Him."

217

Rhonda Calhoun

I turn toward Mount Lebanon and run unhindered, fueled by the love that consumes me. Arriving at its base, I stand in the downpour, watching, waiting and listening. An undetermined amount of time passes. I ask, "He is not here, is He, Captain?"

"No, my lady, He is not."

Looking at the ominous mountain looming over me, I cry out, "You put Your myrrh-drenched hand over my heart, tenderizing and wounding it and then fled from me like a gazelle! O, my Beloved, return to me that Your love might heal this gaping wound, for You alone have the power to heal and satisfy the desires of my heart!"

Silence; nothing but awful silence, and rain and thunder. Nothing but emptiness surrounds me. It seeps into my being, one drop at a time until I am full yet painfully empty.

I have a feeling that He is not coming back today. Who knows how long it will be before I see His face or hear His voice again. My heart sinks. I whisper, "I search for You but cannot find You, yet I love You still and always will!"

Turning away, I say, "We can return now."

Sick of heart, I slowly plod home, not bothering to avoid the mud puddles along my path. I am nearly home when Comforter comes to mind. Surely, He will know where my Beloved is! He knows everything, He will know where my Beloved King has gone and when He will return. Feeling a glimmer of hope, I quicken my pace.

Whatever will I do? Comforter has taught me to be completely dependent on my King. How will I ever make it without His presence? His absence leaves me like a bird without wings, like a sheep without a shepherd, like a heart without a beat and like a book without words. I am nothing without Him. How shall I ever endure His absence even for one day?

By the time we arrive, I am shivering violently. Without stopping to remove my mud-caked sandals or to wash my feet, I run into the cottage leaving a trail of mud and water. The couch is empty except for a folded blanket. Lying on the table is a note. With trembling hands, I pick it up and read:

Lovely Lady,

Your Bridegroom King is committed to you. He understands that your dedication to Him must be based on the strength of His commitment to you, not on the strength of your love for Him or your ability to do what is right. There is nothing you can do to cause your Beloved to love you any more than He already does. Neither can you do anything to further attract His attention, for you have already conquered His heart and His thoughts are continually on you.

Your King neither sleeps nor slumbers. He intercedes for you day and night. He will see you through! He is enough. You cannot save yourself.

Lovely Lady, I, too, must step behind the scenes for a season, but remember that I am always with you. It is for the sake of love that We allow this fiery test. And remember that love bears all things, believes all things, hopes all things and endures all things. Love *never* fails!

Forever Your Friend and Companion,
Comforter

Standing in the open doorway, I see that the rain is falling harder than ever; the sky is torn apart with thunder and lightning. The gusting wind threatens to break the weak and immature trees. Peace is nowhere to be found, and I am painfully alone. *Wind of God, this storm that You send blows hard against me. Will I be broken or will I bend with You? Will I survive this storm? I do not know, for I have become very comfortable in my life. I do not like to suffer at all. I prefer ease and comfort and predictability.*

The Captain comes around the corner; his arms filled with wood. "I thought you might benefit from a fire, my lady."

I am shivering uncontrollably, though I suspect it is from more than just my cold, wet clothing. "Yes, that would be nice," I answer without really thinking.

"I will mop up that water for you," he states.

I look down and see that I am standing in a large puddle. "Thank you, Captain, but you needn't do that. I will see to it."

I go to my room and change into dry clothes. When I return, the floor has been mopped and dried. A thick blanket and several large pillows have been laid in front of the fire.

Snuggling under the warm blanket, I open the Book of Remembrances. After reading several chapters, I give up and toss it aside. The stories that have always been so fascinating to me no longer hold my attention. I stare into the dancing flames and listen to its crackling. I pray, but there is no answer, no comfort. Nothing. It feels as though my prayers are hitting the ceiling and bouncing back on my head. The day seems to last forever. I am eager for night to come in hopes that I will wake on the morrow to find that this has been nothing more than a bad dream.

Weak and exhausted, I do not bother to go to my bed, but crawl to the couch dragging the blanket behind me. I sleep, but in reality, I neither sleep nor slumber, for my sleep is that of a lovesick heart desperately searching for the Object of its desire.

I open my eyes. Someone is in the room.

O, my soul, could it be my Beloved?

My eyes focus and despair fills me; it is only the Captain putting more wood on the fire.

"Well, hello," he says.

"Good morning," I whisper, discovering that my throat is on fire and I ache all over.

"Don't you mean, 'good evening', my lady?"

I try to sit up, but my body refuses to co-operate. "Evening? It can't be," I answer, cringing with every word.

"I am afraid that you are quite sick, my lady. But do not worry, I have sent for Mercy. She will care for you until you are well."

He offers me a cup saying, "Here, I made you some broth."

Again, I try to sit up, but the pounding inside my head is more than I can endure. "Thank you, but I will drink it later."

I close my eyes and drift in and out of a fitful sleep, for I am devastated by Love. I fight to climb out of the deep hole that I find myself in, only to continually fall back into its endless depths. My mind is filled with visions of my Beloved. I run with Him through the mountains as we rescue lost sheep. I walk with Him through the gardens, harvesting priceless herbs. I climb the Tree of Life and eat its fruit, then dive into the crystal clear waters of the River of Life. I float for what seems like days. In the distance, from a surrounding mountain top, I hear singing. The tune grows louder and more distinct. I strain to understand the words but cannot. There is something about this tune that is very familiar, but what is it? Suddenly, I remember — it is the Song of the Lamb!

I roll over and open my eyes. My head is pounding, my body aches and my throat is still quite painful. An elderly woman is bending over the fire stirring a kettle. I muster all the strength within me to listen to the words as she sings, "My Beloved is mine and His desire is for me.[363] My Beloved is dazzling and ruddy, outstanding among ten thousand...."[364]

Her song abruptly stops as she turns around. Her appearance is that of a kindly woman. Her complexion is rosy and her skin is amazingly smooth. Her snow-white hair is fastened in a tight bun on the top of her head and her crystal blue eyes smile down at me. "Well, I'm glad to see that you are finally awake, child. I suppose you are wondering just who I am?"

She lowers her pleasantly plump frame on a stool by my side and continues, "My name is Mercy; I am the King's nurse. The Captain sent for me when you first fell ill. The way I figure it, that was nearly three weeks ago."

"Excuse me," I say, ignoring the pain, "did you say *three* weeks?"

"That is right, child; you have been terribly sick for three weeks now."

"And what about the King? Has He returned?"

"I am sorry, child, but He has not," she answers.

"My friends in the village and my family, how are they?"

"Stephen continues to make the trip to the village every day. Your family is well and your friends have been praying for your recovery. They will be so glad to hear that you are better."

Returning to the kettle, she says, "Now, try to drink some of this broth. It will help restore your strength."

"I am not very hungry, Mercy, but thank you."

"Now, child, I won't take no for an answer. Just try to drink a little, it will do you a world of good."

With Mercy's persistent encouragement, I manage to

drink about half the cup. I have so many questions, but find that I am too weak to ask them. I quickly fall asleep and dream of the Master Shepherd standing before me with His rod and staff in hand. He leads me beside a gentle stream where He invites me to lie down. He lays His hand on my heart and strength and comfort pour into me. Reaching behind His back, He hands me two pieces of fruit. I eagerly devour them without any pain. He says, "Surely goodness and mercy shall follow you all the days of your life and you shall dwell in the house of the Lord forever."[365]]

I wake with a start. Sitting upright, I cry out, "Is He here?" Has He come?"

Mercy is by my side in an instant. She scoops me up in her loving arms, saying, "Shhh, child. Everything's gonna be just fine. Your Beloved hasn't come, but He will—He surely will."

Tears pour down my face. "Mercy, I am sick with love!"[366]

I cry until I can cry no more. Mercy holds me close, rocking me back and forth. When my tears cease, she whispers, "Yours is a sickness of the heart, child. This sickness can only be cured by the One who loves you most."

"O, how I miss Him, Mercy."

"I know, child, I know." Resting my head against her bosom, she hums the Song of the Lamb. "That song never fails to comfort me." I say.

"That is because it is the Song of all songs, which will be sung on the King's wedding day. The Song of the Lamb flows from the heart, child, for it is the story of *true* Love."

"Why don't I know the words then?"

Running her hands through my hair, she answers, "You will know them when the time is right. There is an appointed season for everything and a time for every event under heaven. A time to give birth and a time to die. A time to plant and a time to uproot what is planted; a time to kill and a time to heal. A time to tear down and a time to build up; a time to weep and a time to laugh. A time to mourn and a time to dance.[367]

"You see, child, the King makes everything beautiful in its appointed time."[368]

I remain snuggled in Mercy's arms for a little while longer. as she hums the Song of the Lamb. I drift in and out of sleep. Mercy wakes me saying, "It is time for more broth, child."

She props me up with pillows and hands me another cup. "Would you like for me to tell you stories about the King?" she asks.

"O, please tell me everything, for I am desperate to know all that there is to know about Him!"

Her stories are like hot bread to my starving soul. But, as hard as I try, I cannot stay awake. The last thing I remember is about a Baby being laid in a manger while His virgin mother and adopted father looked on.

Rhonda Calhoun

Chapter Twenty-four
DEATH VALLEY

I searched for him, but I did not find him. [569]

$\mathcal{T}$he days turn into weeks and the weeks into months. On the first day of fall, Mercy announces that I am strong enough to go for a short walk. Captain and Stephen stand outside the cottage waiting for my grand appearance. During my illness, which lasted nearly five months, I became quite thin, extremely pale and very weak, but I am very much in love.

Stepping outdoors, I am blinded by the light. I lean against the door frame waiting for my eyes to adjust. It feels so good to be outside with the sun on my face and drinking in the fresh air.

The trees are various shades of orange, red and gold; they are so lovely. The dancing stream reflects the bright blue sky and the brilliant sun. Multitudes of birds fill the air with their songs and a large family of white rabbits hop along the water's edge.

"Hope Valley is the most beautiful place on earth!" I exclaim.

Stephen replies, "It is lovely...but not nearly as beautiful as you."

"Stephen, you made her blush," Mercy says, poking him

in the ribs.

"Stephen, thank you for everything you did while I was sick. Thank you for caring for my friends in the village and for helping my family. In a short time, I will be strong enough to join you again, my friend."

Turning to the Captain, I add, "And, I want to thank you, Captain, for your devoted service as well. You and your numerous guards have been a tremendous blessing to me and have protected me in ways that I will never know."

"It is my pleasure to serve you, my lady," he responds.

Stephen picks up several bags filled with produce from the King's garden. Throwing them over his shoulder, he says, "I must be off to the village. I will see you this afternoon, Lovely Lady."

"May the King grant you favor, my friend," I reply.

Mercy takes my hand saying, "Come now, child; the Captain has spread a quilt for you under your favorite tree."

I spend several hours resting beneath the shade of this magnificent tree, remembering the wonderful times I have had here with Comforter, my Father and my Beloved. It is exhilarating to be here, but not nearly as good as it would be if my Beloved or Comforter were here with me.

The day crawls by at a snail's pace, so I retire early. Just like every other night, I have trouble sleeping because my mind is so busy searching for clues of where I might find my Beloved.

The following morning and every morning thereafter, I force myself to walk a little further. After several weeks, my physical strength is nearly restored, but my lovesick heart still suffers greatly.

I wake this morning feeling stronger than ever. Stepping outside, the Captain greets me, "Good morning, my lady. Where will we be walking today?"

Looking at the garden gate, I answer, "There is one place I would love to walk, but it is locked and my Beloved alone has the key."

Mercy steps out of the cottage smiling broadly. Holding up the golden key, she says, "The King left this with me. He said that you might desire it one day."

"Can it be true!?" Tears flood my eyes. "Am I to once again walk where my Bridegroom walked? May I see His garden, run among the flowers and eat again from the Tree of Life?"

"The key is yours, my child," Mercy answers, placing it in the palm of my hand.

I walk to the garden; the Captain follows close behind. With trembling hands, I unlock the gate. Turning to the Captain, I say, "I won't be long." I want to be alone in this paradise.

I enter the garden with a pounding heart. Everything is so beautiful here, but I am not here because of the beauty or for my pleasure. I know where I must go and what I must do. I must die to all ambition and pride, to all my fears and desires. I must go to Death Valley where I can find the bitter herbs that grow under the Great Rock. My Beloved said that all one has to do is follow the Path of Life, also known, at times, as the Path of Sorrow and Suffering. I know that path well; it is the same path my Beloved walked.

Hurrying along, I find the narrow gate that leads to life, but, in my case, it will lead to my death. Lifting the latch, I hurry through it. I soon come upon the vines where goodness and mercy grow. I stuff several in my pocket; I might need them later. Pushing aside the thick vines, I hurry on.

Suddenly, the path grows extremely narrow and increasingly steep; it appears that I am climbing a mountain.[370] My physical strength is not what it was, but my heart is strong because it is fueled by fiery love. I stop to rest. Not too far away, I see a pack of lions watching me from the mouth of a cave.[371] A movement behind me causes me to jump.

Was that a leopard?

Fear fills my heart.

Perhaps, I should turn around? What should I do? I cannot go back; I must continue on.

I cry out, "Father, purify my heart and give me strength, I pray!"

A still, small voice whispers within, "It is not your commitment to Me that will keep you, but My commitment to you. Have no fear, for I am always with you...even when you can't see Me."

Having learned the power of prayer, I continue asking for help until the fear leaves. The sweet fragrance of frankincense fills the air. Encouraged, I start out again, entrusting my safety to my Father. The path grows steeper, causing me to slide and fall many times. My knees, shins and arms are bruised and bleeding. The sun has burned my pale skin, and I am drenched with sweat. Dust clings to my entire body. My mouth is parched. I constantly think of turning back. This path is extremely difficult and quite painful.

Perhaps, I should just return to my comfortable cottage and wait for my Beloved to come to me. Surely, if I wait long enough, He will return.

Again, I stop. Sitting on a large rock, I pray, "O my Beloved, You know the way I take. You know the difficulties, for You traveled this same path. Help me, guide me, and when You have tried me, I will come forth as gold. My foot holds fast to Your path; I have not turned aside nor given up. I treasure the words of Your mouth more than necessary food or personal comfort. It is You who have made my heart faint and Your ways confuse me, but I will not be silenced by fear or the darkness that may cover me."[372]

Having made that confession, I resume my quest with greater resolve; I cannot turn back now.

The way seems to be easier or perhaps it is just because I am focusing on my Beloved rather than on my suffering. Either way, I am thankful for the respite. Trying to climb over a large boulder, I fall backwards, which knocks the breath out of me. I am flat on my back, trying to suck air into my lungs and all the while my heart cries for help.

Once I am able to breathe normally, I sit up. I landed in a thick patch of velvet-like plants. I pick one of the very large leaves and lay it against my bleeding knees. The bleeding stops immediately, so I cover my legs and arms with them. In doing so, I notice what looks like plums growing beneath the leaves of this soothing plant. I pick one and recognize it as the gift my Beloved gave me in the garden, a gift called Grace. *O, how I need grace!*

I eat one and store several in my leather pouch. Within

minutes, the entire sky turns an ominous purple color. Fierce winds are ushering in a storm.

I cry out, "Father, will I ever find my Beloved? Where is hope? Where is joy? Where is the sun?"

The howling of the wind is the only response that comes. "O, north winds, you threaten to drive me into the earth! Will I be able to endure the strength of your blasts? I am alone and ever so weak. Yet, I know that even this storm is for my good, for all things along the path of life affect me by reason of perfect Love. Kind King, You love me, this I am sure of! Your love sustains me. My body faints, yet my heart is steady because of Your great love, which keeps me on course. This storm will not last forever. It may last the remainder of my natural life, but it will not follow me into my eternal home with You!

"O, north winds, you blow away my mask and my walls of self-protection, exposing the real me. I see the weakness of my heart and yet You say that I am lovely! You find me desirable and worthy of Your affections! O, how great is Your love! It is indeed strong enough to see me through anything! O, Beloved of God, come and lead me through the storm and through the wilderness, for my life belongs to You!"

An ear-splitting clap of thunder shakes the ground beneath me. The sky clears as the storm frantically flees from the blinding, burning rays of the sun.

With a revived heart, I rise. Continuing on, I shout, "My Beloved, You are my rock and my fortress. You are the love of my life and I will follow You all my days!"

After two more days of difficult trails and great obstacles, I finally make it to the top. The wind blows so violently that it nearly knocks me over. From this high place, I recognize the surrounding mountains; I have climbed and conquered the dreadful Mountain of Myrrh!

I should have known that the path of Sorrow and Suffering would lead to the Mountain of Myrrh. I know this mountain well; Comforter and I spent six long months here. It was here I learned the beauty of self-denial. The built-up tension within and the difficulties of the past three days suddenly flood to the forefront of my being and I start laughing uncontrollably. Within

Rhonda Calhoun

minutes, the laughter leads me directly to the depths of my heartache. My knees buckle as I sob, not because of my difficulties, but because of lovesickness.

The gut-wrenching waves of heartache finally stop; I look heavenward and pray, "O my Beloved, I have nothing to bargain with. I have nothing to offer You. There is nothing good within me that could attract Your attention. There are no rewards due me. There is nothing I can do or say that would motivate You to come to me. I am at Your mercy. I surrender! I surrender to Your perfect will for my life."

Forcing myself to stand, I see that I am overlooking Death Valley. This is the place my Beloved told me about. He said I would come here one day. Little did I know I would be alone, but then, I suppose I am not alone. This place is a dry, barren land where very few travel. A dry, dusty riverbed divides the valley from north to south. The only living thing in sight is a distant Weeping Willow tree. "How appropriate," I whisper.

Without wasting another moment, I begin my descent. The way down is extremely treacherous because of the steep bank and loose rocks. The relentless sun beats down on my already burned flesh, but my heart is fixed on one thing and that is my Beloved.

About midway, I stop to catch my breath. I can now see a tiny, solitary cactus struggling to grow in the dry riverbed. *That is how I feel!*

Without my Beloved's presence in my life, I am like that cactus, alone and desperate for a drop of water where there is none.

"I thirst!" I cry out.

Voices suddenly flood my mind. Doubt comes tumbling in and thoughts of turning back fill me while fear threatens to choke the life out of me. I must not allow these thoughts, my emotions, these 'little foxes', to stop me.[373] I cry out, "Even though I walk through the valley of the shadow of death, I will fear no evil, for You are with me—even if I can't see You!"[374]

As the truth echos off the mountains washing over me, the tormenting fear flees and a blanket of peace settles over me once again. Suddenly a voice from behind me shouts, "Just who is this King you claim to love? He says He loves you—He also said that He would never leave you, but just look around. I don't see Him! He is nowhere to be found!"

I turn around to find the one who accuses my Beloved, but see no one.

"What is the name of your unfaithful Friend? Where is He now? I still don't see Him, and how long has it been since you have seen Him? You've done nothing wrong, so why is He treating you like this? I would certainly never treat a follower of mine so dreadfully. Your King cannot be trusted!"

The voice suddenly loses its accusatory tone taking a much kinder, gentler approach. "Little girl, I'm here to keep you from wasting your life. If you follow your King, you will miss out on so much. If you follow me, I'll lead you down a path of success, comfort and pleasure. I'll be your best friend."

The voice grows quiet; I can feel the pull his words have on my heart.

I am tired and exhausted and...."No!" I shout, "I love Jesus more than I love comfort and pleasure and success! And besides, I am already successful because I am loved and I love! I don't need you or your pitiful offers of momentary pleasure because I will live for all eternity with the King of kings, who you will bow down to one day!"

"And furthermore, my Beloved told me that you are a liar and the father of liars!"

The voice responds with a vengeance, "You say that I am a liar; it is your God who is the liar! He said He'd never leave you! He said he'd take care of you! He said—."

"Stop it! Just stop it!" I shout, placing my hands over my ears. "You don't know Him like I do! My heart has been conquered by a King who is good and kind and trustworthy; it is impossible for Him to lie. Just because I cannot see Him does not mean that He is not here. The only reason He hides His face is to cause my love to mature while purifying my heart. He knows that if I rely on the strength of my dedication to Him, it will fail me sooner or later. Therefore, because of His great love for me, He is allowing me to walk this path that I might die to myself and trust in His commitment to keep me, not my commitment to keep myself."

I fall to my knees and cry out to heaven, "Father, if suffering means that I become more like You, if death to my flesh means victory, then take my life; take my heart and crush it. Render me helpless, wound me in my innermost being; but whatever You do, do not leave me alone. I can't live without You!"

My Beloved loves me. I know it is true! I refuse to believe these vicious accusations. Because of my King's unfailing love and relentless grace, I will persevere, I will believe! [375]

I resume my descent. I have come too far to turn back! My Bridegroom said that if I chose to follow Him I would have to die. He said that I would have to run on this mountain, and that is exactly what I have set my heart to do.[376]

Looking heavenward, I proclaim, "Who is God, but the Lord? And who is a rock, except our God, the God who girds me with strength and makes my way blameless? He makes my feet like hinds feet, and sets me upon my high places. He has given me His shield of salvation and His right hand holds me up."[377]

The voice in my mind does not relent. It bombards me in response to my cry, while the voice behind me continues, "But what about success, and what about your pitiful ministry in the village? You won't get very far in this world or be very productive following someone like your King. If you follow me, I'll make sure you're famous, rich and successful. I will give you power!"

"Success? Ministry? Power? I'm not interested. I do what I do for love, not so that I will be successful or famous or have power. Let me tell you something, if the fig tree never blooms and there is never any fruit on the vines, if the fields produce no food and my flock is cut off from its fold, if there are no cattle in the stalls and everything around me fails, then I will rejoice in my King for He is my strength and He is my salvation![378] It does not matter what you promise me, for I will love no other and will worship none other."

Without realizing it, I have reached the valley floor. Strangely, the voice instantly grows silent. My eyes eagerly and hungrily search for the Great Rock. It takes only moments to locate it. There, on the south side of the valley, hidden underneath the Weeping Willow tree, is the Great Rock. I run as fast as my weak, wounded legs can manage.

The Great Rock juts out from the side of the mountain and sits precariously against the top of a large flat rock forming what looks like a slightly open mouth. I cautiously stick my head into the three-foot opening and wait for my eyes to adjust to the darkness.

The cave itself is the size of a small room. In its furthermost recesses, I see two small plants.

That has to be the plants that I am looking for, but how can they possibly grow in such darkness, such hiddeness?

I step back from the opening. To reach the prize, I will have to climb through the narrow opening and then crawl on my belly to the back of the cave. Fear engulfs me. The rock sits so precariously on the edge of this mountain that it looks as if it will collapse at the slightest movement.

I lower my head and pray, "Father, the Book of Remembrances says that whoever falls on the Rock will be broken to pieces; but on whomever it falls, it will scatter him like dust.[379]

"O Good King, come now and do what You must do in my life that I might crown You with my love. I pray that You would increase within me and that I would decrease, for You are my Rock and my Salvation."[380]

Pulling out a piece of the Grace fruit, I continue, "Your grace is sufficient; Your power is perfected in my weakness."[381]

I eat and tremendous love for my Bridegroom fills me. Suddenly, nothing else matters but Him. No price is too high, no sacrifice too great. I will lay down my life for His sake. "I trust in you, O, Lover of my soul. You are my Rock and my Fortress; my life is in Your hands.[382] Crush this life that, in death, a sweet fragrance might be released before Your throne. Make me the vessel You desire me to be—that You may be glorified. Live or die, I am Yours! You hold my life in Your hands."

Having fully committed my all to Him, I place my pouch, which contains the Grace fruit, just inside the mouth of the tiny cave for safe keeping.

Once inside, I crawl about fifteen feet, but it seems much further. Arriving at the plants, I am surprised to find that they

Rhonda Calhoun

are extremely plain looking. There is absolutely nothing notable or attractive about them—no flowers, no fruit, no fragrance—absolutely nothing. I would consider these plants to be completely worthless except for the fact that my Beloved values them and even proclaims that they are to be highly desired.

I quickly pick a handful of the leaves then hold my breath, fully expecting the Rock to come crashing down on me. When nothing happens, I turn around and crawl back to the small opening where I can examine the leaves in the light.

The leaves from both plants look identical. There is nothing remarkable about them. I have been told these plants are extremely bitter, but are sweet once swallowed.

Consuming the Humility and Sacrifice leaves, I pray to be consumed by these virtues.

What I was told is true—they are unbelievably bitter. So bitter, in fact, that it is all I can do not to spit them out! I force myself to swallow, then wait for the sweetness to come, but it does not. The bitterness not only fills my mouth, but also my stomach.

What have I done? This is awful and for what purpose?

My head hurts. I am cut, bruised and bleeding. My face and arms are sunburned. I am thirsty, hungry and in need of rest.

I have walked halfway around the world for what? For a couple of bitter weeds that have accomplished nothing for me. Why did I even bother to pursue this path? I knew better. After all, very few ever travel here and now I know why. They are much smarter than I.

I roll over onto my back. Immediately, I find myself thinking about my family and friends in the village.

They are probably sitting around the well, eating and laughing and having a great time. They have a good life; they certainly aren't suffering as I am. My life shouldn't be like this. After all, I am promised to the King! I am the daughter of the Ancient of Days! I have personal bodyguards who never leave my side day or night...except for now when I really need them. Where were they when I was bombarded by those horrid voices? Where were they when I fell knocking the breath out of myself and nearly died? And where is the King? He said He would never leave me, but I haven't seen Him in so long that I can barely remember what He looks like.

Why should I have to endure so much suffering and hardship? I did nothing wrong. I got up when the King knocked on my door. I was willing to go with Him, but He ran away with not so much as a word! I certainly deserve better than this!

The bitter taste in my mouth and stomach grows even stronger. In an effort, to do something about the awful taste, I grab my pouch and quickly eat a piece of the Grace fruit.

O, how sweet it tastes! So much sweeter than I remember.

Its sweetness convicts me and I bury my face in my hands. It feels as though a bright light is searching my heart, exposing and bringing to the surface my awful pride, selfish ambitions, hidden agendas and impure motives.

O, how wretched I am! O, how unworthy!

I cry out, "Father, forgive me, for I am a sinner!"

A gentle breeze blows into the mouth of the cave; love and peace flood my soul. The bitterness in my heart and stomach disappears and sweetness envelops me. I whisper, "Your grace is enough! Though You slay me, yet will I trust You." [383]

I love Him because He first loved me.[384] Revelation floods my soul; I finally grasp and embrace the truth that I cannot earn His love, neither is there anything I can do to cause the King to love me any more or any less than He already does. He loves me even in my weakness and immaturity! His love for me never changes! He remains faithful even if I don't!

The love exploding in my heart fills me with a great desire for the One who is perfect and good while exposing my sinful and selfish nature. "Release me from my prison, Good King, and set me free from my self focused life!" I cry out.

It sounds as though the ground is cracking. I quickly turn and watch in amazement as a seedling breaks through the rock floor. In a matter of minutes, the sprout becomes a full-grown Everlasting Virtues plant. Faith, Hope and Love bloom before my very eyes. The sweet fragrance of myrrh fills my tomb-like cave.

No longer fearful and no longer mindful of my rights, my pride, or my comforts, I crawl back to the furthermost recesses of the cave and touch the Everlasting Virtues' velvet-like petals.

Rhonda Calhoun

I pick the one called Love and whisper, "And the greatest of these is Love."

Lying on my back, I lift my voice and sing, "I love You, I love You, I love You! I know You are here, even though I cannot see You. You love me, even though my circumstances accuse You of not caring. You are for me, even though it seems otherwise."

I sing myself to sleep.

For three days, I lie alone in the cave during which time I allow God to search my heart and soul. I lay down my vain fascinations and all my earthly ambitions. I die to my past, my present and my future. I accept the fact that I will never be perfect or good or worthy — there is only One who qualifies for such titles. His death has become enough for me. His death makes me whole. His death grants me incredible freedom. His death gives me freedom. His death gives me life everlasting.

On the morning of the third day, I wake, but wonder if I am still asleep, for I feel strangely empty. I have no more excuses, no other loves, no hidden agendas and no selfish ambitions. There is nothing left of me except a tiny ember of Divine affection burning deep in my heart.

Alone in the darkness I whisper, "I will embrace no other, for You are God and You are pure love in its truest form. Even though it seems that You are a million miles away and the heavens are made of brass, I will trust You. I love You, my King and I worship You alone."

Suddenly, a shaft of glorious light appears in the corner and my tomb is filled with a sound like that of water crashing over a great precipice.

With eyes of fascination, I watch as the pulsating light slowly moves toward me like a cloud moving across the sky. It comes to rest directly above me and fills me with holy fear.

What is this?

"My Glory," a Voice whispers.

Shall I dare reach out and touch this manifestation of glory?

"Draw near to Me and I will draw near to you," the Voice responds to my thoughts.

Mustering all my courage, I stretch out my trembling

hand, which immediately is swallowed up in the glorious light. Hope surges through my body like lightning racing through a tree. Lying flat on my back, trembling, I am filled with the knowledge that my future is secure, my steps are ordained by my King, and I am loved completely.[384a]

No sooner does this wave subside when another wave of revelation hits me. Faith explodes within my heart and mind unveiling the truth that absolutely nothing is impossible for my Beloved. I can do all things because of the One I love; He strengthens me and all that He has is mine.[384b]

Within the confines of my cocoon, I shout, "For the King and for His kingdom! May He be glorified within and without! O, take me away, my King! Take me away with You! Draw me and let us run together on the highest mountains and in the darkest valleys, for I am Yours!"

My plea echoes throughout the cave until it is finally absorbed by the Rock of Ages.

The sound of thunderous waters once again surrounds me. In the midst of it, I hear the still, small voice of the One I love. He whispers, "I am the resurrection and the life; whoever believes in Me shall live, even if he dies."[384c]

I respond, "O, wash over me, wave of God! Kill me, that I might live! Crucify my flesh that I might rise again! O, that I would decrease and You would increase! Father, grant that I might be forever lost in Your love!

"Wash over me love of God and fill me with who You are, for I have found my reason for living—I have touched Your love!"

Perfect peace fills me as perfect Love surrounds me. A glorious weight from above rests on me. Something like warm oil covers me and soaks into me, flooding my soul and coursing through my veins like life-giving blood. The voice of my Beloved whispers, "What you feel, My perfect one, is merely the shadow of My furious, infinite, unconditional, all-consuming love for you."

The shadow?

Suddenly, all grows perfectly quiet. I am completely content. I am fully satisfied. I have no desire to be anywhere else

Rhonda Calhoun

but here in His sweet embrace, resting under the shadow of His wing. His love completely fills me. I am in no hurry; I have no agenda, no plans, no great feats to accomplish. I float in this glorious state, content to never leave. I am lost in an ocean of perfect, infinite Love. I have no idea how much time passes, for time does not exist beyond the confines of this world. Eternity is forever, as is my Beloved's love for me.

O, that I could stay in this place with God, never to return to the imperfect world! How marvelous, how glorious it is to be in my Beloved's presence, held in His arms of love!

Experiencing a taste of eternity causes me to think about how great the King's love must truly be. After all, He left a place where He had no restrictions, no boundaries, no limits, no heartache and no suffering. He came to a fallen world where He poured Himself into the confines of the mere shell of a man that was made from dirt. This King who bowed to no one, this King who spoke and everything that exists was created, this King who directed myriads and myriads of angels — is the same King who stepped into skin and became a servant to mankind.

I lift my voice and sing, "Amazing love, how can it be that you, my King, would die for me?"

He responds, "I want you to understand that I not only love you, but I like you, too. I love and enjoy you in the same way that My Father loves Me."[384d]

"How could You ever care for someone like me in that way and to that degree?"

"My love makes no sense because it is freely given to My enemies and to My friends. It is given to people who reject Me over and over again, to unfaithful people. Because I always love this way, you are free to run to Me when you stumble and fall rather than running away from Me."

I bask in the glorious effect His words have on me as He continues, "True freedom means you have nothing left to lose. The richest, freest place you will ever be is when you come to the place where all you have left is the truth that God loves you and you love Him. And, in that place, you are content."

I respond, "I lay it all down again, my King. You are all I want and You are all I ever needed. I crown You King over my life and commit to tell others that You are indeed the Bridegroom King!"

The rock above and beneath me suddenly shakes violently bringing my glorious encounter to an abrupt end. A sound like that of rolling thunder comes from outside the cave. Forcing myself to move, I crawl to the opening. There, riding furiously toward me, are a multitude of soldiers. Their swords are raised above their heads reflecting the bright light of the sun.

In a matter of minutes, they are just outside my cave. Wasting no time, they leap from their horses. As the dust clears, I am relieved to see that it is the Captain and his mighty men. He motions for me to stay where I am and then quickly leads his army up the Great Rock shouting, "For the King and for His kingdom!"[385]

The sounds coming from above are frightening. I try to pray louder than them, but find that I am only partially successful. Finally, all grows quiet, so I cautiously stick my head out. Hearing and seeing nothing, I shout, "Captain, is all well?"

"Yes, my lady, the enemy has been defeated, for there is no foe strong enough to defeat your King. It is now safe for you to exit."

Wasting no time, I join the Captain on top of the Rock. He points to the edge of the rock and says, "They were waiting to devour you, my lady."

Nearby, several lions lie in a bloody heap. A cold chill runs through me. "O thank you, Captain, for rescuing me."

"It was not I, but your King who conquered your enemies, my lady."

"My Beloved was here? He knows where I am? Where is He?"

The Captain responds, "He has left, my lady."

An overwhelming joy fills me; I dance around the bodies of my enemies singing, "There is no mountain my Beloved cannot conquer! There is no enemy He cannot defeat! My Bridegroom loves me and He will return to me! When? I do not know, but He will surely come!"

My song and dance are interrupted when I notice, just at the edge of the Great Rock, growing out of a small crack, a

Rhonda Calhoun

small patch of beautiful snow-white lilies.

O, how good my Beloved is to me! Once more He has placed a reminder of His lovingkindness in my path.

I break into song once again, singing, "I am the lily of the valley, and my Beloved cares for me! I am unable to bring life from devastation, but nothing is impossible for Him! My Beloved causes life to spring up in the most impossible situations. The King exchanges the ashes of my life for His great beauty. O, how good He is to me! You are good to me!

"There is no place too far, too high, or too deep for my Beloved to reach. There is no darkness too deep for His light to consume and there is no pain too great for His love to heal. Like a small child, I will cling to my Beloved. Goodness and Mercy shall follow me all the days of my life and I will dwell in His house forevermore."[386]

I suddenly realize that the Captain and his men are staring at me. They look quite bewildered. "What?" I ask.

"You look different, my lady."

"In what way?" I ask, fully aware that my outward appearance must be dreadful, but not really caring.

"Your face is glowing. You are quite a mystery, my lady," the Captain answers.

"What mystery?"

"The mystery is your love for the King."

"That is no mystery, my friend. I am merely one whose heart has been stolen by a King who loves me infinitely regardless of the state that He finds me in. He loves me just as I am! O, what freedom there is in this great truth!"

"And that is the greatest mystery of all," the Captain responds, shaking his head.

"I would agree with that statement, dear Captain."

Taking my hand, he leads me down from the Great Rock to the valley floor. Waiting below is the King's prize mare. "Your King thought you might like to ride home," the Captain says.

Laughing, I respond, "My Beloved is exceedingly kind and ever so good to me!"

"He watches over you with great care, my lady," he responds.

"Indeed, He does."

I leave Death Valley with a deeper love for my Bridegroom and with a greater understanding of what it means to be His bride. I leave behind my pride and personal ambitions. I leave behind my right to be right. I leave behind my agendas and my future plans. I leave behind who I was that I might become who He sees.

I take with me a large supply of leaves from the Sacrifice and Humility plants, for I have learned that I cannot live successfully in this kingdom without them.

A fiery furnace of devotion now consumes me. 'Tis a love that nothing can extinguish—not pride, success, fame, weakness, fear, doubt, accusations—not even sorrow, and suffering.[387] I am now fully His and fully in love. I belong to my Bridegroom King and to Him alone.

The

Majestic God

Chapter Twenty-five
HAVE YOU SEEN HIM

This is my Beloved, this is my friend. [588]

$\mathcal{I}$t takes a little over a week for my wounds and sunburn to heal so that I can resume the search for my Beloved. No longer afraid, no longer self-focused, I decide to search the surrounding mountains and then ride to the village. I tell Mercy of my plans, and she responds, "Little One, your body is still so very weak."

Running the back of her hand along my cheek and taking my hands in hers, she continues, "But I see that your devotion is stronger than ever. Your Beloved will give you the strength you need and will surely lead you into His arms."

"I pray that you are right, Mercy," I reply.

"Come and eat; you will need the nourishment."

I eat as quickly as possible and then grab my shawl. Mercy follows as I hurry out the door. Catching up, she hands me a satchel filled with more food than I could ever eat in a day.

"Thank you, Mercy," I say, wrapping my thin arms around her neck and kissing her cheek.

The Captain helps me into my saddle, then effortlessly mounts his stallion. Raising the flag, he shouts, "For the King and for His kingdom!"

As usual, the guards echo him, but this time I remain

silent. My thoughts are consumed with one thing and that is finding my Beloved Bridegroom King.

Passion drives me forward as I search Hope Valley and the mountains. I repeatedly call out to Him. My voice soon grows hoarse. [389] The Captain, riding beside me asks, "Perhaps, I could call out in your place, my lady?"

"Thank you, Captain, but the longing in my heart is so great that I cannot remain silent."

Convinced that He is not here, I turn my mare toward the village. We race across the valley into the dark and dangerous wilderness. There was a day not so long ago when I was much too afraid of this place to ever venture anywhere near it. But that is no longer true, for love has gripped my desperate, aching heart to the point that fear no longer has a hold on me. I cry out, "O, that I had wings to fly!"

My mare increases her speed. She leaps over every obstacle and gracefully makes her way around every hindrance. We explode out of the wilderness in no time at all. My heart leaps; I know the village is only a short distance. The Captain, who has gone before me, now pulls alongside me. Neither of us speak.

Arriving at the village gate, I tie my mare to a nearby tree. Rushing in, I ask everyone I encounter if they have seen my Beloved King. Their response is always the same—no one has seen Him.

The noonday sun beats down on me, causing my recently burned skin to form new blisters, but nothing can keep me from searching for the One I love. Turning the corner, I see several shepherds coming my way. Saul, whom I knew from David's congregation, makes his way directly to me, roughly grabbing my arm he asks, "What are *you* doing here?"[390]

"Please, you don't understand. I am simply searching for my Bridegroom King. He has been gone for so long and I am desperate for Him. Tell me, have you seen Him?"

Saul replies, "You're an ignorant girl who has given herself to fantasy. All you talk about is love and beauty and the *Bridegroom.*

"You act as though you are the only one who reads the

Book of Remembrances. Actually, I'm an expert on that Book; I know the law well, child, and I also know that you are very dangerous with all your talk of love and forgiveness and grace. If you knew anything, you would know that preaching grace to people only gives them a license to sin."

I respond, "My friend, there is a love that flows from the King's heart that washes away all sin. His grace does not encourage those who truly love Him to sin; on the contrary. It has been my experience that grace enables people to do and to be all that God has created them to do and be, which includes living a life of purity and holiness.

"Saul, I do not follow the King out of a sense of duty or for the sake of appearances. I follow because I am in love with Him. You say you know the law. Then, you know that the King said that the greatest commandment in the law is to love Him with all your heart, strength, soul and mind. The second is to love your neighbor as yourself.[391]

"My Beloved's kingdom is one that is built on love, and everything we do should flow out of that. It is not about being perfect, which is a good thing, because none of us will ever be perfect. And neither is it about getting your doctrine exactly right, no one will ever understand the ways of God perfectly. Eternal life is all about knowing the Father and His Son intimately. And once you know Him all you want to do is obey Him."

I am suddenly and violently knocked to the ground. Several shepherds laugh and mock me while Saul repeatedly hits me with his rod. Standing over me, Saul shouts, "Just who do you think you are, preaching to me?"

He kicks me in the side saying, "I'll tell you who you are—you're just an ignorant girl who loves to pretend that she is somebody special."

Saul's eyes are cold and his face is red with anger. He kneels beside me saying, "You're no longer welcome in this village, pitiful one."[392]

He turns his back on me. Immediately, the other shepherds deliver a few punches of their own. Hearing a shout, they stop. Uncovering my face, I see two watchmen running toward us.

The watchmen will protect me, that's their job. Perhaps they will even help me find my Beloved.

Saul and his friends step away, looking at the ground. Ignoring my pain, I force myself to stand. I do not recognize either of the watchmen, but hobble over to the one closest. Clutching his arm, I plead, "Please, tell me, have you seen the King?"

"What's going on here?" he asks.

Saul lies to them saying that I tripped and fell. He then says that I am a troublemaker, lying about the King and causing division in the village. One of the watchmen shoves me away, causing me to fall. "I've heard about you," he says, the disgust clear.

Lying face down in the dirt, I pray, "Father, they don't understand this love that possesses me. Those who should be watching over my life have turned against me. They think that I have been forsaken and that there is no one to deliver me."

Pushing myself up, I cry out, "Father, do not be far from me; hasten to my help!"[393]

Enraged, Saul snatches my shawl from me, saying,[394] "From this day forth, you may no longer minister in this village! You are no longer part of us!"[395]

They leave me lying in the dirt. I watch them go. My body may be battered, but my heart burns with love. I pray, "Father, from the beginning, all I have wanted was to know the Master Shepherd intimately and to run with Him in ministry. You were so good to answer my prayer, but now I have lost both. I can't find my Bridegroom anywhere and they have taken away the ministry You gave me.[396] I now have nothing left but You, and it is enough for me."

Raising my eyes to heaven I continue, "You have taken hold of my right hand. Who is there besides You? I desire nothing on earth but You. My flesh and my heart may fail, but You are the strength of my life and my portion forever. I have made You my refuge that I may tell of all Your works. I will rise up and seek You."[397]

My mouth is cut and bleeding, my ribs and back are

throbbing and my ankle hurts. I remind myself of the agonies my Savior endured to make me His bride. He was stripped of His garments; I have lost only my shawl. He was mocked; I have merely been misunderstood. He was rejected and beaten; I have suffered a few blows in heart and body. I shall not complain, for I have not even come close to the sufferings my Beloved endured.

With renewed vigor, I resume my search crying out as I go, "Have you seen my Bridegroom? Have you seen the One my heart longs for?"

I think of Comforter's words: "Always remember that His commitment to you is based upon the reality and truth of His word, not on your ability to see or hear Him. And the Book of Remembrances says that He will never leave you nor forsake you."[398]

My Beloved is here, somewhere.

I hurry once more to the garden where I found Him last time, but find only Charity and Mary. Falling at their feet, I cry out, "Have you seen the King?"

Looking somewhat perplexed, they slowly shake their heads. "Has He left you?" Mary asks.

"My Beloved has indeed withdrawn His presence."

Charity kneels beside me, saying, "What has happened? You are hurt and bleeding."

I answer, "Sweet Charity, I am not aware of any physical pain or discomfort. My tears do not flow because of any abuse I have suffered. These tears are a result of my Beloved's absence. Without His presence in my life, I shall wither and surely die!"

Grabbing Charity's hand, I continue, "If you find Him, please tell Him that I am faint with love. Tell Him that though my physical strength grows weak, my love grows more fervent with each passing moment!"

"What are you saying?" Charity asks.

"I would rather be faint and in love with my Beloved than living in ease and in love with this world."[399]

Charity responds, "You are a strange girl....you have always been such a plain and simple girl, but look at you—you have become quite beautiful!"

I answer, "For the first time, someone beside my Beloved

Rhonda Calhoun

calls me 'beautiful'. My dear friend, I am beautiful only because I have my Bridegroom's image stamped upon me. His unconditional love has transformed me."

Taking my hand in hers, Charity asks, "Your Betrothed has abandoned you and allowed you to be misunderstood, mistreated and rejected, and you still love Him? I don't understand this kind of love."

"O, Charity, He is good through and through. There is no malice nor deceitfulness found in Him! I will always love Him! Tell me, have you seen Him? Have you seen the One I love?"

Mary responds, "You plead with us as if we know where He is hiding. We do not. But I must know, how is your Beloved better than other loves?[400] What kind of Beloved is He that you would seek Him with such fervency when He has abandoned you? What is it about Him that causes you to cling to Him so desperately?"[401]

"You ask me who this Man is and why I love Him so? I will tell you. He is the lover of my soul. He lifts me up when I am down. He heals my broken heart and removes my shame. He loves me whether I do good or do bad. He is my life, my hope and my all!"

Divine love floods my heart, and I pour out my adoration in song:

> 'My Beloved is wholly desirable!
> He is one of incomparable perfections.
> He is dazzling and as radiant as the sun,
> He is the Lion and the Lamb, beautiful in holiness.
> He is pure through and through
> and overflows with sacrificial love and devotion.[402]
> He is fully God and fully Man;
> therefore, He fully understands my pain.
>
> My Beloved is wholly desirable!
> He is outstanding among ten thousand;
> others pale in comparison to His greatness.
> Such beauty is found in none other. [403]
> His leadership is Divine and sovereign,

and His thoughts toward me are excellent and higher
than the tallest mountain.[404]
His undying dedication towards me is filled with
zeal and passion; it is beyond our comprehension. [405]

My Beloved is wholly desirable!
He never grows weary; His affections never waver.[406]
He said that I have dove's eyes,[407]
but He is the One who has the eyes of a dove —
chaste, clear, devoted, loyal, pure and ever so kind.
He is all-knowing; He sees the past, present and future
with infinite compassion and perfect discernment,
with a single eye, focused and resolute.
He is pure, merciful, innocent;
and He sees me as beautiful.[408]

My Beloved is wholly desirable!
His emotions are a heavenly garden
filled with extravagant and diverse perfumes,[409]
which are more fragrant than the richest flowers and
perfumes; He revives and refreshes my soul.[410]
His speech is powerful and like the lilies —
full of inspiration, grace, and purity,[411]
bringing death to all that hinders love.[412]

My Beloved is wholly desirable!
The work of His hands is not haphazard or random,
but purposeful and filled with power and authority.[413]
His tender compassions are rare, priceless and lovely.[414]
His plans are carried out with strength and dignity,[415]
in an orderly manner, stable, and steadfast,
and will endure forever.[416]

My Beloved is wholly desirable!
His appearance is like the mountains of Lebanon —
holy, majestic, visible, rich and fruitful![417]
My Beloved is full of grace, compassion and strength.[418]
His communication is intimate and filled with secrets.[419]
He is altogether lovely! [420]

Rhonda Calhoun

My Beloved is wholly desirable!
From head to toe, in every way, He is excellent!
His leadership over my life is perfect in every way;
nothing He does is selfish—all is done for love.
You ask me about my Beloved?
There is nothing or no one I desire more!
He is the lover of my soul, and He is my best Friend![421]
This is the One in Whom my heart has found its home!
This is my Beloved and my Friend!

Charity and Mary are speechless.

Taking their hands in mine, I continue, "My dear friends, the King is the only One Who can fully satisfy the human heart. Despite His greatness and perfection, He does not consider it beneath Himself to be a true and affectionate Friend to the greatest of sinners, of which I am one. How can I not search for Him when He is so excellent, so beautiful and so majestic?"

"Dear ones, how can you *not* love One who is so pure, so good and so Divine? This is He in whom I trust, and from whom I expect all good, for He is my Savior and Friend."

Mary lays her hand on my shoulder, and says, "If He is this good and this kind, then I want to seek Him with you that I might know Him. Tell me, most beautiful among women, where has He gone?"[422]

I wish I knew.

"Father, where is my Beloved?" I whisper to myself.

A still, small voice answers, "I have come into *My* garden, My sister, My bride."[423]

Throwing my hands up in the air, I shout, "I know where He is!"

"You do?" Charity asks.

"My Beloved has gone down to His garden, which is fragrant, beautiful, productive and filled with grace and rest.[424] It is in that place that He feeds His flock, surrounding Himself with purity and beauty."[425]

"But we're standing in the garden and He is not here," Charity replies, obviously confused.

"Charity, the King has a garden called His church, which

is destined to be His eternal bride. He dearly loves her and finds great pleasure in her love. He enjoys her sweetness and is intoxicated and strengthened by her love.[426] That is where we will find Him—in the church!"

Without wasting another moment, I run to the village square with Mary and Charity following closely behind. Upon arriving, I search through the crowd until I see Him. I cannot move; I cannot speak. I can only gaze on this beautiful Man as He passes out bread to men, women and children.

How awesome He is in this place! How good and how kind He is to both friend and foe!

Charity and Mary are right behind me. I stand here with nothing to offer, yet cling to the truth that I belong to Him and He belongs to me.

Glancing over my shoulder, I say, "Charity, Mary, look! There He is! There is my Beloved and there is my Friend.[427] He is sitting among the pure in heart and feeding both old and young bread from heaven![428] Is He not the most beautiful King you have ever seen? He is the great King of all the ages! There is no one like Him!"

I do not hear their response, if there even was one, because my Beloved suddenly, and with great grace, stands to His feet and looks directly at me.

Joy floods my being. Not one word has been spoken, not one movement made and still my heart leaps within!

The King hands the remaining bread to David then rushes through the crowd toward me. Unable to contain the joy exploding in my heart any longer, I shout, "I am my Beloved's and He is mine! I am His inheritance and He is mine! My Beloved feeds His children only the best and purest of foods! "[429]

Walking up to me, He exclaims, "My love, you are as beautiful as Tirzah and as lovely as Jerusalem, the two strongest and most beautiful cities in My kingdom! You have come through the fire of testing and you now shine like gold. You are victorious and overwhelmingly lovely. Your beauty is strikingly obvious among believers and unbelievers alike.[430] You are like a powerful army dressed in battle array before which both friend and foe must surrender."[431]

Rhonda Calhoun

No longer divided in my affections, no longer veiled in shame, no longer filled with self-love or selfish ambition, I look into the eyes of my Beloved Bridegroom. My breath catches in my throat. My gaze is steady, but my frame trembles.

He doesn't just like me and He doesn't just love me — He is in love with me!

I look deeper into His eyes of fire, those endless wells of compassion and zeal.

He is consumed with love! It is the essence of His being, not just one of His characteristics. God is in love with me! God thinks I am wonderful! God finds me delightful! God likes me! Oh, how glorious, how marvelous, how amazing!

Tears fill my eyes spilling over and running down my cheeks.

Filled with tremendous emotion, my Beloved says, "My darling, My beautiful one, you refused to be offended with Me even in the midst of persecution and sorrow, even though I hid My face from you, even though it appeared as those I had abandoned you. O, how beautiful you are! O, how beautiful is your love for Me!"

Tears glisten like diamonds on His eyelashes. I reach up and touch His cheek, staring into His eyes of love.

My Beloved says, "My bride, turn your eyes away from Me! Turn your eyes away from Me, for they have overwhelmed Me!"[432]

I take His hand and respond, "Where else shall I look, my Lord? There is no one as lovely as You, and no one worth gazing upon but You."

His hands are shaking.

Does the King of kings stand before me trembling?

Wiping the tears racing down my face, He says, "My love, there is no power strong enough, no enemy great enough and no foe wise enough to conquer Me, but you have succeeded to do so. Your devotion, in the midst of great persecution and perceived abandonment, has overwhelmed Me. I stand here before you a conquered King."[433]

"And I stand here before You a lovesick bride," I respond, kissing the palm of His hands where my name is carved. My heart is flooded with overwhelming adoration as I fall into His wonderful arms of love.

With my head tucked under His chin and His arms wrapped tightly around me, He continues, "My darling, I was there with you on the Mountain of Myrrh. I watched as you picked up your cross and followed Me. I saw you face your fears as you allowed My love to be the driving force in your life. I watched as you silenced the enemy of your soul. I saw you die to yourself as you ate the bitter herbs. I watched as you entered into the fellowship of My death.

"Your devotion and dedication to Me in the midst of that fiery test is glorious and ever so beautiful.[434] For momentary, light affliction has and is producing in you an eternal weight of glory far beyond all comparison."[435]

Charity and Mary join us. My Beloved nods and smiles, acknowledging their presence, but quickly turns His attention back to me. "My bride, you have made incredible progress. Your ability to receive instruction has increased considerably. Your meditation on My Word has washed away those things that made you unfruitful in the past. You have now brought forth twins: love for Me and love for others, which are the first and second greatest commandments in My kingdom.[436]

"You have endured many trials and tribulations, which have helped to purify and beautify you. You are now secure in My love for you, which enables you to stay true during difficult, painful seasons. You are and shall be very fruitful, My love."

I blush. He softly laughs, and says, "I love your emotions."[437] You are as pure and innocent as a little child.

"You remained faithful to Me, even in the midst of severe testing. When all you had to give Me was your broken heart, it was enough. Even though you could not see Me, I was there. I am always near. Your tears are more precious to Me than diamonds and I treasure each one. Even in your weakness, you are lovely to Me."[438]

I am deeply moved by this Majestic King and His tender affections. I reply, "Lovely? You say that I am lovely? The only reason I am lovely is because You see me through eyes of unconditional, infinite love. You have lavished Your extravagant

Rhonda Calhoun

affections on me. Without Your love, without Your presence, I would be like a solitary cactus seeking water where there is none."

"What's not to love about you?" He asks.

Before I can give Him a long list, a little boy tugs on his garment. With no effort, He scoops him up in His arms. The little one tugs on His beard, obviously trying to get His attention. My King looks at him and smiles. The boy whispers something in His ear to which He replies, "I love you, too."

Turning to the watching crowd, He proclaims, "Except you become like a little child, you can not enter into My kingdom."[439]

His words create quite a commotion among many of those gathered, but that does not stop Him from speaking the truth. I step back to listen, leaning against the meeting hall where I spent so many hours listening to teachers, preachers and shepherds. So many memories, so many lessons, and so many delights were experienced in this place, not only for me, but for many others as well.

My eyes fall on a red rose lying on the church steps; it has obviously been trampled. My heart is gripped by the sight of something so beautiful being trodden underfoot. I cannot take my eyes from the pitiful little thing. Cradling it in my hand, I see how this once perfect flower is now crushed to the point that it barely resembles a rose. Sadness sweeps over me.

I look at the face of my beautiful Bridegroom; He is like this rose. He never stops placing Himself in the paths of those He loves, always praying that they will draw near enough to see His beauty or smell His intoxicating fragrance. But more often than not, He is trampled upon and rejected, and yet He never stops giving of Himself.

The King speaks to the crowd of His great love. My heart aches—a few are listening while others are obviously bored.

When He is finished, I hurriedly return to my Beloved's side. He turns to me; His eyes are swimming in a pool of tears. "Will you be My partner? Will you tell them about My perfect love?" He asks.

With a fire of love blazing in my heart, I speak about the beauty of my King. I tell them about Faith, Hope, Love, Grace,

Goodness and Mercy. I explain the beauty of dying so that one might live. I speak of the immeasurable riches found in the King and the wonderful gifts found along the path of Sorrow and Suffering. I end my message with a plea for them to surrender their lives to the Bridegroom King.

No one moves. I look into their eyes and see nothing but emptiness. Anguish fills my soul. I turn my eyes to my Beloved. He is in great agony over their decision. A rush of love for Him floods my heart and I cry out, "O, my Beloved, I want to live in Your presence forevermore! You have chosen me and set me apart for your good pleasure. I am forever sick with love! I live for the warmth of Your loving embrace and for the beating of Your heart!

"Jesus, my King, my Beloved, my Bridegroom, I love You! No one, nothing satisfies me like You! Your heart burns with love for me and sets my heart on fire! You are glorious! You are holy! You are altogether beautiful!"

I look into His eyes and see that His pain has been eased. I have brought my Beloved a moment of pleasure! He is satisfied and my soul rejoices!

The King stands before the crowd and says, "My bride tells you of My glory, but let Me tell you about her incredible beauty and immeasurable worth.

"My heavenly kingdom is filled with a multitude of angels of various ranks and callings, but My dove, My perfect one is more desirable than them all.

"She walks in great grace and heavenly beauty. She is kind to all and eager to serve with no regard to a person's status. The Royal Court, My ministering angels, all know her well and highly esteem her; they call her 'blessed'.[440] She is the one I desire.[441] My bride not only burns with love for Me, but also for you. She longs for you to join her passionate pursuit of Me.

"My bride is pure in heart and is known by all as one who ministers with great compassion. She is unique and highly valued; she is her mother's only daughter, which makes her even more highly treasured. I am wholly committed to her good."[442]

Charity looks at me through tear-filled eyes and declares, "I can see Him now! I can see the Bridegroom King and He is

Rhonda Calhoun

every bit as lovely as you said!"

Charity and two shepherds fall at His feet in tears. He deals tenderly with them as they confess their sins, all the while lavishing them with His unconditional love.

"Charity, the King loves you and He will make you absolutely beautiful," I respond as tears of joy stream down my face.

My Beloved spends the remainder of the day answering questions and showering those who allow Him with His unending love. He stands to leave and says, "I am the Good Shepherd. My sheep know My voice and follow Me. I am the Light of the world; He who follows Me shall not walk in the darkness, but shall have the light of life."[442a]

Turning to Charity and the shepherds, He says, "Stay close to David, for he will carefully watch over you as a shepherd watches over his sheep."

He then turns to me, takes my hand and says, "Come away with Me, My love. It is time for us to return to Hope Valley."

I shout, "I am going home! Home to the place my Beloved built for me!"

Embracing Charity, I whisper, "I am so happy for you!"

"I only wish I had listened to you a long time ago," she replies.

"Yesterday is gone; no regrets. Today is a new day. A day to rise and shine; for your light has come and the glory of the Lord is risen upon you."[442b]

"Indeed He has," she replies.

My Beloved and I bid everyone farewell. We walk away arm in arm. I turn to the One I love and say, "I believe today was the happiest day of my life."

"You have many more days like this one ahead, My love."

We walk a short distance and my Beloved says, "I want all of your affections; I refuse to share you with any other. You must have no other gods before Me. I am to be your all in all, your everything. I am a jealous God. I am committed to having you all to Myself. Why? So I can love you forever."

"I do not understand the depth of Your love for me," I respond.

"I went to the depths of hell for you so you would never have to."

"O, I do not understand such love!"

"There is a day coming when you will, My love."

We walk on in peaceful silence. I am thoroughly content and completely satisfied and so is my Beloved Bridegroom King.

Rhonda Calhoun

Chapter Twenty-six
MY BETROTHAL CELEBRATION

Who is this that grows like the dawn? [145]

$\mathscr{I}$t is the first day of spring. The morning breaks bright and clear. Today, is the day of my betrothal celebration. I am so nervous that I can barely think. My beautiful white linen gown, a gift from my Beloved, is laid across the foot of my bed; a pair of white sandals wait nearby. Everything is ready—everything, that is, except me. I still have so far to go before I am transformed into the image of my King.

With great care I slip the lovely gown over my head. Looking in the mirror, I am surprised at how elegant I look, except for my hair. I have worn my hair in braids for most of my life, so I do not know how to style hair. I try once again to make it look presentable, but lay my brush down in frustration and pray for help. Within minutes, there is a knock on my door. I open to find Mercy and another friendly looking lady standing there. Mercy embraces me, saying, "Allow me to introduce my sister. Her name is Goodness."

"I didn't know you had a sister," I say as I take her baby soft hand in mine. "It's nice to meet you, Goodness."

She kisses my cheek. She seems so familiar. "Have I met you before?" I ask.

"Does not the Book of Remembrances say that Goodness and Mercy shall follow you all the days of your life?" Goodness responds.[444]

"Well, yes it does," I reply.

She chuckles and says, "Lovely Lady, every word in the Book of Remembrances is true. We are the King's messengers, His servants. Mercy and I have followed you since the first day the Master Shepherd called you to His side. We are always with you, but there are times when it is difficult to recognize us because we come disguised as pain and suffering, hardships and difficulties. The King works all things out for good to those who love Him and are called according to His good purpose. Time reveal's the goodness and mercy that are hidden in painful, difficult situations and tragedies, if one will only look."

Her voice is sweet and so kind, much like my Beloved's. Holding up the Book of Remembrances, she continues, "The words recorded in this Book are eternal and delivered by the very breath of God. It is absolutely impossible for even one word found in here to fail."[445]

"You sound like Comforter, which is a compliment, by the way," I say.

"Of course it is, Lovely Lady" she responds.

Mercy throws her loving arms around me, saying, "We thought you might need some help getting ready."

"Oh, do I ever! Are either of you good with hair?" I ask, as I grab their hands and eagerly pull them into my room.

Without wasting another moment, Goodness picks up my hair brush and goes right to work.

"Comforter could do wonders with my hair. I sure do miss my dear Friend. I was certain He would return once I found my Bridegroom, but I haven't seen Him."

Staring at nothing in particular, I add, "Today will not be the same without Him. I cannot imagine Comforter not being at my betrothal celebration. He has helped me so much and has worked so diligently to get me ready for this day. I miss Him so!"

Mercy answers, "It is too soon to stop hoping, Lovely Lady; the day isn't over yet. After all, love bears all things, believes all things and *hopes* for all things. Never stop hoping for the best and never stop believing, for you might be giving up on the brink of a miracle."[446]

Turning the mirror towards me, Goodness says, "Tell me, what do you think of your hair?"

Looking at my reflection, I cannot believe my eyes! Goodness has styled my hair in exactly the same way Comforter did the afternoon I first dined with Father. "How did you know?" I ask.

"I have been with you from the beginning," she answers.

"Thank you, Goodness!" I throw my arms around her neck. "My hair is absolutely perfect."

"I am glad you are pleased. Now, may I help you with your jewelry? After all, you don't want to be late now, do you?" Goodness asks.

"This is one event I certainly would not want to be late for."

Handing her my gold bracelet with the silver hearts, I say, "This gift came from Comforter, Father and my King. The silver represents redemption and holiness, and the gold represents Divine character and purity. When I first came to this cottage, Comforter told me that He, my Father and my Bridegroom would make me beautiful, just like this bracelet."[447] I run my fingers over its delicate chain.

Mercy responds, "And so they have, Lovely Lady," as she fastens the bracelet around my wrist.

While putting on my earrings, I say, "These diamonds are a gift from my dear Father. He personally delivered them to me just last night. He told me that He has been waiting for this day since before creation. He cried and I cried.

He told me that a diamond is really a chunk of coal that has undergone great pressure, which transforms it into a glorious jewel. He said, 'You, Little One, are like these diamonds. You have gone through great pressures and tremendous suffering, but it has done its good work and made you shine like My Son.'

I will never forget His words. It was a very special time for me."

Taking my silver necklace out of its cedar box, I hand it

Rhonda Calhoun

to Goodness who puts it around my neck. Running my fingers over the pendant shaped like a gold heart, I say. "And this was a gift from my Beloved Master Shepherd. He gave it to me when I was just a child. I did not realize the value of this precious gift at the time, but I never forgot His words. Placing it in my hand, then closing my fingers tightly around it, He said, 'Realizing you had nothing to give Me, you gave Me your heart. Realizing I had everything to give you, I gave you My very life.'

"How little I understood that day; I was but a child. I had no idea He was giving me the most precious, most valuable treasure imaginable, His very heart, His very life."

So much has happened since my Bridegroom brought me to His garden. I have changed so much. I am happier than I ever thought possible. My fears have been overcome, my shame has turned to joy and the pain in my heart has been replaced with tender compassion for others.

Mercy lays her hand on my shoulder and says, "Pardon me for interrupting your thoughts, but it is time to go, Lovely Lady."

I whisper to myself, "He has traded the ashes of my life for beauty; my mourning He has replaced with joy."

Taking my hand in hers, Mercy says, "You have been clothed in fine linen, bright and clean; for the fine linen is the righteous acts of the saints. Your dress represents the deeds you have done and will do on this earth, Lovely Lady."[448]

As I turn, Goodness straightens my long, flowing skirt. Glancing one last time in the mirror, I quote from the Book of Remembrances, "But we all, with unveiled face beholding as in a mirror the glory of the Lord, are being transformed into His image from glory to glory."[449]

"Indeed you are," Mercy responds.

Opening the front door, seeing the palanquin shining in the sun, I abruptly stop, which causes Mercy and Goodness to nearly run into me.

I forgot about the palanquin.

The morning sun, shining on the gold and silver, causes the couch to appear as if it is on fire; it is absolutely breathtaking!

Stephen, handsomely dressed in the finest of clothing,

stands straight and tall beside the Captain; both are staring at me as if I were a complete stranger.

The King's mighty men surround us with their swords drawn. As far as the eye can see, a long line of royal coaches make up my betrothal procession. Stephen approaches, smiling. Offering me his arm, he says, "I've never seen you look lovelier, my lady."

Taking his arm, I reply, "I cannot take credit for any beauty that I might possess, as you well know. By the way, Stephen, you look very handsome."

"The King gave me His royal garments. In doing so, He told me that He was giving me His righteousness. From homelessness to royalty! If only my old friends could see me now! Can you believe this is happening to you and to me?" Stephen asks, almost whispering.

"I most certainly can, my friend."

The Captain interrupts saying, "My lady, the King has sent me to bring you safely to Him. He had His palanquin delivered for you, just as He said He would."[450]

Leaning close I whisper, "Captain, were you able to find Comforter?"

"No, my lady, I am sad to report that He remains hidden. I did send out word as you requested, but have not received any reports of His whereabouts."

I let out a deep sigh, which causes the Captain to respond, "He may yet come, my lady. Do not give up on Love."

He pulls back the curtain for me to enter. The entire floor of the palanquin is filled with beautiful gifts. "Where did these gifts come from?" I ask.

"From the King and His Father," the Captain answers.

Such extravagance, such love overwhelms me! Trembling, I step into my royal chariot and whisper, "What a glorious Family I have!"

Eight of the King's strongest men lift the couch on their broad shoulders. The Captain and his guards surround us as we make our way to the village. I am thankful for the broad canopy and curtains because they protect me from the burning rays of the sun and the curious looks of travelers. Goodness and Mercy follow closely behind, as well as the entire Royal Court. Passing through the Wilderness of Life, I have no fear, for the King's valiant soldiers completely surround me, protecting me from thieves, animals of prey, or any other thing that would threaten my welfare or prevent my safe passage. Such is the diligent care of my the King for His eternal bride.

I look closely at the interior of my couch. It is even more beautiful on the inside than the outside. Gold and silver of the finest quality surround me, but the true beauty of this couch is my Beloved's workmanship. The King said that He fashioned this couch to be a reflection of my beauty; He has made this couch and me what we are.

Could it be possible that He sees me as being as valuable and exquisite as this beautiful, glorious palanquin?

I run my fingers over the intricate designs carved in the rich wood. Looking closer, I discover that they are not designs at all, but words. I read, "I have hidden Your Word in my heart that I might not sin against You."[451]

What I thought were designs are actually quotations from the Book of Remembrances. I read each of them and realize that every one of these passages are the ones Comforter instructed me to memorize.

His words are written on my heart.

After what seems like a very long journey, the Captain announces our arrival at the village gate. The watchmen on the walls blow their trumpets welcoming the King's bride-to-be. I suddenly feel extremely nervous. The last time I was here, the shepherds and watchmen rejected and wounded me. They took away my shawl, which was a gift from my Beloved, and forbid me to ever minister in the village again.

The couch suddenly stops and the men lower it to the ground. I open the curtain to see what is happening. The Captain rides up alongside me.

I ask, "Is there anything wrong, Captain?"

"No, my lady; on the contrary, there is something very right."

The Captain steps aside and my heart leaps! There standing behind him is my dear Friend, Comforter! He is dressed in white from head to toe and holds a large bouquet of lilies and wildflowers.

"Oh, Comforter, you have come!" I exclaim, as my eyes fill with tears.

"I would not miss this day for the entire kingdom, Lovely Lady, for I have been sent by the King Himself as a Gift to you," He answers as He steps inside the couch.

He hands me the flowers, saying, "This bouquet is for you, Lovely Lady, on this your special day."

"Comforter, they are so beautiful! Thank You for them and thank You for coming! I have missed You, my Friend. So much has happened, but there isn't time to tell You now," I say holding Him close as tears of joy course down my face.

"I know everything. Lovely Lady; I was with you through it all, even when you could not see Me. I was there as you lay on your sickbed and also in the cave. I never leave your side, just as your King never leaves you. But, there are times when it is best for Me to work behind the scenes where you can't see Me."

"Comforter, Your ways are higher than mine. I clearly do not understand how things work in this kingdom, but I am so glad You are here. Thank You for all that You have done in getting me ready for this day." I squeeze His hand so tightly that I am sure I left a mark.

"The King is the One who paid the price to make this day possible. It is His love that has made you the lovely bride that you are," He answers.

The palanquin is once more lifted and we are carried through the village gates. Our procession continues down the streets, which are crowded with people waving and shouting greetings.

"Comforter, is this real?" I ask, parting the curtains.

"This is more real than the air you breathe."

The couch arrives at the Village Square and is once more lowered to the ground. Comforter turns to me saying, "Wait here, Lovely Lady."

He steps out and quickly disappears into the meeting hall. Peering through the curtain, I see many people that I recognize. I look for Charity, Mary and my family, but do not see them. I feel a twinge of sadness, but it is momentary for the joy I feel outweighs the

Parting the curtain on the other side, I see, tied to a tree, my Beloved's beautiful white steed.

Suddenly, the front door of the meeting hall opens. Every eye turns in anticipation. The Ancient of Days steps out with Comforter by His side. My Father is dressed in glorious white attire and shines like the noonday sun. I am flooded with love for Them. Never has anyone in all history been loved like I have. My Beloved, my Father and Comforter have poured all that they are into me. They have withheld no good thing from me, freely giving me eternal life, unconditional love, undeserved forgiveness, abundant mercy, lovingkindness and empowering grace.

I tremble as my Father approaches. He throws open the curtain and smiles. "I am happy to see you, Little One," He says, offering me His hand.

Silence has fallen on the crowd. I step out holding my bouquet; the crowd gasps and then grows absolutely quiet.

Comforter steps back and exclaims, "Who is this that grows like the dawn, who is as beautiful as the full moon, as pure as the sun, as awesome as an army returning in victory?"[452]

My Father faces the crowd and answers, "I will tell you who she is. My daughter is one who has faced severe testing and persecution. She now shines like the radiance of the noonday sun. She has endured the dark night of the soul without losing her splendor. She reflects My glory and My beauty to a dark and fallen world. In the midst of trials and testing, she has learned to love selflessly. She returns to this village victorious, with a pure heart and filled with love."

Peering deep into my eyes, He continues, "She does good to everyone she meets. She will lead many to Me. The powers of this world will surrender themselves to her gifts and graces. She is My triumphant daughter and will reign with My Son as His bride throughout eternity."[453]

Comforter responds, "Let us rejoice and be glad and give glory to the Father, for the bride is to be betrothed to the King of kings!"

I look at the faces of the crowd. Many look shocked, a

few look angry. I see Saul standing in front of a shepherd named Adversary. Adversary leans over and whispers to the lady beside him; her countenance reveals her disgust. She points at me and shouts, "Isn't this one a friend of Compromise?"

Before I can respond, someone else shouts, "It is indeed the same girl, for I know her well."

My heart stops and my breath catches in my throat. I know that voice. The blood drains from my face. I fear I will faint. I frantically search for him as if finding him could somehow keep him from revealing my deep, dark secret. Everything, except my heart, seems to be moving in slow motion. I finally locate him—Compromise is pushing his way through the crowd toward me.

In the distance, I hear an elderly woman cry out, "Look at her, she's so lovely! How is it that a poor shepherd girl stands before us today as the one who is to be betrothed to the King? What has brought about such a dramatic transformation?"

I look at Compromise who now stands only a few feet from me.

What will I do? What shall I say?

Another voice calls out, "Who is this lovely lady?"

Compromise smirks. He points at me, shouting, "I'll tell you who she is!"

Without taking the time to think, I step in front of him and interrupt saying, "You don't know me!"

Looking over the crowd, I continue, "I will tell you who I am. It is true that I was just a common shepherdess dressed in rags. It is also true that I had a divided heart and left my Beloved in pursuit of fame and fortune, but the Master Shepherd found me and loved me. His wonderful Father adopted me and called me His own. I was given a Teacher and a Friend, who trains me in the ways of the kingdom.

"You ask who I am. I am the daughter of the Ancient of Days. I was bought with a price, redeemed by the blood of the Lamb, made pure and spotless for His glory and honor. I am destined to rule and reign with the King as His eternal partner, His bride. My Bridegroom is the Sun, and I am the moon. I have no light of my own, but merely reflect His glory, His beauty. I

Rhonda Calhoun

delight in this. It is only because of His amazing grace that I stand here today as the One He loves. This is who I am."[454]

My exuberant, confident response appears to have stunned Compromise; he stands before me speechless. My Father bends down and writes with His finger in the dirt. The color drains from Compromise's face as he reads the words. He quickly turns, forcefully pushing his way through the crowd, desperate to escape.[455] Several people leave with him.

Father stands and takes my hand. He whispers, "They each had the same opportunity to know My Son as you have, but sadly they have chosen the Path of Least Resistance. But you, Little One, have chosen the path that leads to life everlasting."[456]

"Thank You, kind Father, for loving me so much."

"It delights My heart to love you, Little One."

Scanning the crowd, I see many who have rejected the King; sadness fills me. They have no idea that they have rejected Love in its purest form.

The crowd parts before us as my wonderful Father leads me across the square to the steps where Comforter stands waiting. My heart pounds so furiously that I fear it will burst.

Comforter tenderly kisses me on the cheek. He whispers, "You are the loveliest of all women. Your complexion is like milk; your cheeks are like breakable alabaster, and your lips are like a scarlet thread. You are like the dove — pure, loyal, kind and filled with devotion. I am honored to present you to the King today."[457]

"Thank You for everything, Comforter! You have been so good to me. There is no one like You, my Friend."

Father then kisses my forehead, saying, "You are filled with My righteousness, having no spot or wrinkle or any such thing. You stand before Me holy and blameless."[458]

"That is because You have cleansed me and dressed me in Your robes of righteousness, my dear Father.[459] It is Your salvation, grace, redemption and mercy that has made me thus."

Balancing on my tiptoes, I kiss His cheek.

"You are the perfect bride for My perfect Son. Come, let us not make your Bridegroom wait another moment longer."

We ascend the steps as Comforter follows close behind.

We stop just inside the foyer. The meeting room is packed with friends. Flowers fill every available space, filling the room with the sweetest of fragrances, yet not sweeter than the glorious fragrance of my King.

We step inside the meeting hall. I see my Beloved standing in front of the altar. He, too, is dressed in white from head to toe, except for a crimson sash tied around His waist and a red rosebud pinned on His lapel. My Beloved wears a glorious crown and holds a golden scepter, which He immediately raises toward me. His face is radiant; His eyes are sparkling. He nods, smiling broadly.

Oh, how glorious He is, how magnificent, how stunning!

All else fades away. The only sound I hear is the furious beating of my heart. "I feel faint," I whisper.

My Father puts His arm around my waist and says, "Lean on Me, My dear, dear child. I will never let you fall."

That is exactly what I do and strength pours into me.

How do those who do not know this wonderful Father make it through this life?

Father, Comforter and my Bridegroom have become the very source of my existence. I have become completely dependent upon Them in every way.

Comforter steps in front of me and kisses the back of my hand, saying, "It is time for Me to take My place by your King, Lovely Lady."

"Thank You again for all You have done. You are truly a dear Friend."

"And you have made yourself ready," He bows ever so slightly, then hurries to the King's side.[459a]

"Shall we join your Beloved?" my Father asks.

"I cannot think of anyone I would rather have by my side than You, Father."

We begin our journey down the aisle when, ever so quietly, I hear my name called. I turn in the direction of the voice and see Mary, Stephen and many more of my friends. How happy I am to see that they are here! I take another step and then stop. My heart skips a beat when I see my mother and two brothers. Completely overcome, I ask, "Is it true? Have you come to know

Rhonda Calhoun

the Bridegroom? Can you see Him?"

My brothers nod. My mother quietly answers, "It is true."

A cry of joy escapes from my mouth as tears fill my eyes. Looking into my Father's eyes, I whisper, "Thank You for hearing my prayers! You have made me the happiest girl in the whole wide world!"

He responds, "You sowed in tears and now you reap in joy."[460]

"Father, it has been worth it all, every dark hour, every tear, every hardship, every battle and every wound. I am so thankful that You found this lost sheep and saved me. I am so glad that You are kind to sinners like me, for Your love has transformed my life."

"And I am glad you said 'yes' to My invitation."

We arrive at the altar and my Father turns to the packed house and says, "My dear friends, I am so glad you are here. It is with great pleasure that I present to you My Son and His lovely bride on the day of their betrothal celebration."

Facing me, my dear Father kisses my forehead and says, "It is with great joy that I present you to My Son." He then places my trembling hand in my Beloved's steady one.

Looking into my Beloved's eyes, I open my hands exposing the crimson stain from the henna plant, which marks me as one who belongs to Another. "I have been bought with Your blood and my life is no longer my own. From this day forward, I belong to You alone. I will have no other gods before You," I say.

"I am yours and My delight is in you," my Bridegroom responds.

He then displays the palms of His hands. Incredible joy fills me; my name is carved there! My trembling fingertips trace the outline of each letter. He whispers, "Behold, I have inscribed you on the palms of My hands. Your life is continually before Me. I will never forget you."[461]

I look up into the fiery eyes of my Beloved. His deep affection for me is obvious.

Following tradition, I circle my Beloved three times signifying the love and devotion I feel for Him, my Father, and Comforter. Stopping at My Beloved's right hand, I look into His eyes of love and say, "I am Yours."

"And I am yours," He responds.

Our friends look on as I surrender my entire existence, my heart and my all to my King. I hold nothing back as I give Him my past, my present and my future. I give Him my failures, my sins, my weaknesses, my victories, my strengths and my talents.

My Beloved kisses the back of my hand. Scenes from the past four years fill my mind. I remember the day I left the Master Shepherd to follow my worldly ambitions. I think of Compromise and what a great tragedy that was. I shudder as I think of the night I was too afraid and too comfortable to follow my Beloved so I sent Him away.

Oh, how selfish I have been! Apathy, complacency and unbelief have been my greatest enemies.

I stand in awe of this King who desires me in spite of my many weaknesses and failures. I have been transformed because of His incredible grace and lovingkindness.

His unconditional love has brought about many changes in my heart, but how will I ever be good enough to be His Bride?

Knowing my every thought, He responds, "You are perfect because of the blood I shed for you. I have clothed you in My garments of righteousness, making you white as snow. I have ironed out every wrinkle and removed every spot. I am not asking you to be perfect in your own strength. I am asking you to lean on Me and on what I did for you on the cross. I am asking you to surrender your life to Me.

"Let Me be your Savior; I am much better at it and more qualified than you will ever be. You cannot perfect yourself, but you can lean on the One Who can perfect you. Do not fear rejection, for I do not reject imperfect people; I embrace them if they will allow Me to do so."

He gently lifts my chin and continues, "Have no fear, My darling one, for I am making you an instrument of praise."

"I give You my heart and my devotion, for it is all that I have to give," I say in response.

Father ushers us to a table where a cup of wine sits. Comforter holds my chair. My Beloved hands me a katubah, which is a legal, written document. He says, "This is the New Covenant, which was ratified by the blood of the Lamb, the blood of My very own Son."

I read it. It states the bridal price, the promise to provide and care for me and the terms of the marriage to come. Father asks, "Do you agree to the terms of this Covenant, Little One?"

"I do," I reply.

Father then picks up the cup of wine and says, "I offered this cup to My Son in the garden of Gethsemane and He drank it. The only thing left to do is for you to drink it. If both parties do not agree, the marriage never happens."

Holding out the cup to me, He asks, "Little One, will you drink the cup?"

Trembling, I turn to my Beloved and say, "I accept Your gift and Your life, and I give You my life in return. If you find me desirable, then I am Yours. All that I am, everything that I have is Yours, for You redeemed and transformed me. I will go with You wherever You lead. I say 'yes' to this invitation to be Your eternal partner, Your eternal bride."

Reaching up, I wipe the tears running down His face and whisper, "Behold, the hand-maiden of the Lord; be it done unto me according to Your Word."[462]

He replies, "I paid the bridal price on the cross — an extravagant price it was, but you are worth it, My bride. "

He reaches into the small pocket over His heart and brings out a gold ring, which He places on the index finger of my right hand. Looking into my eyes, He says, "I have loved you with an everlasting love; therefore, I have drawn you to Myself with lovingkindness. I betroth you to Me forever; I betroth you to Me in righteousness and in justice, in lovingkindness and in compassion. I betroth you to Me in faithfulness.[463] Behold, you are consecrated to Me. With this ring, I seal our love. You are set apart unto Me until our wedding day."

The guests looking on shout, "Consecrated!"

Father motions for Comforter to take His place on my left; My Beloved stands on my right. The King continues, "I have gifts for you, My love. The most important gift I have for you is the gift of the Holy Spirit, whom you know as Comforter. He will dwell within you, for He is My pledge to you, a token that I will surely come back for you and make you My bride." His gentle breath covers me as Comforter intertwines His fingers with mine. "I will never leave you nor forsake you. From this day forth, I will reside within you and without," He whispers.

Father steps forward and announces, "The betrothal ceremony is now complete. From this day forth, you belong to Another, you are set apart for the King of kings!"

Laying His hand on my shoulder, He says, "Your identity now is that of one who has been bought with a price. You are no longer your own, but belong to the King and have entered a season of consecration and sanctification in preparation for the wedding of the ages."

My Beloved adds, "Put Me like a seal over your heart, over all that you do, for My love is as strong as death. Nothing can extinguish this fiery love—not water, nor flood, nor river."[464]

He kisses the back of my hand and continues, "My love, you were worth it all—every dark hour, every tear, every hardship, every battle and every wound."

"You heard me!" I say, thinking back to my conversation with Father only moments before.

"I not only hear your every word, but I also know your every thought," He responds.

Comforter hands my Beloved a golden tiara adorned with diamonds, rubies, sapphires, pearls and emeralds. I kneel before my King, and He places it on my head.

I cannot believe this is happening. How does a peasant girl become royalty? Only in this upside-down kingdom can such a thing happen.

Once again addressing my thoughts, He says, "Whenever a king marries a peasant, it is costly and extremely painful, but it is worth it."

Looking up into His wonderful eyes, I say, "I wrote a song for You."

"Let Me hear it, for your voice is sweet to Me," He responds.

Turning, I take both His hands in mine, look directly into His eyes and sing:

Rhonda Calhoun

"My heart is set apart for our wedding day
when my Beloved will take my hand and say,
'You are My bride forevermore.'

When all my doubts and fears are washed away
and the wedding song begins to play
to the beating of Your heart.

Hold me, my Love, so close.
Show me Your passion,
and I will follow after You.

My heart is yearning for the day
when You will come and say,
'My love, dance with Me!'

Dance! Let the music play
to the beat of Your heart,
to the song of the bride.

My heart is set apart for our wedding day
when my Beloved will take my hand and say,
'You are My bride forevermore.'[465]

Everyone claps, but their applause means nothing to me.
I bow low before my King who says, "How beautiful you are,
My bride!"

I nod.

He continues, "I promise to care for you, to provide for
you and love you. I will remain true and faithful to you. I will
never stop thinking about you. I will not sleep or slumber; I will
intercede for you night and day. I will allow nothing to touch
your life that does not pass through My hands of love first. I will
remember mercy instead of judgement, and I will hide you under
the shadow of My wing. I will surround you with angels — the
Captain and his mighty warriors will be your constant
companions.

"I will be your Savior, Redeemer, Deliverer, King,

Shepherd and Friend. Seek first My kingdom and its righteousness, and I will provide all you need. I will always be here for you."[465a]

I respond, "With Your love and grace as my strength, I will remain true and faithful to You."

The music begins to play, and I immediately recognize the tune. I turn to Comforter and whisper, "The Song of the Lamb?"

He nods, smiling.

I close my eyes and, for the first time, I know the words!

My Beloved takes my hand and asks, "May I have this dance?"

"My answer is 'yes' and always will be."

Gazing into each other's eyes, we dance, face to face, heart to heart. The love I feel for my Beloved pours out as we sing the Song of the Lamb to each other. We sing of selfless love and extravagant sacrifice, of glorious grace and eternal beauty. We sing of eternal love and heaven's beautiful mysteries.[466]

The music stops but we do not. No one moves and not a sound can be heard. I whisper, "Your extravagant love makes me sing!"

My Beloved bows ever so slightly. "I have longed for this day, My bride. Nothing will ever separate us; death cannot, nor life, nor angels, nor principalities, nor things present, nor things to come, nor powers, nor height, nor depth, nor any other created thing.[467]

"My darling, you are safe in My care and I will keep you in My love. The day will come when you will spend all eternity discovering the many facets of My perfect love. Eye has not seen and ear has not heard the delights that await you. It has not even entered into your mind all the wonders that I have prepared for you. Your future is secure."[467a]

"You are mine, and I am Yours," I respond.

Chapter Twenty-seven
MOUNTAINS OF LEBANON

Who is this as beautiful as the full moon, as pure as the sun?[168]

$\mathcal{M}$y Beloved, Comforter and I leave in the palanquin and go to our Father's palace where He has prepared an extravagant banquet to celebrate.

As we are carried through the streets, I ask, "How is it that You describe me as being so wonderful and beautiful and delightful? I know my heart and see all its flaws and its propensity to sin and cannot understand how You can see me in such a favorable way."

"My love, when you entered into a relationship with Me, you were hidden in Me in God."[468a]

"I don't understand."

"Then, allow Me show you."

He laid His hand on my shoulder. I looked up and saw what I can best describe as a vision. Before me, standing in a doorway, was my King. He stood with His arms stretched out as though He were on the cross. I ran to Him expecting Him to embrace me, but instead, I went into Him. I traveled through Him as beams of light pierced me. I looked down and saw what appeared to be gold forming within my being.

After some time, I came out the other side and was standing before the Mercy Seat. Blinding light flooded the room, which caused me no harm. I wondered why the only emotion I felt was pure love. I looked down at myself and discovered that my body was gone and all that was left of me was pure, beautiful light. I looked behind me and saw my flesh, my sin nature, my impurities and my sorrows all hidden within the Son of God. I shout, "You traded my sin and my sorrows for Your perfection! Oh, how good You are to me!" And the vision ended.

"This is how I can say that you are altogether lovely and there is no spot or blemish in you. You are hidden in Me in God."

"Your love is better than the choicest wine, greater than the highest mountain and deeper than the deepest ocean! Your love makes me who I am!"

"You are exactly right," He responds.

We arrive at the palace and Comforter holds the huge door open for us. *The Trinity are the greatest servants I know.*

With my two dearest Friends each holding my arm, I am escorted into the foyer. Lavish decorations and exquisite flowers fill the place. Every detail has been carefully thought out. The palace is alive with anticipation, for our Father declared it to be a day of great celebration.

We stroll through this breathtaking palace. Magnificent flowers and golden candles fill every available space. Heavenly music seems to come from above, and servants dressed in white hurry here and there carrying food and gifts.

We finally arrive at the dining hall where the banqueting table filled with delicious looking and smelling food awaits us. A large number of men, women and children fill the hall. They stand and bow when they see the King and Comforter. "Where did all these people come from, and who are they?" I ask.

"Father sent invitations throughout the entire kingdom inviting everyone to come. He desires that none be left out; therefore He extends the same invitation to all. These, My love, are the ones who have accepted His invitation to be part of His family. Sadly, many more than this refused Him."

"Why would anyone refuse Someone as wonderful as He?"

"There are many excuses, but none are valid," He answers.

Our Father, the Ancient of Days, enters the room and everyone stands again bowing low. After greeting me with a kiss, Father leads us to the head of the table. I am seated to the right of my Beloved who sits to the right of His Father.

These seats look more like thrones than chairs.

I look down the table and see my mother, brothers, Charity and many others from my village.

How absolutely, perfectly happy I am!

Father stands, holding a loaf of unleavened bread, and the room grows perfectly quiet. He speaks, "This is the bread of the covenant. It was baked without leaven representing the body of My Son who lived and died free from sin. Today we celebrate His betrothal to His beautiful bride. In doing so, let us eat of this bread and remember the price that He paid to make you His."[469]

Everyone nods in agreement.

Father breaks the bread and hands it to my Bridegroom King, who passes the thin bread to me, saying, "I will not eat of this bread again until I eat it with you on our wedding day."

I break off a piece, then pass it to the next person. As I eat, I think of His death; I remember His life. Tears flow from every face, my Beloved's included.

Father then lifts a gold goblet and says, "This is the fruit of the vine, which represents the spilled blood of My Son, which was shed for you. Take, My friends, and drink deeply of its richness."

Raising my glass, I gaze at my beautiful Bridegroom King. "Thank you," I whisper.

"You are worth the price," He replies.

I drink and find that it is amazingly sweet.

Hearing a commotion behind me, I turn. A man hurries through the doors and makes his way toward my Bridegroom. He is dressed in fine apparel and looks very distinguished.

It is obvious that he desires an audience with the King. Surprisingly, my Bridegroom holds up His hand. In response, the Captain and his men surround the man. My Beloved stands and gently says, "Friend, you are not dressed in the King's garments, but your own. Why have you come in here without

Rhonda Calhoun

proper attire?"

The man stands before Him speechless; he drops his head in shame. The King orders the guards to escort him out. Bewildered, I watch as they lead him away.

I lean close and whisper, "What was wrong with that man's clothing? He was dressed in garments that appeared to be quite expensive."

"My love, it matters not what one looks like on the outside. It is easy to disguise the outward appearance and it is easy to appear righteous, but one can never disguise the heart. This man refused My garments. He refused My forgiveness, preferring to do his own thing and go his own way. He thought he could come into My house dressed in his own righteousness, which are nothing more than filthy rags to Me.[470] There is only way to into My kingdom and that is through Me. You cannot earn it and you cannot be good enough. Many are called, but few are chosen, My love."[471]

"But, maybe he didn't know," I respond.

"He knew, but he chose another way—his own way."

"'Where are Your guards taking him?"

"They are taking him to a place prepared for Satan and his angels, a place that was never intended for humans. There are those who insist on going there, and so I must allow them to do so, but it was never My intention," He answers.

"How sad," I respond.

"Indeed it is, but this is not a day for sadness, My love. It is a day for celebration." He motions to the servants for the food to be served.

With a touch of His hand, my joy returns.

The festivities continue late into the night. When the last guest retires, my Bridegroom informs me that it is time to leave. I hurry to my Father's side. "Father, I want to thank You for everything, for loving me and calling me Your child. I love You so very much!"

I throw my arms around His neck; He holds me close. "You are a delight to this Father's heart."

Kissing my forehead, He bids me farewell. Once I am settled in the palanquin, I quickly fall asleep nestled against my

Beloved's shoulder and remain there until it comes to a stop.

I am surprised to see that it is morning. "Where are we?" I ask.

"We are on the high places of Mount Lebanon," He answers.

"Why have we come here?"

"Upon entering into this Covenant with Me, your life is no longer your own. You have been set apart for Me and for My purposes. In this place, your love will mature and you will learn the ways of the kingdom, for you are being prepared to rule and reign with Me. The remainder of your life will be spent in preparation for the day you will become My bride. You are to gather oil and prepare your wedding garment."

"Why should I gather oil?"

"On that day, if I should come and find that your lamp has gone out, I would be greatly insulted, for it would communicate to Me that you were not watching for My return. Gather oil now while you still have time, My love, for it that hour it will be too late."

"What kind of oil should I store up?"

"The oil that I speak of is the oil of intimacy, your history with Me, for that is what keeps the fire of your heart burning."

Within my heart, I commit to intimately pursue the King all the days of my life.

He continues, "Be aware that many will come to you with invitations and good ideas, many of them will be good things, but it will be most important for you to only say 'yes' to those things that I have called you to.

"I have built your new home on the high places so that you can see this life from My point of view and not from the perspective of human wisdom or manipulation."

Pulling back the palanquin's curtain, my Beloved steps out and takes my hand. I am taken aback; before me is the most magnificent palace I have ever seen. "What do you think of it?" He asks.

"I don't know what to say. It is absolutely lovely, extravagant and magnificent!"

I look all around.

I cannot believe my eyes, the view from this high place is astonishing!

"This, My bride, is your new home. I built it just for you.[472] Come, let us go inside."

I enter through double doors made of cedar. The foyer floors are made of cypress. The walls are made of polished cedar and are inlaid with gold and ivory. The beams are cedar and so are the many pillars. Every door frame has been carved with magnificent artwork and quotes from the Book of Remembrances. The walls are filled with oversized windows providing a breathtaking view of the world.[473]

"How beautiful!" I whisper.

Running my hand over the intricate carvings on the banister, I say, "This looks like the same wood that is in the bridal couch."[474]

"You are very observant, My dove. This is indeed the same exquisite wood. It was cut from these very mountains."

"In the past, I have been afraid of high places, but You are my Bridegroom King in whom I have put my trust; I shall not be afraid."[475]

Comforter, Mercy and Goodness step out from around the corner. Goodness places a vase of lilies and wildflowers on the table. "My friends, you are all here!" I exclaim.

Mercy responds, "Goodness and Mercy will follow you all the days of your life. Remember?"

Comforter laughs, adding, "And you will dwell in the house of the Lord forever."[476]

And here I am and here they are.

Could a person be any happier?

My new home is grand. I spend weeks exploring its many rooms and delightful treasures. I do not believe that I will ever come to the end of it.

Each morning, I rise early and sit on the veranda reading and meditating on the Book of Remembrances. My desire to understand this book only grows with each reading. I have found it to be invaluable. As I read, gazelle, deer and other delightful animals frolic nearby. I love watching them; their gracefulness and agility remind me of the King.

In the evenings, I watch the shepherds lead the sheep in from the pasture. I have named every one of them and have been training them to come when I call. Sheep are not very intelligent, so this takes a lot of effort and a great deal of time, but I so love being with them that I don't mind.

This morning, after my prayers and scripture reading, I hurry to the sheep pen to see if Sunshine has given birth. To my delight, I find that she has two beautiful lambs nestled close to her. "Sunshine, your lambs are absolutely beautiful!"

I carefully scoop one of them into my arms. She wakes. Sunshine watches me closely. I gently rub the newborn's ear and whisper, "I'll call you 'Pansy' because you are as beautiful as a field of flowers."

Laying her down, I pick up the other little bundle. She is mostly black with a few patches of white. Rubbing my face against her smooth coat, I say, "I'll call you 'Lily' because you are dark, but ever so lovely just like me."

Each evening, I watch for Sunshine and her twins to return from the pasture. It takes Lily only a couple of months to learn her name. She is an exceptional little lamb.

This morning, the sun is unusually hot, so I decide to read and pray under the shade of a large tree that overlooks Hope Valley. As I climb a large rock, I see Samuel, the shepherd boy, leading the sheep to pasture. I laugh as Pansy wanders away from the flock in pursuit of a butterfly. Samuel whistles, but she ignores him. He hurries after her with his staff.

What a free-spirited little lamb she is!

I sure hope Samuel can tame her. If not, he will have to break her legs and carry her across his shoulders while she heals. Sometimes that is the only way to keep a lamb from wandering away. The time spent across the shepherd's shoulders bonds the lamb to him, which often keeps them from wandering away once they are healed.

I miss being a shepherdess. It's not that I am not happy; I am. But, I would love to be able to both tend sheep and live in the courts of my King as His bride.

Samuel and his flock soon disappear from sight. Turning my attention back to my reading, I find myself missing my

Rhonda Calhoun

Beloved and aching to be by His side. He left only three days ago, but His absence is excruciating. Just before He left, He gave me a gift. Opening the package, I found the most exquisite shawl in existence. My Beloved said to me, "This is to restore what was unjustly taken from you."[477]

Tears filled my eyes as I remembered the shawl the watchmen took from me. That was the day they took from me the ministry the King gave me.

Running my hand over the smooth fabric, I look over the valley. Across from me, on the highest peak, is the Tower of Lebanon, which helps to protect my Beloved's kingdom from His enemies.[478] Below me is the beautiful Hope Valley and just beyond that is the dark, and sometimes dreadful Wilderness of Life.

My Beloved is somewhere out there. "Where do You go and what do You do when You leave me? If only I knew, I would follow," I whisper.

I look toward the east where the King's fertile fields and orchards stretch as far as the eye can see. *The fields are white unto harvest.*

That's it, that's where He has gone! He has gone to bring in the harvest![479]

I gather my things and hurry inside. Comforter and the Captain are engaged in what appears to be an important conversation. Too excited to wait, I interrupt, saying, "Please excuse me, but I must ask You a question."

"Yes?" Comforter asks.

"It is no longer good for me to stay behind while my Beloved works in the fields. He desires a partner and I desire to be that partner. I want to be with my Beloved in His garden. I long to see the buds, the leaves, the flowers and the fruit appear in the lives of His people.

"So, I was wondering if You would allow me to go find Him? May I work alongside Him caring for His garden and for His sheep that I might have something to give my Bridegroom on the day of our wedding. Comforter, I must be where He is! Please say 'yes'."

Comforter responds, "This is a holy thing you desire. You

should pursue your Love at once."

With just a glance from Comforter, the Captain responds, "I will prepare the horses."

Goodness and Mercy appear in the doorway, saying, "We are ready to follow you."

"Thank you, dear friends," I answer, laughing at my two faithful shadows.

Comforter prepares a food basket for our journey while I gather a few things. Placing the Book of Remembrances into my pouch, I throw it over my shoulder and then quickly step into my sandals.

The Captain announces that all is ready. I race outside, eager to be by my Beloved's side. Climbing onto my prize mare, I exclaim, "For the King and for His kingdom!"

"For the King and for His kingdom," the Captain and his guards echo.

Rhonda Calhoun

Chapter Twenty-eight
THE ORCHARD

I went down to the orchard of nut trees. [480]

We travel as fast as possible down the mountain. Goodness and Mercy follow close behind me the entire way. Midmorning, we stop to water the horses. I sit on the river bank dangling my hot feet in the cool water. "Comforter, I would sure love to see my family and Stephen, David and Charity. I wonder if Saul and Martha have surrendered their lives to the King? And what about the others in the village? Have they come to believe in the King?"

"Some have; others remain unconcerned about their future, Lovely Lady."

"I cannot understand how anyone could not be concerned about their future. After all, the way they live their lives now determines how they will spend eternity."

"And eternity is a very long time," Comforter adds.

I watch as the Captain brushes down my mare.

"Why does the Captain do what he does?" I ask.

"Because that is his job; that is why he was created."

"But, that's not why I was created. You said I was created primarily to love and be loved."

"The Captain is an angel, Lovely Lady. He was created

to serve the King."

"Does he love the King?" I ask, ever so curious.

"Angels are servants and do not have the same privilege as humans. They cannot enter into a personal relationship with the King. Humans are in a class all by themselves. Angels can't be redeemed or saved, they aren't part of My bride. That is why they watch you and wonder at your love. This is something that is not available to them. They are in awe of this relationship between the bride and the Bridegroom."

"But, I am a servant."

"You serve because you are loved and you love; you serve by choice. Your primary identity is to be a lover, not a servant," He answers.

"My Beloved has so captured my heart that my greatest desire is to be His constant companion. I desire to remain by His side, reflecting His glory to a dark and dying world. I have a strong desire to see others come to know His unconditional love and experience His infinite kindness."

"And so you shall," Comforter says as He helps me to my feet.

We continue on our journey arriving just on the outskirts of Hope Valley just before the noon hour. I bring my horse to a stop wondering where we should eat our lunch.

"I would suggest that walnut orchard," Comforter answers, without me asking. He points toward the large walnut orchard on the other side of the river.

No longer surprised that Comforter knows my thoughts, I respond, "Then, to the King's orchard it is."

Having finished our meal, we travel through the heart of the orchard, which is a blessing because the large trees provide a respite from the burning rays of the sun. We ride only a short distance when I hear people crying. Turning my mare towards the sound, I soon come upon a small gathering of men, women and children huddled close together.

A shepherd quickly approaches, greeting us rather weakly, "Good-day, friends. Do you come in the name of the King or another name?"

Comforter looks at me, obviously waiting my response. I

answer, "We come in the name above all names—the King of kings. Is there any way we can be of assistance to you, kind shepherd?"

"Oh, that someone could help us. You see, we are a group of friends who meet together each morning to study the Book of Remembrances. This morning, a mountain lion invaded our gathering and snatched away a young woman's infant. As you can imagine, she is devastated."

Wiping his eyes, he continues, "I fear for her sanity, my lady, for this tragedy has followed the sudden death of her husband by only a few months."

I look to Comforter for guidance. My eyes plead with Him that we might stay and offer some assistance. Knowing Him so well I can see the yes in His eyes. "Of course we will stay, for that is what the King would do," I respond.

I quickly dismount and follow the shepherd. The distraught mother looks up and I nearly faint when I see that it is none other than Martha. My knees feel weak and my heart is sick. I run to her. She throws herself into my arms, telling me a story that makes no sense. I look at Comforter, who stands beside us.

"I sent the Captain and his men to search for the babe," He says.

The Captain took more than a dozen of the guards with him and the remainder formed a circle around our little group keeping us completely safe from any and all predators.

Martha and I collapse on the ground, leaning against an ancient walnut tree. Her friends and I begin to pray for a miracle.

Martha lays her head in my lap and I stroke her hair. Comforter sits beside us and lays His hand on her shoulder. He speaks ever so softly to her, but I cannot understand what He is saying. Goodness and Mercy stand nearby, quietly singing over her.

I have no words to speak, no wisdom to give and no answers to the questions Martha keeps asking. I have never, in all of my life, felt such helplessness and grief. All I have are my prayers and my love, and for the first time, I find myself wondering if they are enough in the face of such a horrible

Rhonda Calhoun

tragedy.

It takes a while, but Martha finally begins to relax. Her grief-filled eyes look up into mine as she whispers, "The King was here this morning. He sat with us for a while. Just after He left, it happened."

Her sobs prevent her from saying more. I hold her small frame and stroke her hair and pray. Oh, how I pray!

Suddenly, Martha sits up and shouts, "Why didn't He do something? He is the King! He can do anything, so why didn't He?!"

She throws herself against me and buries her face in my skirt. Her gut-wrenching cries fill the orchard.

After some time, she sits up and shouts, "No lion would ever dare to come near when the King is present. Why didn't the King stay? He knows everything. He knew the lion was coming. He knew — Oh, He knew!"

"Martha, I don't have the answer to your questions. There are many things that happen in this life that we cannot understand and make no sense. But, I can tell you no matter have awful our circumstances, no matter what tragedy comes our way, our King cares and He is good through and through. When you are brokenhearted, He is ever so close. Even if the mountains were to crumble before you and the hills shake, His lovingkindness would not be removed from you. He is full of compassion and great in power. Martha, regardless of what happens, you must cling to this truth and never let it go."[481]

Martha collapses. She is perfectly still; no tears, no questions, no sounds. I am not sure if she is asleep or just resting.

I suddenly become aware that my hand is hurting. I lift it and find a shattered walnut under it. Its outer shell is crushed, its wounded heart is exposed just like Martha's. Walnuts are extremely valuable because they are not only good for food, but they are also good for cleansing and healing. However, they are useless until their hard outer shells are broken.[482]

Just as my Bridegroom was crushed, so is Martha and so it must be for all who follow Him.

I continue to run my hands through Martha's hair as I sing scriptures over her. I am so thankful that she has become a follower of the King. I am also thankful for her godly friends because she will need much love and many prayers to see her through this tragedy.

I hear the sound of horses approaching and anxiously look up. The Captain and his men have returned, cradling a small bundle wrapped in a cloak. The shepherd hurries out to meet him. Mercy and Goodness step forward blocking Martha's view. I lean to the left so I can see. The Captain hands the small bundle to the shepherd. I strain to see the shepherd's countenance for some sign of the outcome, but cannot for his head is down. I am scarcely breathing by the time he looks up. He is crying. I look into his eyes and the excruciating pain I see there says it all. Grief explodes in my heart.

Why did this little one have to die? Why was she a victim of such a cruel enemy? And what will happen to this young widow who is now completely alone and without hope? I know that my King is greater than any mountain lion. I know that He holds life and death in His hand. And, yet, He allowed this tragedy. For what purpose, and to what end?

I do not understand. I have no answer or explanation. I find myself having to heed my own advice and cling with all my strength and might to the truth that my Beloved is good, even when circumstances say otherwise.

The shepherd's shadow falls on us. Martha groans. He kneels down and gently lays the little bundle in her lap. She uncovers her baby's face and kisses her forehead. The infant simply looks as if she is asleep.

Comforter places His hand on Martha's arm and lovingly says, "Martha, I know that your pain is great. I want you to know that I am with you; I will never leave you. I will comfort you and see you through. You are not alone nor will you ever be."

"Where is my baby?" she asks.

"Your precious baby now rests in the arms of her Father in His kingdom. She knows no pain or sorrow, nor will she ever. Right now, at this moment, she is clapping with delight at the wonderful mysteries being revealed to her. She is happy and loved. She will live in perfect peace forever. One day you will

Rhonda Calhoun

hold her in your arms again."

"I know that is true, but I want my baby with me now. She would be happy with me," Martha cries, "She was such a good baby and so beautiful. I don't understand. First, my husband and now my baby. Why? Someone tell me why!"

Comforter wraps His arms around her and holds her close, all the while whispering in her ear. After a while, a measure of peace settles over her and she falls asleep. Comforter holds her close for hours.

When Martha finally stirs, she rocks her precious baby as she sings over her. Tears stream down Comforter's face.

The sun sets and Martha finally hands her little bundle to Comforter. He says, "Blessed are those who mourn, for they shall be comforted.[483] You shall be comforted in this great hour of pain and tragedy."

Martha collapses in my arms and lays her head in my lap. She soon falls into a restless sleep. Mercy brings out the basket of food Comforter packed and passes it out to Martha's weary friends. I am amazed to see that after everyone has eaten there is still food left over, which is impossible. Such a small basket could never hold enough food for this many people.

I hold Martha throughout the long night. Pain sweeps over her like ocean waves, causing her to cry out and groan in her sleep. All I can do is hold her close and pray. Each time she cries out, Comforter lays His hand on her and whispers words I cannot hear. His touch never fails to comfort her.

I wake to the sound of muffled sobbing. In the early morning light, I see Martha's shepherd lying face down on the dirt. It is his cries I hear. Sometime during the night, the King arrived. He now lies on the dirt beside the shepherd, His arm draped across his shoulders. Comforter stands over them.

Martha is still asleep and so are her friends. The baby has been laid nearby in the hollow of a tree and covered with beautiful lilies.

How will Martha ever survive such a tragedy? How will she go on?

I look back at the shepherd who continues to cry out on Martha's behalf. It is obvious he loves his 'flock' and has laid down his life for them. I look at Martha's friends sleeping around her and know that they, too, will love her with the love of the Lord. I also know that the King, Comforter and Father will watch over her with great care, never leaving her side.

The kindhearted shepherd slowly rises to his knees. Comforter kneels in front of him, while my Beloved lays His hand on his shoulder and joins His prayers with those of the shepherd's.

A young woman who introduces herself as Dorcas quietly sits beside me. She whispers, "How long have you known Martha?"

"Martha and I grew up in the same village. I have known her since we were children. What about you?"

"I met Martha two years ago when she and my brother were betrothed. They married just over a year ago. Shortly afterward, my brother caught the fever and died and now this. Do you think she will be okay?"

"I know it looks like her life is over, but I have seen my Beloved heal many broken hearts, mine included. The King works miracles. Comforter loves her and will never leave her side. Father is the kindest, most loving Father there is. They are incredibly wise and are wonderful Counselors. They are more than able to heal her shattered heart and restore to her what was lost."

Pointing to the now prostrate shepherd, I continue, "And your shepherd obviously cares for her as do all of you. With love like this, I am sure she will be healed."

Dorcas lays her hand on my arm and says, "My lady, you remind me of the King."

Looking at Him, I respond, "Thank you, Dorcas; that is the best compliment anyone could ever give me. But, I can take no credit for any virtues I may have, for every gift and grace in my life is a result of my Bridegroom King's great love for me. I am nothing without Him."

At this moment, my King looks up at me. I see the weariness etched in His face. Grief fills Him. He nods at me then turns away, heading into the deepest, darkest part of the orchard.

Comforter returns to Martha's side.

Rhonda Calhoun

"Comforter, why does my Beloved leave? Where does He go? It seems to me that He should stay close and comfort Martha."

"Your King has not forgotten Martha or her friends," He says as He lays His hand on Martha's arm. He looks into my eyes and says, "Lovely Lady, your King has gone in search of a lion."

Chapter Twenty-nine
THE VILLAGE

I went down to see the blossoms of the valley,
to see whether the vine had budded. [184]

We bury Martha's precious baby underneath the walnut tree where she and I spent the night. We travel only a short distance when Martha runs back. She throws herself on the tiny mound of dirt, sobbing. Comforter kneels by her side saying, "Dear one, your baby is not there."

"In my head I know that is true, but my heart cannot believe it," Martha says.

"Then we will sit with you until your heart is ready."

We all join Martha and Comforter around the grave. One day turns into three. As the sun rises on the fourth morning, Martha looks up and says, "My baby is not there, is she?"

"No, she's not," Comforter answers.

"She's in heaven with God, isn't she?" she asks.

"She is being held in the arms of her loving Father at this very moment, Martha."

With Comforter's help, Martha stands. Taking His hands in hers, Martha weakly says, "Then, let us return to the village."

We make it to the edge of the orchard and Martha

Rhonda Calhoun

collapses. Thankfully, Comforter is there to catch her. Others offer to carry her, but quickly grow tired. It seems Comforter is the only one strong enough to carry such a heavy heart.

As we get close to the village, David hurries out to meet us. It is good to see him. Laying his hand on my shoulder, he says, "We heard about Martha's tragedy. Come, we have made preparations for your arrival."

We travel through the dusty streets and are soon joined by Stephen. Embracing me, he says, "I have brought food from the King's garden. All is ready. We have also made arrangements for all of you to have a place to sleep, knowing that you would most likely be hungry and extremely weary."

"How did you know about this tragedy, and how did you know we were coming?" I ask my two friends and fellow shepherds.

"The King sent a messenger ahead of you with the tragic news. He also told us that you were on your way here." Wiping his eyes, David continues, "Our hearts are heavy with grief. We have been on our knees night and day."

"Thank you so much. You are true shepherds. This is a good thing that you have done," I reply.

"We have done only what our Beloved King would have done had He been here in flesh and blood," Stephen replies.

I nod, fully understanding that we can take no credit for any services we render on behalf of our King. We cannot even take credit for the love that burns in our hearts, for it is the King who plants and cultivates such love. And the only reason we love Him in the first place is because He first loved us.[485]

We walk the remainder of the way in silence. Comforter carries Martha to the room prepared for her. Comforter, Goodness and Mercy stay with her. David, Stephen and several others wash our dirty feet and then serve our weary group more food than we can possibly eat.

Martha's shepherd and her friends linger late into the night waiting to hear news concerning her. Once Mercy announces that she is resting peacefully, they retire to the rooms prepared for them.

My Beloved has just arrived; He and David are engrossed

in conversation. I look in on Martha and find her in a deep sleep. Comforter sits by her bed holding her hand. Goodness and Mercy are singing softly over her. Seeing that she is in the best of care, I join Stephen on the meeting hall steps.

We sit in silence, staring at the bright moonlight. I look around this village and wonder at the many changes I see, both good and bad. "Nothing ever stays the same, does it?" I ask.

"Not on this earth, but there is One thing that stays the same and that is the King," Stephen responds.

David joins us. He sits with us as we stare in silence at the sky. The pain in my heart is excruciating. I wrestle with the fact that the King could have stopped this tragedy from happening, but chose not to. I war within my soul, reminding myself that He is good all the time, in every way, even when it does not look like it.

Tragedy has a way of revealing what one really believes and where your trust lies. When the world comes crashing down around your feet, when all that you believed is challenged, do you still believe that God is good and that He cares? That is the questions I am facing.

David speaks, laying his hand on my shoulder, "The journey through life is often painful and very difficult, is it not?"

"It is difficult, but I have been told that, in the end, it will certainly be worth it," I answer.

"I know that to be true. The King is our strength and our refuge and we must lean on Him at all times, especially when things don't make any sense," David says.

Stephen adds, "We may not have the answers, my friends, but I am certain of one thing and that is there is One who does. And He can be trusted. That fact will never change, even if everything around us should crumble and fall."

"I know that to be true in my head, but it is difficult to feel at times like this," David responds.

"I have learned that the wilderness is designed to reveal the weaknesses within the soul so that we might fall more in love," I state.

"Things are certainly strange in the kingdom of heaven," David says.

Rhonda Calhoun

Laying my hand on David's shoulder, I ask, "So, how are things in the village, my friend?"[486]

"The kingdom continues to grow in strength and purity. Charity and Mary have become strong leaders, full of zeal and love for the King. They testify with great boldness as to the identity of the Master Shepherd. Charity has been having a lot of dreams and visions. It seems that the Lord has given her a strong prophetic gift, which is so encouraging to those she ministers to.

"And just two weeks ago, Mary gave her entire inheritance to the King on behalf of the poor. Her friends do not understand the intensity of her devotion and have rejected her. Their persecution causes her to suffer greatly, but her heart remains steadfast. She has nothing left on this earth, but I tell you the truth, her riches are stored up where neither moth nor rust can destroy and no thief can go.[487]

"As for Stephen, he continues to grow in grace and power. He is a mighty man of faith fully devoted to our Beloved King," David answers.

Stephen is obviously uncomfortable that the focus has turned to him. David lays his hand on his friend's knee and continues, "Stephen has been used by the King to heal the sick on several occasions. We are blessed that the King has seen fit to grace this humble little fellowship with such a godly man as Stephen. As you and I both know, what makes Stephen so wonderful and delightful are not his gifts and talents, but his steadfast love for our Bridegroom King and those who are part of His family."[488]

Stephen responds, "Our King is indeed good and glorious and worthy of our praise. All glory and honor goes to Him and Him alone. He is good to the just and the unjust."[488a]

David lays his hand on mine and continues, "I want to tell you what happened just last week. One of the village watchmen confessed that he was one of the men who beat you the day you were seeking your Beloved. He said you never once treated them with contempt, but your only concern was finding your Beloved. He also said that he couldn't forget the look of love in your eyes while you were being beaten. He has surrendered his life to the King and has given himself to prayer and fasting ever since."

"Which of the watchmen was it?"

"Nabal," he answers.

"How wonderful for Nabal! I must find him tomorrow and welcome him into the kingdom. But what of Saul? Has he come to know the Bridegroom King?"

David answers, "I have talked with Saul many times, but he only grows more bitter and jealous. He still comes to our gatherings, but I fear his motives are less than pure."

The compassion and love I feel for Saul surprises me. "I pray the day will come when he will see the truth and fully surrender," I say, looking up at the endless sky decorated with brilliant stars.

"I pray that day will come for him and for all those who don't know the beauty of our Bridegroom King," David replies.

Our beloved King suddenly stand before us. We quickly make room for Him on the steps. His very presence calms my soul and fills me with peace. There is nothing on earth that equals the joy of being with my King whether in private or among the people.

My heart is heavy for Martha, so I lay my head against His broad shoulder. Laying His hand on my head, He whispers, "My peace I give to you."

I breathe deeply of His love and grace, for He is the source of my strength and hope. He is my very reason for living, and He is enough to see us through this painful ordeal.

When everyone else has retired for the night, I ask, "Is it wrong for me to ask why You allowed this tragedy?"

"It is never wrong for you to ask Me anything. There are things in this earth that surpass human understanding. When you find yourself faced with such things, that is when it is most important to fight the good fight and trust Me, for I know the future and My ways are always perfect. I know what I am doing."

Chapter Thirty
COME BACK!

My soul set me over the chariots of my noble people. [489]

The next morning, I hurry to check on Martha and find her still sleeping, so I go in search of the repentant watchman. Finding him sitting under a sycamore tree, I offer my hand of friendship. At first, he finds it difficult to believe I could ever forgive him. But after I share my journey, he is able to receive my gift of forgiveness and we quickly become grand friends.

As the days go by, I eagerly give myself to the tasks that my Beloved asks me to do. I delight in serving Him because I am in love. I find that I am not as easily offended as before, neither do I tire easily or quit when difficult things come my way. I now move with ease among the people and thoroughly enjoy their company. It is much easier to love people now that I know how much I am loved and how weak I truly am. I have learned to keep the eyes of my heart fixed on my Beloved, for He is really good at helping me love well.

I know now that I was created to receive love and give it away. I was born to be a partner to the King both now and forever and that is what delights my heart more than anything this world has to offer. I am in this world, but not of this world. [489a]

Rhonda Calhoun

My real home is with my Beloved and He alone satisfies.

Because of my daily involvement with the people and before I am even aware of what is happening, my heart is tightly knit with them. I find it easy to speak to all, even those who make fun of me and reject the truths presented.[490] In spite of their attitude, compassion fills me. I am compelled to continually reach out to them in kindness and I do not hesitate to do so. I love these people, even though they are unable to love me back.

One evening, as I am drawing water from the well, one of the most antagonistic women in the village approaches me. She taps her foot impatiently while waiting for me to finish filling my buckets. A still, small voice speaks to my heart saying, "Lovely Lady, never forget the power of kindness."

Kindness?

I turn to the woman and ask, "May I fill your buckets?"

Suspicious, she responds, "Why would you want to do such a thing?"

"Because I noticed that you are favoring your arm."

"It hurts, but I can take care of myself. I've been doing so my entire life," she answers as she pushes me out of the way.

I stand behind her quietly praying.

Every day, at the same time, I meet her at the well and offer to fill and carry her buckets. After several weeks, she finally agrees. As I carry the buckets to her cottage, I quietly sing about the love of my King. After several more weeks of doing the same, she finally asks me about Him. I share my journey with all its failures and victories and how the Master Shepherd loved me while I was a sinner.

We are both in tears by the end. She looks up and says, "Your kindness captured my attention, but His kindness has won my heart. I would like to meet this Bridegroom King of yours."

Wasting no time, I take her by the hand and lead her to the chambers of the King. What a glorious end to another day!

The following day, with Comforter's encouragement, I begin to pray for the sick in the village and many are healed.

What a delight it is to see the power of the King at work in the lives of hurting people!

Each and every day, I sit with Martha. Some days she

ask me to read from the Book of Remembrances while other days we sit in silence. Her pain is great, but she holds fast to the thin thread of hope she has. Comforter, Father and the King never leave her side.

This morning, Comforter informs me that the King is returning to Mount Lebanon, and I am to go with Him. Though my heart is sad to leave my friends, I quickly pack my few belongings, for I must follow my King.

With bag in hand, I hurry to the old meeting hall to bid everyone farewell. The news that we are leaving has traveled fast. The room is full. I slowly make my way through the crowd, saying good-bye to all.

Martha clings to me as I hold her tightly. I have grown to love her as a sister. The thought of being separated from her is quite painful, but to not follow my King would be unbearable. I kiss her cheek, and whisper, "I love you, dear one, and I will keep you in my prayers. Remember, Comforter, Father and the King are always with you, and They will keep you."

"Thank you, dear friend. You have been so kind, even though I was dreadfully hateful to you in days gone by."

Placing my fingertips on her lips, I respond, "My dear sister, there is no need to speak of those days, for they are in the past. As far as I am concerned, you have been nothing but kind to me."

"Thank you, dear friend and sister," she replies.

As I put my hand on the latch, someone cries out , "Come back, come back, peaceful one! Come back that we may gaze on your beauty, for your words are filled with life! You have matured in wisdom and revelation. You now walk in peace regardless of the circumstances that surround you. We have much to learn from you. Come back and teach us from your wealth of knowledge!"[491]

Suddenly, old and young alike begin to cry out for me to remain. I understand their need, but my heart must follow my King. I must obey the King, for He is the one who gives life and purpose to this poor heart.

"Dear friends, my Beloved has called so I must go; but I am confident that we shall return to you again. Farewell."

Rhonda Calhoun

I open the door and find myself face to face with Saul and Adversary. A cold shiver runs down my spine. Saul pushes past me and Adversary follows, nearly knocking me over. They stop in the middle of the room as Adversary furiously whispers in Saul's ear.

Adversary then steps back as Saul addresses the crowd, "Why should you gaze at this—. What was it you called her? Oh, yes, I remember—this *'peaceful one'*? Don't you know that she causes division everywhere she goes? Just look around you."

Whispering fills the room. A strange thing begins to happen. Several people move closer to Saul while others move near David. As for me, I am in the middle.

Saul continues, "Why would you waste your time listening to someone like *her?*"[492]

Looking in the eyes of those who have sided with Saul, then looking at those standing with David, I see an amazing difference. The countenance of those with Saul appear dull and lifeless, but the faces of those with David are bright and filled with joy.

At this point, Comforter enters the room. Adversary quickly cowers behind Saul. Comforter takes His place beside me and whispers, "Lovely Lady, this is the age-old clash between religion and holiness. The two can only dwell together for a limited time before religion raises its jealous head and attacks holiness. Dull hearts are uncomfortable around burning hearts—it is the story that never ends."[493]

Saul takes a step forward and clears his throat, saying, "I am glad to see that some of you are coming to your senses. As a shepherd in this village, I say that it is time someone takes a stand, and I guess that someone is me.

"We like things the way they are. We have the law and the prophets—what more do we need? We certainly don't need some little shepherd girl telling us stories about a King who wants to make us His bride. Whoever heard such a tale? I tell you that message is not for us. We are perfectly content with the way things are."

All the while, Adversary moves around the room, whispering into the ears of those who will allow him to. He finds a man who not only listens, but nods his head in agreement. This man then steps up to Saul and lays his hand on his shoulder. With a nod, Saul concedes. The man then addresses the group saying, "Why do you want this shepherdess to remain here? She's nothing but a weak, insignificant, peasant girl parading around like she's somebody special. Once a peasant girl, always a peasant girl, I say."

Martha makes her way to my side. Every eye focuses on her as her gentle voice fills the room. "You ask why we want her here. I will tell you why."

She faces me and says, "Daughter of royalty and excellence, how beautiful are your feet in sandals! Wherever you go, you speak of your Beloved Bridegroom with zeal and great grace. You are successful because you have learned how to walk in the King's authority. There is a grace and beauty surrounding your gait unlike any peasant girl I have ever seen.[494]

"I look at the way you live your life and I see our Beloved King. I see the strength of your life, your dedication, devotion and dependence upon the One you love, which is a precious and rare thing to behold. I know that you did not gain this victory, this beauty on your own. It is because of the love of our King that you stand before us today, mature and adorned with great beauty."[495]

Taking my hand in hers, she continues, "The values and motives of your heart are pure and in right order, bringing you strength and maturity.[496] You are indeed lovely."

David steps forward. He lays his hand on my shoulder but faces Saul and says, "Obviously, you do not realize who this Lovely Lady is, so I will tell you. This one is a pure and innocent servant of the Most High who lives for her King. She follows Him wherever He goes—whether in sweet fellowship or in the harvest fields, it matters not to her. Because of her great love and devotion, she will reap a bountiful harvest of souls. Many will come to know the King because of the way she lives her life. Rest assured, she is one who is and will be surrounded by disciples who are devoted to the King and are committed to living lives of purity and holiness."[497]

Stephen now steps forward and speaks, "I will also tell

you about this peaceful one. Not only will many souls come into the kingdom because of her, but she will also edify and nurture others, enabling them to grow and mature so that they are able to nurture others just as she does."[498]

My friend, Nabal, pushes his way from the back of the room and boldly says, "Men and women, it would be to my detriment if I were to remain silent any longer. I, too, must tell you about her. She has proven herself to be pure and upright. She is resolute in her commitment, but submissive to those in authority, which is a rare trait and costly in its attainment.[499] Many find safety in her ability to see clearly and warn others of wrong motives and actions.[500] She also has an incredible gift to discern correctly, which protects not only herself, but also those around her. Last but not least, she is one who remains true during times of suffering."[501]

Mary joins him saying, "Your thoughts are powerful and full of compassion and wisdom. You, my friend, give hope to the hopeless.[502] I have watched a peasant girl, who was filled with shame, guilt and failure grow into a strong tower, a woman of royalty and excellence.[503]

"I remember the day when the King told you to turn your eyes away from Him because your dedication and devotion had overwhelmed Him.[504] Well, I see that same love burning in you now and it is truly inspiring."[505]

Mary suddenly stops speaking. She is staring at the door with a look of both awe and fear. Everyone follows her gaze. There, standing in the doorway, is the King of kings dressed in His glorious royal attire!

Oh, how stunning He is! How worthy of all affection! He is awesome in power and more radiant than the sun!

The room suddenly becomes a flurry of activity as different ones scurry here and there. Adversary and Saul scramble to the back of the room, pushing and shoving people out of their way.

The King's piercing eyes scan the room coming to rest on Adversary. My Beloved holds his gaze until he looks away. The King then turns to face me. With His eyes fixed on mine, He addresses the congregation, saying, "You have rightly spoken about My bride. All that you have said is true, but there is still more to be said about My perfect one."

Speaking directly to me, He says, "My love, how lovely and pleasant you are in all your ways. Nothing on this earth delights My heart like you."[506]

He takes my hand in His. "You have grown strong and stately like the palm tree. Your roots are firmly established as your heart reaches upward for your King. You have learned to depend on Me in fair weather and in storms. You walk with maturity and resolution. You are fruitful and graceful. You have learned how to find water in the midst of a drought, life in the midst of death, hope in the midst of despair. Your love runs deep, My love.[507]

Looking around the packed room, He continues, "I want you to care for those in My kingdom, loving them the same way I loved you. Feed them from the rich things I have taught you, not from your old way of life.[508] Do you remember how I brought you under the shade of the Tree of Life and fed you from it?"[509]

"I can never forget Your gracious, tender-loving care, my King," I answer.

"It is important that you do the same for others. Lead them to Me so they, too, can find rest and comfort under My branches that I might feed them with Truth and flood them with My love.

"I see your maturity, My bride, and say that now is the time for all that I have worked in you to flow out to others. It is time for you to come away with Me."[510]

Turning, He laid His hand on Nabal's shoulder and said, "Always remember that I do not demand perfection, for you will never be perfect. What I am seeking are those who will love Me with their whole hearts while pursuing holiness and allowing Me to be their perfection."

Turning His gaze back to me, He continues, "It is important for you to nurture others; refresh them with all that Comforter gives you. But most importantly, never stop pursuing Me, for your greatest battle will always be for intimacy. There will always be a thousand voices calling to you, but remember that it is My voice, My heart, My friendship that you need first and foremost. As simple as this may sound, you cannot accomplish such a feat in your own strength. I must always be your source and your strength."

"I rejoice in this, for it is my salvation," I reply.

Looking at the sea of faces, He continues, "My promise to you and to all those who will believe in Me is that I will send the Comforter to you and He will give you all that is needed.[511] You will see the sick healed, the lame walk and the deaf hear. You will love the rich, the poor, the orphan, the widow, the sinners and the afflicted.[512] You will go into the highways and byways compelling all to come into My Father's house."[513]

Turning His attention back to me, He takes my shawl, His gift to me, and wraps it over my shoulders, saying, "Today, I am commissioning you as a messenger of the Good News. Feed My sheep.[514] Your shawl, your ministry, which was taken from you, is being restored to you in a greater measure.

"From this day forth, may your public and also your secret life be wholesome and clean. In this way, those who come in contact with you will be refreshed and filled.[515] May you go into My vineyards, proclaiming My message, while remaining close to My heart. Never allow yourself to get so busy working for Me that you forget Me.

"The battle will always be over the issue of maintaining an intimate relationship with Me, My love. May others see the joy you find in loving Me, for this is what sets you apart from all others. May you be at peace with all men as much as it lies within your ability to do so. I love unity in the midst of diversity, My love."[516]

I fall at His feet and respond, "I am no longer fearful, and I am no longer offended by any requests You might make of me. I fully trust You, and I am committed to stay close by Your side. Your influence is like wine—it goes down smoothly, my Beloved. I receive Your instruction and counsel with delight. You lead me even in subtle ways. You have given me a new boldness to wake those who sleep, to shake those who slumber, to reveal Your beauty to those who do not know You that they might live a passionate life of worship."[517]

I look at the faces, many of which have come to know my Beloved just recently. I suddenly realize that my transformed life has had an impact on many of them.

"My Beloved, I had no idea that when I accepted Your will for my life, choosing to follow you on the Path of Sorrow and Suffering instead of the Path of Least Resistance, others were watching."[518]

I pause as revelation floods my heart.

My success comes from the fact that the King loves me, not because of anything I do, or how perfectly I live my life. It really has nothing to do with me, just like Comforter said in the very beginning. I was too immature to understand what He meant then, but now I see that my entire existence revolves around Him rather than revolving around myself.

The truth is I belong to my Beloved, and He is all I care about! I am totally His, and all my labors and sacrifices flow out of my great affection for this beautiful Man. I will serve Him without condition or limitations.

His desire is for me. He enjoys me, longs for me and delights in me! I am His! I will refuse every voice that accuses or condemns me, for my Beloved never accuses or condemns anyone. Adversary is an expert at that; he also encourages anyone who will listen to do the same to others.

I will not be cast into depression when others criticize or slander me. Why should I be distraught when the most perfect, loving and glorious King in existence finds me irresistible?

I look into His dancing eyes and whisper, "I will give myself to whatever You desire, to whatever concerns You have. I will honor and value what You honor and value, my King."

I kneel before Him. He replies, "Then you must honor and value yourself, for My most prized possession is you, My bride. You are what I love, value, honor and cherish above all else."

"*Me?* You value *me* above all else?"

"It is true, My love. I love you in the same way and in the same measure that My Father loves Me. I chose you because I love you."

"*You* chose me? I didn't choose You?"

"I chose you even while you were lost in sin," He answers. *What kind of King loves unfaithful people, people who reject*

Him over and over again?

I remember back to a time as a small child when the Master Shepherd spent hours and hours with me. He would talk with me, listen to my fears, successes and failures. He bandaged my cuts and laid His hands on my bruises. He instructed me in the way I should go and warned me concerning things that would be harmful to me. I didn't always listen and often learned the hard way that He is always right, every time.

He was the One who sought me out time and time again. He tenderly watched over me and captured my affections. He put the desire in my heart to be a shepherdess and then taught me how to not only be a skilled shepherdess, but to lovingly care for those in my charge. He was always there, always helping, always encouraging and always speaking truth. I did not know that He was preparing me for this day when He would call me to take care of His flock, His people.

The day came when He introduced me to His wonderful Father, Who called me His own. And, as if that was not good enough, He sent His precious gift, Comforter, to help prepare me for eternity where I will rule and reign with Him.

What a precious gift His lovingkindness is!

This same Shepherd, who rescued me from a life of sin, pain and loneliness, now stands before me as my Bridegroom King. Taking His hand, I say, "You not only love me, but You also *like* me! I am valuable! I am precious to You! I am loved and cherished!"[519]

Overcome with emotion, I declare, "I belong to You and Your desire is for me! My life is all about You and what You desire!"

Turning to the watching crowd, I shout, "I am my Beloved's and His desire is for me!"[520]

I look up just in time to see Adversary and Saul quietly slip out the back door.

Chapter Thirty-one
COME AND LET US GO

There I will give you my love. [521]

$\mathcal{T}$he King and I set out for the mountains of Lebanon early the next morning. I am a tangle of emotions, knowing that I will miss my very dear friends, while understanding that I cannot be truly happy apart from my Beloved. Where He goes, I must follow. I love them, but I love Him so much more.

Goodness and Mercy follow close behind as my Bridegroom and Comforter set the pace. Being with my dear Friends makes the long horseback ride quite delightful as I never tire of being in Their presence.

I must be asking more questions than usual because at one point Comforter says, "Lovely Lady, it will take all eternity for you to ask all the questions that fill your mind."

"That is probably true, my Friend. But, how happy I will be abiding in the King's presence, feasting from His table, ruling by His side and hearing unfathomable mysteries throughout all eternity!"

My Beloved responds, "I am the One who will be happy, My love. The day I am crowned with your love will be the day of the gladness of My heart."[522]

We arrive at our lovely mountaintop home. Before going

Rhonda Calhoun

inside, I run to the sheep pen. Samuel is just closing the gate.

"Good evening, Samuel. I must know, how are the sheep? How are Sunshine, Pansy and Lily?"

"It is good to have you home, my lady."

"Thank you, Samuel."

"To answer your questions, the King's flock continues to grow. Sunshine and her lambs are well. Pansy has grown so much that you may not recognize her. As for Lily, she finally settled down. They have just now gone into the pen."

"I am so glad to hear that Lily is no longer wandering, for I was so afraid you would have to break her legs."

Throwing open the latch, I hurry inside. There, lying near Sunshine, are her lambs. "You are right, she has grown a lot," I call back to Samuel.

"Do you remember me, Pansy?"

I scratch behind her ear. Sunshine walks over and presses her body against my leg, obviously eager for attention. "Are you jealous?" I ask, scratching her thick coat.

Lily rubs up against me, bleating softly. Sitting on the thick hay, I rub behind her ears.

It is so very good to be home!

I wake the following morning to the sound of my Father's voice. Dressing faster than ever, I hurry into the dining room. Running into Father's waiting arms, I hug Him so tightly that He laughs and says, "Little One, you are going to squeeze the life out of Me...if that were possible."

Letting Him go, I respond, "It is just that I have missed you so much, Father. I have missed the sound of Your voice and Your amazing hugs. Do you know how often I have thought of You?"

"Many are My thoughts toward you, Little One. So many, in fact, that they are too numerous to count."

I smile so big that my face hurts.

"Perhaps you would like another one of those hugs right now just to make up for lost time?" He asks, chuckling.

"I will take every hug You will give me," I say, throwing my arms around His strong neck.

Goodness and Mercy fill the table with food. We enjoy a

grand feast while taking great delight in being with each other.

To think that I am the daughter of the Ancient of Days, betrothed to the King of kings, and my best Friend is Comforter, who is kinder and more loving than anyone I know — it is overwhelming!

The sun shines through the windows casting its golden light on my Beloved's kind and beautiful face. I look at Comforter, my Teacher and dearest of Friends. He is deep in conversation with my good and affectionate Father. I am overwhelmed and whisper, "A day in His courts is better than ten thousand elsewhere."

My days are filled with prayer, meditation and study. It seems the more I learn, the more I realize just how little I know.

At the cool of each day, Father takes me on long walks. Just being in His presence makes my love to grow deeper and stronger.

My Beloved continues to lavish me with His love. I wake each morning and read the scripture that is painted around the top edge of my bedroom wall. It reads, "The Lord is in your midst. He will rejoice over you with joy; He will be quiet in His love; He will rejoice over you with shouts of joy."

Daily, Comforter continues to train me in the ways of the kingdom. Goodness and Mercy continue to follow me everywhere. I have grown so accustomed to their presence that, at times, I forget they are there. The two are a constant reminder of how good and kind my Beloved is. The Captain and his mighty men faithfully watch over me, keeping the King's enemies and mine far from me.

The hot summer days have grown shorter signaling the soon coming autumn. Today has been unusually cool. After dinner, my Beloved invites me to walk with Him through the garden we planted. Always eager to see what new thing has bloomed or what new plant has taken root, I hurry to join Him. Holding open the white picket gate, He says, "I have a gift for you, My love."

"You do? What is it? Where is it? Please tell me." I am so excited that I jump about like a goat experiencing its first wide-open pasture.

Rhonda Calhoun

"Be patient, My darling," He says, laughing. "Patience is a thing to be desired, you know."[523]

"I will wait patiently then," I say, taking His hand.

We barely make it through the rose garden when, unable to contain my excitement any longer, I ask, "I was wondering..., how long must I be patient?"

Laughing, He answers, "As long as it takes to walk through this apple orchard."

"That isn't so long—not if we run," I say, dragging Him behind me as I break into a run. Our laughter echoes through the orchard as we run together.

I know that my King only gives good and perfect gifts, which heightens my desire to see what gift He has chosen for me.[524]

We come to the edge of the orchard and collapse. Catching my breath, I prop myself up on my elbow and say, "So, what is this gift You have for me?'

"Come, and I will show you."

Standing, I take His hand and pull. He resists me, thoroughly enjoying the game. I pull even harder. My hand slips from His, sending me tumbling backwards. I land on the ground on my bottom, and we burst into laughter.

Now it is His turn to help me up. He offers me His hand. "I will make you wait no longer. Come and see what I have for you."

We step out of the orchard and into a large, beautiful field, which is full of wildflowers. "This pasture is My gift to you. It has several underground springs and numerous ponds. It is yours to do with as your heart desires."

"*This* is for me?"

"Yes, My love, it is for you. Tell Me, what will you do with such choice, fertile land?"

He picks a daisy and tucks it behind my ear. I answer, "I don't know; I will have to think and pray about it."

Like a young child, I skip through the field as my Beloved sits under the shade of a nearby tree watching me.

What will I ever do with this wonderful piece of property? Whatever it is, it must be something really special.

The sun is beginning to set when my Beloved suggests we return to our house. Slipping my hand in His, I say, "Thank You for such an extravagant gift—I just love it!"

"You are most welcome, My love. It brings Me great pleasure to bless you."

As I lay in my bed, I suddenly know exactly what I will do with the property. I decide to keep it a secret from my Beloved because it is going to be a gift for Him. I am so excited that it takes me forever to fall asleep.

The following morning as my Bridegroom and I walk through our garden, I say, "I have decided what to do with the property You have given me. But, I have a small problem. I want to keep this a secret, but You are always with me, even when I can't see You. And, besides that, You know everything. How will I ever surprise You?"

"Nothing is impossible for Me, My Love."

"Then You won't peek?"

"No, I won't peek."

"Good! I must go, for I have work to do." I run off leaving Him laughing in the garden.

Comforter joins me. We work until sunset. What a great feeling to know that I am working for the One I love and not for myself.

Each day, the Captain and several of his men follow me to my field and assist me with my plan. They have strict instructions to keep silent about this and to warn me should the King come near. After several weeks of backbreaking work, the Captain asks, "Why do you work so hard, my lady?"

"I do what I do because I am in love with the King. I know that this will please Him, that it will satisfy His heart, which is all that matters to me."

Throughout the fall, Comforter brings me daily reports of Martha's recovery. She continues to grow stronger and her heart is slowly mending. Father, Comforter and the King never leave her side. I know that it is true, even though They are always with me. How can They be with me, and also with everyone else at the same time? I do not know the answer, I only know that it is true. This is another one of those mysteries I intend to ask

Rhonda Calhoun

about in eternity.

The winter comes and the snow begins to fall. It is quite beautiful being on the mountaintop overlooking the valley. Early each morning, hundreds of gazelle leap across our backyard, gracefully making their way down the mountain and across the valley. The evergreens are covered in snow and numerous bright red cardinals add their beauty to this glorious place.

My mountain home is truly a wonderful place. My every need is met. I love everything about this place, but something strange is beginning to happen in my heart. I have a growing desire to go out into the surrounding villages and tell others about my wonderful Savior and King.

Now that it is winter, I can't work in my field, so I spend the warmest part of the day wrapped in a blanket, sitting on the large rock that overlooks the valley. It is a great place to pray and read the Book of Remembrances. My Beloved sits with me often and shares the secrets of His heart with me.

This morning He said to me, "The winter season prepares the ground for the coming spring when new seeds are planted and old things grow again."

I knew He was speaking about me.

Winter seems long, but it is good for me to have this season to soak in the presence of my King that I might grow deeper in His unchanging love and learn His ways. I remember His words and pray about the new things that spring will bring.

At the first sign of spring I eagerly resume working in my field, which we have made into a vineyard for my Beloved. And on its perimeter, we built several homes for children who have no families.

Goodness and Mercy work by my side, as does Comforter, whose wisdom and guidance have proven to be invaluable. One of the lessons He has taught me is that left to themselves, the vines will grow wild and vigorously but will produce little fruit. I have learned that pruning the unnecessary shoots is the most important thing I can do to insure a bountiful harvest. I understand this is true in my life as well, therefore I diligently watch for the little foxes that try to sneak in and spoil those virtues that have been established in me thus far. I continually submit myself to Comforter, for He knows my heart and is such a kind and faithful Counselor. He keeps me from straying.

It is not even summer when my desire to go out increases significantly. I love working in the vineyard, but my thoughts are increasingly on the great numbers of people who have never met the King and are ignorant concerning His love for them. Many know *about* Him, but few truly know Him personally. I have come to understand that there is a big difference between the two. Comforter told me that even the demons believe that Jesus is the King and are doomed. He said that one must *know* the King as opposed to knowing *about* the King, in order to become His eternal bride."

I long to go and tell the lost, yet I have no desire to go without my Beloved and He is nowhere to be found.

As the weeks go by my heart grows heavier. I dreamed last night that the people of my village were in a ship that sank. There was an island nearby where they could find safety, but no one told them it was there. Because of this, my heart is heavier than usual this morning.

Comforter joins me at the edge of the orchard and we walk the rest of the way together. "What is troubling you, Lovely Lady?"

"Comforter, I can no longer bear the pain that is in my heart. I love being here, but the vineyard is planted and doing well. The houses are filled with children who now have godly parents. It seems that it is time for me to move on. My heart is no longer content to keep the love of my King to myself. I long to tell others there is a Bridegroom who loves them and desires to make them His bride. I want everyone to know Him as intimately as I do."

"That is the King's desire as well, Lovely Lady. Perhaps, you should tell Him what is in your heart."

"Comforter, that is exactly what I would do...if I could find Him!"

"He is in the garden picking lilies, Lovely Lady."

Turning, I hurry to the garden.

I cannot describe the joy and relief I feel when I arrive and find Him teaching a dozen or so shepherds. Overwhelmed

Rhonda Calhoun

with love, I remain at a distance, watching.

What an excellent King He is! He sits among the poor and the commoner feeding them from His garden. What king is there on earth that would humble himself in such a way?

He ends by saying, "Every circumstance that comes into your life is an opportunity for God's manifold wisdom to be revealed. So, go and transform the world, for that is why I came."

One of the young men asks, "You came so that we could transform the world?"

"I came to show the world what God looks like with skin," He answers. "That is what will transform the world, My friend."

After handing each a rod and staff, He blesses each one, laying His hand on their heads and anointing them with oil. He then sends them off with His blessing.

Not wasting another minute, I hurry to Him and cry out, "Come, my Beloved, and let us go into the country and into the harvest fields. Let us see how Your kingdom fares."[525]

Pansy, who had been asleep at the King's feet, comes to my side, eager to play. I ignore her, but my Beloved calls her back and scratches her neck while listening to my every word.

"I refuse to go without You. So come, and let us travel throughout Your kingdom. Let us spend the night in the outlying areas where many have never had the opportunity to meet You Let us go to the harvest fields, for they are white.[526] We will rise early and go to the vineyards where Your Word has already been planted and grows.[527] Let us reach out with unconditional love to the people we encounter. I want everyone to know and experience the beauty of Your presence and the unending fountain of love that You possess."

"This is quite an undertaking that you propose," He responds. "It will require great dedication, much inconvenience and tremendous sacrifice on your part. Are you certain you want to leave this place of refuge, this place of comfort and subject yourself to such hardships?"

"My life is all about You now. The cost to me no longer matters. I desire to be Your partner both in private and in public. I can no longer hide away while souls are being lost.

"Come, my Beloved, and let us go to the poor, the broken,

the lost. Let us also go to those who are already part of Your kingdom and see how they fare. As for any inconveniences I might suffer, that will be nothing in comparison to what You endured for the sake of love.[528] If You suffered, it is only right that I should, too. After all, a servant is not above her Master, is she?"[529]

Kneeling before my Beloved, I continue, "Dearest King, I know that You desire to be with those who love You, and I also know that You long to go to those who don't know You, to those who are lost and hard to reach. That is now my desire, too.

"So, let's go to them. We will go to those places where others do not want to go. We will lodge there; I am willing to pay the price and stay as long as You instruct me to stay."[530]

He captures a wisp of hair that escaped my braid and tucks it behind my ear. "You are highly favored among women, My love."

"My Beloved, You are the One who is good, perfect and true. I have learned to love You in private, and now I will love You in public.[531] In doing so, I will not sacrifice the love that is in my heart on the altar of ministry—I will remember Your love. Because of Your commitment to me, I will never leave Your side, even when success threatens to sweep me off my feet or when failure threatens to take me out.

"There, in the fields and in the villages, where the risk of persecution, hardship, sacrifice and conflicts are unavoidable, I will give You my love, for I am no longer afraid.

"I will run with You on the mountains, in the fields and in the villages. As we run, I will remember Your love. I will keep my eyes fixed on You, even while I work in Your vineyard and feed Your sheep. I will love You even when surrounded by rejection, persecution and difficulties."[532]

"As we labor together in the harvest fields, my love will blossom; it will be a sweet fragrance for You, my King. Because of Your love, our ministry will be pleasant, fruitful and delightful. At our gates, there will be a rich harvest of souls. I will draw upon all that You have taught me and will see with my own eyes the fulfillment of everything You have promised. Then, on the day of our wedding, I will cast every accomplishment and

Rhonda Calhoun

also every failure at Your feet, my Beloved."[533]

He replies, "Then come, and let us run together. Let us lodge in the villages. Let us rise early and go to the vineyards. We will see if the vine has budded, whether the grape blossoms are open and the pomegranates are in bloom. We will gaze on the state of My church and see how she fares."

I respond, "I have loved You in secret; now I will love You in public. I have worshipped You in private; now I will proclaim Your beauty and glory in the nations. There I will give You my love."[534]

Joy floods my soul as I take His hand. Together, we leave to prepare for our journey.

Chapter Thirty-two
RUNNING WITH MY BELOVED

Over our doors are all choice fruits.[555]

$\mathcal{F}$or the next eight months we travel together far and near. I am saddened to find that many people are not even interested in personally knowing my glorious King. Every day, I grow more in love with Him as I watch Him show unconditional love and incredible compassion to both friend and foe.

It is easy to love a friend, but the true test of character is when one is able to love his enemies. My Bridegroom King is One who does just that.

This morning, to my delight, my Beloved announces that we are going to my family's cottage. I am so eager to see them that when He suggests that we stop to rest, I plead with Him to continue on. Chuckling, He agrees.

We finally crest the hill overlooking my family's small cottage. Nudging my mare to a gallop, I ride ahead. I hurry to the door; I can hear my brothers talking. Throwing the door open, I shout, "Surprise!"

No one responds; something is very wrong. Stepping inside, and looking around, I ask, "Where's Mother?"

"She's very sick with the fever these past three days now,"

my youngest brother answers.

Without waiting, I run to her bedside. Stroking her sweaty forehead, I whisper, "Mother, why did you not send for me?"

Slowly opening her eyes, she weakly answers, "My little girl has come. I so wanted to see you again." Her voice fades away as her eyes close.

"Mother, I am here now, and I will take care of you."

I hurry to the kitchen for some water and a cloth. Goodness and Mercy have already begun preparing food. My Beloved is quietly talking to my brothers.

I hurry to my Bridegroom's side. "Mother is very sick. Perhaps, we could stay a while that we might see to her needs?"

"That is why we have come, My love."

"You are so good! I must go now and see to her fever." I fetch a bowl of cool water and a cloth and then hurry to Mother's side.

Four long days come and go. My mother continues to grow weaker by the hour. It is late and everyone is asleep except my King and me. The lamp by her bedside has nearly consumed all its oil; its flame is but a flicker, but I dare not leave my mother's side to search for more.

"I fear that she will not survive," I whisper.

"This sickness is not unto death," my Bridegroom responds.

"It will take a miracle, my Lord."

"Is anything too difficult for Me?"[536]

"Nothing, my King," I answer.

"You need more oil," He says looking deep into my eyes.

Revelation floods my heart. *I do need more oil.* I respond, "Lord, I believe, but help my unbelief."

Pulling out a ring of church keys from His leather bag, He says, "I have the keys to death and hades."[536a]

"She won't die?"

"She won't die," He answers.

My Beloved wipes my mother's forehead while I hurry to the cupboard for more oil. I quickly fill the lamp then return to her side where I sing and pray over her. Just after midnight, the King kneels by her bed and takes her hand. I take hold of my mother's other hand and whisper, "Nothing is impossible for the King, mother. Even should you die He will raise you up."

He smiles broadly then says to my mother, "Dear one, I have come to make you well."

I lay my hand on my mother's forehead. It is hotter than ever. She has been unconscious for several hours. He places His hand on top of mine and says to her, "You shall live and not die."

Power surges through my hand and into my mother. Instantly her body relaxes and a visible peace settles over her. Her forehead is cool, the fever is gone!

Throwing my arms around my Beloved's neck, I cry out, "You healed her! Oh, thank You, thank You!"

I hold Him close as my tears of gratitude fall on His broad shoulders. A sweet fragrance fills the air, a fragrance that is very different from myrrh. It is quite delicate and very refreshing. Intrigued, I ask, "What is this fragrance and where does it come from?"

"It is the fragrance of undistracted love and it flows from your heart," He answers.[537]

"From *my* heart?"

"From your heart. You have fixed your gaze on Me and have chosen to believe."

I lean back against my mother's bed drinking in the beautiful fragrance. Exhausted and greatly relieved, I quickly fall asleep and dream of my wedding day.

The sun's rays flood through the bedroom window waking me. I quickly check my mother's forehead and find that it is still cool. Overjoyed, I run outside spinning and twirling, laughing and crying at the same time.

What a beautiful King! What a glorious day!

I gather some wildflowers and place them in a vase on the kitchen table then hurry to the sheep pen to tell my brothers the good news. Astonished, they race to the cottage, outrunning me. We find mother sitting at the table talking nonstop to Mercy and Goodness who are preparing breakfast.

"Mother, you've been dreadfully sick; you should be in bed," my eldest brother proclaims.

Rhonda Calhoun

"Don't be silly. I feel just fine!"

She looks great. She does not look at all like someone who has been sick for days.

Mother continues, "I smelled food cooking, so I came out to see if there was enough for me. To my delight, there is."

Mercy places a plate before my mother that is filled with eggs, fruit and hot bread. I am delighted and quite amazed to see my mother hungrily devour the food. Once my brothers are convinced that she is indeed well, they join her and eat like they haven't eaten in days. Their lively chatter fills the room. I sit beside my mother, but keep my eyes fixed on my Bridegroom, who sits on a bench on the far side of the room.

Suddenly, the same fragrance that filled mother's room last night now invades this room. My mother stops eating and asks, "What is that wonderful fragrance? Where is it coming from?"[538]

"That is the fragrance of undistracted love, Mother. It flows from a heart that is fixed on one thing," I answer.

"What one thing would that be, child? I must know, for it is quite intoxicating."

"It flows from my heart, for I am so captured by my Bridegroom that I cannot focus on anything but Him. I cannot stop gazing on His beauty, for nothing on this earth compares to Him. I belong to Him alone."[539]

Beams of sunlight suddenly stream through the window invading the dimly lit room. The beams come to rest on my Beloved's face.

His countenance is glorious, far beyond description. I have never seen anyone or anything that even comes close to matching my Beloved's incredible beauty. His head is like gold, pure gold. His eyes are filled with love and devotion. His mouth is full of sweetness.

Unable to contain the joy filling my soul, I exclaim, "My Beloved is wholly desirable; this is my Beloved and this is my Friend!"

My family appears to have ignored my outburst and quickly resume their conversations.

We spend the entire day with my family and what a wonderful day it is! In the late afternoon, mother hurries out to the vineyard and invites the workers and their families to join us for dinner.

Having finished our delicious meal, my brothers tell our guests about my mother's miraculous healing. Sitting beside my Beloved, I listen with great satisfaction. What a delight it is to see such a transformation in my family!

We soon gather outside under the shade of a large tree. My normally timid mother stands before the group and shares how my Beloved healed her. A young woman sitting beside me begins to weep. I keep the eyes of my heart on my King while laying my hand on her shoulder. "Why are you crying?" I ask.

She whispers, "I knew the King as a child, but I stopped believing in Him a long time ago. I soon convinced myself that He wasn't real. If only I could see Him, then I would believe."

Tenderly, I respond, "Blessed are those who do not see and still believe.[540] The Bridegroom is everywhere. He is here right now waiting for you to glance His way. He will embrace you, not scold you. He will accept you, not reject you. He will restore you, not accuse you. Is that what you want?"

"More than anything," she answers, holding her head in her hands.

My Beloved is making His way toward us. He sits at the feet of this young woman and lays His hand on top of mine. Years of grief and sorrow pour out as my Beloved speaks tenderly to her. She is being set free. Not taking my eyes from my Beloved's face, I reassure her of His acceptance and forgiveness. She finally stops crying and peace settles over her tiny frame. The sweet fragrance once again fills the place. She looks up and asks, "What is that wonderful perfume?"

I look at my mother and we softly laugh. Mother steps forward and answers, "I will tell you what that fragrance is; it is the fragrance of undistracted love, love for the King."

At this point my Beloved leans over and whispers, "It is time for us to go, My love."

He rises and I follow. Excusing myself, we gather our few belongings and bid my family farewell. Mother follows us to the horses, which the Captain has ready and waiting. Taking my Bridegroom's hand, she asks, "How did you know I needed

Rhonda Calhoun

You? And how did You know I was longing to see my daughter?"

"I know everything, dear one. Not only do I know everything, but I also care about you so much that I have counted every hair on your head.[541] Absolutely nothing happens in My kingdom without My knowledge," He answers, kissing the back of my mother's aged hands.

"Thank you for healing this old body, and thank you for bringing my beautiful daughter to see me."

Turning to me, she takes my hands in hers and says, "Daughter, you have become such a lovely lady. Your life is fruitful and full of purpose. You move in great authority. You walk in great grace beside your King. You walk in much wisdom and are full of truth. Your life is filled with treasures the likes of which I have never known."[542]

"Mother, it is only because of my Bridegroom that I stand here before you today as I am. He has taken this poor, fatherless girl and given me a Father who infinitely loves me. He has dressed me in His garments. He took away my shame and guilt and cast my sins as far as the east is from the west.[542a] He has made me rich though I have little money."

My mother kisses my cheek and says, "You are altogether lovely and there is no blemish in you, my child."[543]

She turns her attention back to my Beloved and says, "Capture my heart in the same way You have captured my daughter's, for I desire to live fully abandoned to You. Catch the little foxes that spoil my vines, I pray."[544]

He nods and replies, "My Father, Comforter and I will make for you ornaments of gold with beads of silver, My love."[545]

I remember when Comforter spoke those words to me. It was the beginning of my incredible journey with my King.

I kiss my mother good-bye, then watch as she crosses the yard and returns to her guests.

Taking my Beloved's hand in mine, I say, "The day you first invited me to walk with You in Your garden, I prayed that I might know You intimately and run with You in ministry and You have given me my heart's desire.[546] Everything I have, everything I do and everything I have become I give to You. I will live my life for You alone, my Beloved."[547]

Chapter Thirty-three
AMAZING LOVE

Oh, that you were like a brother to me![548]

We arrive in the village and find David doing what he loves so much, and that is teaching and ministering to his congregation. We quietly take a seat in the back. I see many new faces as well as many old friends. It is good to be here, especially with my Beloved by my side.

I recognize the passage David is reading from; it is Psalm 62. My heart burns within me as I listen to his words, "My soul waits for God alone; from Him is my salvation. He only is my rock and my salvation, my stronghold; I shall not be greatly shaken. Trust in Him at all times, pour out your heart before Him because God is a refuge for us. If riches increase, do not set your heart upon them—."

At this point, David looks up and sees my Beloved. His face lights up and he exclaims, "Behold, the Lamb of God who takes away the sins of the world!"

David then makes his way to my Beloved's side. Throwing their arms around each other, David invites Him to speak to the congregation. My King turns to me and says, "Tell them about Me, My love."

Having learned that the King desires to partner with me,

I step to the front and speak of perfect Love.

The hour passes so quickly that it seems like only minutes. I invite any who would like to surrender their lives to the King to come to the front. I am thrilled to see two strangers running forward. My Beloved embraces them both as tears flow down their faces.

After a few minutes, He says to them, "I know that you both have suffered greatly. I also know that you were on your way to the Path of Least Resistance. You believe that you will find rest there, but that path will only add to your misery. It is void of true happiness and is filled with many obstacles. In the end, it brings great heartache and will cause your life to be a complete waste. Be wise, for the gate is wide and the path is broad that leads to destruction and many are those who enter by it.

"But there is a path that leads to great joy and sweet rest. It is called the Path of Life, but you must enter by the narrow gate, for the gate is small and the way is narrow that leads to life, and few there are who find it.[549]

"I know that you are looking for life — I am the way, the truth, and the life! I know that you are weary and heavy-laden. If you will follow Me I will give you rest, for I am gentle and humble in heart."[550]

The two men immediately fall at His feet. My Beloved continues, "Which path do you want to walk on, My friends? Be certain of your answer, for this is the most important decision you will ever make."

Without hesitation they cry out, "We choose life. We choose You!"

My Bridegroom smiles as He takes their hands. He whispers something to each of them which causes them to smile. They stand and embrace their newly-found Savior and Bridegroom.

While David answers their many questions, Stephen, Martha and several others fill the table with a wonderful feast. Everyone is invited to join in the celebration.

I slip away to be near my Beloved who reclines at the table. Reaching under the edge of the table, I take His hand. He looks at me and smiles. I lean close and whisper, "If only You were my brother, then I could express my love for You in public and no one would despise or criticize me.[551] As it is, I must restrain myself, for it is improper to display public affection to one who is not a brother or sister. Therefore, I must keep hidden my fiery love, for those who have never experienced the depth of such devotion cannot easily understand why I love You so fiercely and so extravagantly.

"I must hold private some of those things You have taught and revealed to me, for those who have not been in Your secret counsel cannot understand the revelation of the love You feel for Your bride."[552]

Mary places a bowl of apples on the table and then hurries to fill our pitcher. I continue, "I pray that You would help me completely overcome my fears that I might boldly proclaim truth to all who will listen. I ask that I might fully walk in love and humility. My desire is not to keep You all to myself, but to bring You, not just to people who have never known You, but also to those closest to me, and to those who have played a part in my spiritual growth."[553]

Mary returns with the pitcher. I fill my Beloved's cup and then hand it to Him, saying, "I desire to serve You in the same way the hostess of a party serves an honored guest. I will honor You and keep You in first place; I will faithfully serve You with a heart of pure devotion.[554] I will give You my absolute best. I will not serve You halfheartedly, but with all that I am and all that I have. I will waste my life on You, for You alone are worthy. You are worthy of so much more than this poor heart could ever give. You alone deserve glory, honor and power, for Your love is stronger than the grave, deeper than the ocean and higher than the heavens!"

I look into His eyes of love; it is obvious that His heart has been deeply touched by my worship. The candlelight casts a golden glow on His tanned skin. His eyes dance in a pool of joy and delight.

I see the marks on His forehead — marks of unconditional, sacrificial love. I silently promise myself that I will follow Him anywhere He should lead and do anything He asks.

Rhonda Calhoun

I whisper, "My King, I pray that You would not only work in my life in ways that are obvious, but also in ways that cannot be seen. I trust You to work behind the scenes, in ways I don't understand and cannot see. Do what is necessary to bring me to that place where I walk with You in perfect unity. I surrender my will to You.

"I also trust You to work in my life in ways that I can see and understand. I ask You to intervene in my life in such a way as to bring about Your purposes for my life. I ask You to release wisdom and authority in my life and surround me with favor."[555]

The King squeezes my hand and whispers, "How beautiful and delightful you are with all your beauty, character, grace and purity!"[556]

David, along with the two new believers, now join us. My Beloved, still holding my hand, gives them His undivided attention, answering their questions and explaining His ways. It is amazing how He speaks with them, constantly encouraging and building them up. His words are creative, never destructive, never condemning.

He loves so freely and so extravagantly. He does not wait for people to prove themselves true before He wraps them in His love.

Several young girls gather at my feet. I look into their eager, hungry faces and see myself.

With a squeeze, I let go of the King's hand.

A little girl named Esther gently tugs on my sleeve. I look at her pretty little face and see tears filling her eyes. She motions for me to come close. With her mouth pressed against my ear, she whispers, "I was wondering — does the King like nine-year-old girls?"

I look into her beautiful eyes and answer, "Of course, He does."

As she tugs on my sleeve again, I lean close. She looks around to make sure no one can overhear, then very quietly whispers, "But does He like nine-year-old *orphan* girls?"

My heart nearly breaks. Taking her small hand in mine, knowing that her parents recently died, I answer, "Esther, not only does the King like you, but He loves you! And, He has a very special place in His heart for orphans. Being an orphan doesn't change who you are; it only makes you even more special to the King. You are a delight to Him and the joy of His heart."

Once again Esther tugs on my sleeve and motions for me to come close. She whispers, "Do you think the King could give me a mother?"

I look into her grief-filled eyes and answer, "There isn't anything too difficult for the King, little one. I will ask Him every day to send you a mother."

"I will too," she replies. Her countenance immediately brightens and after hugging me, she runs off to play with the other children. At the first opportunity, I tell my Beloved about Esther. I see the love in His eyes, the pain in His heart. I want to ask Him why, but decide not to since I already know the answer.

He feels everything we feel, only more acutely, more deeply.

"My King, I am not going to stop asking for a mother for Esther until You give her one."

He responds, "That is the way to the King's heart."

In the months that pass, I remember my promise and pray several times a day for Esther. During this time, I am constantly sought after to help with some task or start some project. I am asked almost daily to join some group. I hate to turn them away, but I must do only those things my Beloved instructs me to do. To do anything else would be a distraction and could easily cause me to drift from the path that my Beloved chose for me.

There are so few workers in the kingdom, so I pray often for more laborers who will not only serve, but will serve with the same loving compassion that burns within the King.

This morning, aware of the increasing number of pleas for help that I am receiving, my Beloved stands before the congregation and says, "I charge you not to disturb My bride until she is ready. She must not be distracted right now. It is important that she stay close to Me and remain focused on Me during this season. I am ordering her steps, for I know the plans that I have for her—plans for good and not for evil, plans to give her a future and a hope."[557]

Facing me, He says, "Come, away with Me, My love."

Without hesitation I rise up, take His hand, and follow.

Rhonda Calhoun

The
Consuming Fire

Chapter Thirty-four
BEAUTY FOR ASHES

I am my Beloved's and His desire is for me.[558]

$\mathcal{I}$ spend the next three days with my Beloved, resting under His watchful eye. On the morning of the fourth day, my King sends me to David with a message. Finding him in the garden, I hurry to his side saying, "David, I have a word for you from the King."

Standing, he eagerly responds, "Pray tell me what it is."

"The King says that before this day is over He will reveal to you a new location for your congregation to meet."

David's congregation has more than outgrown the meeting hall so they have been meeting in an open pasture. They desperately need a place before the snow comes. Over the past four months, the congregation has spent many hours fasting and praying for an answer from heaven.

Feeling very encouraged, David, Stephen and I decide to walk through the village just to see if there might be something that would be suitable and available. The sun begins to set and the three of us collapse on the steps of the hall. "I don't understand," Stephen says. "The King said we would find the place today. We have searched every inch of this village and there is nothing remotely suitable. We have nowhere else to look,"

Rhonda Calhoun

he says, shaking his head.

"The day is not over," I respond.

Just as I said this, I look up and see my two brothers hurriedly coming toward us. I quickly stand to my feet and call out, "How goes it? Is all well?"

My youngest brother answers, "Rest easy, all is well."

After embracing us, my eldest brother turns to David and says, "Several months ago, my brother and I heard that you were in need of a larger place in which to meet. We have come to bring you news of such a place. We have been secretly building a place for you, and with just a little more work it will be finished. We will need to build some benches and, this winter, we'll bring in a couple of stoves to heat the place."

I ask, "But, where is it?"

"It is a short distance outside the village, nestled in a grove of trees."

"I hardly know what to say, except, 'Thank you'," David responds with a big smile on his face and tears in his eyes.

Perplexed, I ask, "I don't understand. The King gave you lumber so you could build a house for yourselves that you might take a wife. You used it to build a meeting hall, didn't you?"

The youngest answers, "It was all we had to give the King."

The eldest adds, "The day mother was healed, we realized that there are much more important things in life than houses and fame and fortune. We began to ask ourselves what we could do to bless the King. It was only a few days later when Comforter told us about David's need, and the rest is history. "

"But where did you get the land?" I ask.

"We petitioned the King for land and He gave us not only land, but also the extra lumber we would need. We were trying to keep it a surprise until it was finished, but little brother and I got so excited about it that we just couldn't wait another day."

I am shocked by their generosity. I know how important being prosperous has always been to them. Standing on my tiptoes, I kiss each brother on the cheek and whisper, "I am so proud of you both."

Like school children, they poke and shove each other in the side. The oldest responds, "I am the one who is proud of you. I know that I caused you great pain, and I'm really sorry. Please forgive me."

"I am guilty, too. Will you forgive me?" my younger brother asks.

I hug them both and respond, "I forgave you both a long time ago."

My oldest brother says, "I've waited a long time to hear you say that."

David slaps each brother on the back and says, "Perhaps now would be a good time to thank our King and Father for all that He has done for us this fine day."

With our arms locked around each other's shoulders, we join our voices in prayer, expressing our heartfelt appreciation and love to the greatest Father and King who has ever lived.

My eldest brother says, "What do you say we get back to work, little brother?"

"I'm right behind you," he replies.

I watch as they walk down the street with a bounce in their steps.

It is amazing how the King's love can change a life.

My Beloved suddenly appears behind us. David falls at His feet thanking Him profusely for His kindness.

He replies, "It delights My Father's heart to give good gifts to His children."

He then looks at me and says, "You have become quite fruitful, My love, and your fruit shall remain. We are looking at some of that fruit walking down the street right now."

"And it is all because of You and for You," I answer.

We sit on the steps and discuss the various members of David's congregation. The King has wisdom that is beyond anything I have ever known or seen.

The following morning just after dawn, David, Stephen and I are standing in the middle of the new meeting house. My brothers, along with several workers, are already hard at work. "What a wonderful job you have done," I shout.

Looking out the door, I see my Beloved coming out of the

woods toward us. I cannot take my eyes off Him. Even in the misty dawn, He is like a majestic mountain.

Oh, how I love Him!

Unable to contain my joy and delight, I run out the door and shout, "What a glorious King You are!"

"And what a delight you are!" He shouts back.

I run into His arms, followed by Goodness and Mercy. "Thank You for providing this wonderful meeting place for David. What a perfect gift! You are so very good and Your lovingkindness is everlasting!"

"There is only One Who is good and that is My Father."[559]

Playfully poking Him on the arm, I reply, "And You and Your Father are One, so that makes You good!"

"We are One, indeed."

"I have never seen any as good as You are," I say.

Taking my hand, He says, "Now come, let us see the gift your brothers have built for My bride and for Me."

We join the others inside. The King places His arm around my brothers' shoulders and asks, "Will you give Me a tour?"

They show Him around the building while thanking Him repeatedly for making it possible for them to build this meeting house. I have never seen my brothers look so happy. They have done such a wonderful job. This place will be absolutely perfect for David's rapidly growing congregation.

My Beloved turns to me and announces that we have been invited to Martha's house for lunch.

David kneels before his Bridegroom King and says, "I give You thanks with all my heart, for Your lovingkindness is better than life. I will sing praises to You all the days of my life. My King, a day in Your courts is better than a thousand elsewhere. I would rather stand in the threshold of Your house than dwell in the most extravagant house of the wicked. You are my sun and my shield. No good thing do You withhold from those who walk uprightly. How blessed is the man who trusts in You!"[559a]

Laying His hand on David's head, my Beloved responds, "From this day forward, I no longer call you servant; I now call you friend."[559b]

We say our farewells, then leave for Martha's house.

Martha was waiting for us in the small garden outside her front door. Sitting across from her, I see the deep sadness etched in her face. What can I say? What can I do?

"What dreams do you have, Martha? What would you like to do with the rest of your life?" I ask.

Twirling the tassels on the end of her scarf, she answers, "I don't have any dreams anymore—they are all dead." She looks away.

Our King speaks, "Martha, your dreams are not dead; you have just given up on them. I have great plans for you. Your future is not determined by your circumstances, but by your King. Rely on Me and I will see to it that you fulfill your destiny. You can still have that home for orphans, if you so desire."

Martha suddenly looks up, her face mirroring her surprise. She responds, "How did You know? No one knew about my dream except my husband. That was something we planned to do together, but everything has changed, making that dream impossible now."

Tears spill down her face. Taking her hand in mine, I say, "Martha, that is a wonderful dream and one you can still do!"

"I'm too broken. I can't," she responds.

"Martha, the Book of Remembrances says that if you bring the poor into your house, give yourself to the hungry and help the afflicted, then your light will rise in darkness and your gloom will become like the noonday sun.[560] Your pain will turn into glorious light.

"Martha, when you reach out to others, healing flows to you. I know a cute little girl named Esther who is praying every day for a new mother. Perhaps, you are the answer to her prayers."

Martha merely looks away.

"Why don't you ask the King what He wants you to do. After all, you live in His kingdom and are part of His bride."

She looks at the King then back at me and says, "He is too busy to have time for me."

"Why do you say that?" I ask.

"Because He was too busy to save my husband and daughter," she answers as tears stream down her face and fall onto her lap.

I look His way. Tears fill the eyes of the King, not for Himself, but for Martha. My Beloved reaches across the table and places His hand on her small one. Looking deep into her eyes, He says, "Martha, let Me tell you a story. Just a few days ago, I was in the village watching people putting money into the treasury. Some rich people put in large amounts.

"But a poor widow, dressed in rags, came into the assembly. I leaned forward, every muscle at attention. The room grew quiet. That was when I heard it — the nearly silent sound of two small copper coins landing on top of a mountain of silver and gold. No one else noticed this widow; she and her gift were lost to all, save One.

"Martha, that woman gave only two copper coins, which amounts to a penny. But, truly, I say to you that she gave more than all those who went before her; for they gave out of their abundance, and she gave out of her poverty, her weakness, her inabilities. She gave what she had. She had nothing left. She had no one else to turn to except Me. To the world her gift was insignificant and worthless, but to Me it was extravagant! It was pure love."

Martha is crying. My Beloved continues, "Martha, I do not expect you to give what you do not have, but I do expect you to give what you do have, and you have a beautiful heart that loves children. You have a home, and you have Me."

She nods and squeezes His hand. He reaches up and wipes her tears. "All I am asking is for you to lean on Me and let Me orchestrate the events of your life. Will you dare to trust Me, one more time?" He asks.

She nods then falls into His open arms. I watch and pray. After quite sometime, Martha sits up and says, "Even though You slay me, I will still trust You."

"That is true love," He answers.

My Beloved turns to me and says, "My love, we must be on our way for we have a long journey ahead of us; we are returning to your mountain home this day."

Martha leads us to the door.

Standing in the doorway, my Beloved takes her hands in His and says, "Martha, do not be worried about anything, for I am always with you and will take care of you, just as I care for the lilies of the field."

He then lays His hand on her head and says, "My peace I leave with you. My peace I give to you, which is better than the world gives. Let not your heart be troubled, nor let it be fearful, for I have overcome the world."[561]

He then kisses the top of her head and bids her farewell.

Embracing my dear friend and sister, I say, "The King will not withhold His compassion from you. His lovingkindness and truth will continually preserve you. He will make haste and deliver you, for He is near to the brokenhearted."[561a]

She replies, "I have no one else to turn to, for He alone holds the power to heal my shattered heart. There is none other. He is my only hope; therefore, I have put my trust in Him."

Walking away, I ask my Beloved, "Will Martha ever know joy again? Will she survive this horrible, painful tragedy? Will she be whole again?"

"There is no heart too broken and no life too shattered for Me to heal. I will surely set her feet upon the Rock and will put a new song in her heart. I will give her beauty for ashes, the oil of gladness for the spirit of mourning."

My heart rejoices as I return to my tent and hurriedly gather my few belongings. I bid my friends good-bye. We travel until dusk and then stop in the heart of the wilderness to set up camp. After eating, I lie down on my mat under the star-speckled sky to sleep. My King sits down beside me and says, "My love, I must leave you now, but will return to you soon."

Propping myself on my elbow, I respond, "I will be watching eagerly for Your return."

Brushing the hair from my face, He smiles. "Oh, how lovely you have become, My sister, My bride, My favorite."

"How can You say that I am Your favorite? You are the King of kings, the Lord of lords, the Great I AM. You are no respecter of persons, loving both rich and poor, Jew and Gentile, alike. So, how is it that You can say that I am Your favorite?"[561b]

He lays His hand on my forehead and says, "Look and see."

Immediately, I see a vision of a large heart the size of the earth. I zoom towards it through outer space. As I get closer, I see that it is covered with millions and millions of keyholes. Each keyhole is a different size and shape. I am drawn to a particular one. Curious, I try to turn and go into another but find it impossible; I don't fit. I go to the one that I am drawn to and discover that it is a perfect fit. I snuggle in this place, which is like a nest lined with thick down feathers. I can hear the beating of His heart.

No one else can fit in this place. I also realize that when I choose not to enter into this place, it creates pain and longing in the heart of God. I matter to Him! My absence hurts Him! I am His favorite and so are the countless others who have a place in His heart.

I open my eyes.

"You have a special place in God's heart that no one else has," the King says, "Not even the angels in heaven nor any other created being has the privilege to enter the heart of God. That makes you unique. That makes you His favorite."

With a wink, He stands. "I must go now. Do not wait for Me here, but travel on to the mountain." He turns and disappears into the darkness.

I am not anxious, neither do I feel fear.

Nearby a pack of wolves are howling, but peace fills me. All around is thick darkness, but a bright light burns within my heart. The night air is bitter, but fierce love warms my soul. I am well cared for, and I am safe because of my Beloved.

I lift my voice in song. Love flows through my heart like a raging river.

Afterwards, I pray for Martha and Esther and countless others.

"Father, I am in love with Your Son, too," I say just before falling asleep.

Chapter Thirty-five
LEANING ON MY BELOVED

Who is this coming up from the wilderness?[562]

T he morning breaks and I rise to find that Goodness and Mercy have breakfast ready and waiting. We sit before the fire as we eat; all the while I think of my Beloved. It seems I cannot think of anything else. He has become my source of strength, my love and the reason I live. He is as necessary as the air I breathe. He is all there is and all that really matters.

We have almost finished eating when the Captain approaches saying, "My lady, the horses ran off during the night. It seems we will have to travel on foot."

"Then...we will travel on foot."

Needless to say, by the end of the day, I am quite weary. When we finally stop, my feet are bruised and blistered. I am so tired that I can barely eat. I crawl under my blanket and quickly fall asleep. I dream of my Beloved Bridegroom.

I wake before sunrise so I quietly worship. I know He is listening even though I cannot see Him. Once everyone else wakes, I jump up, eager to get started.

It is unusually hot for an October day. Thankfully, the dense trees in this wilderness shade us from the burning rays of the sun.

The Captain and his men remain on high alert. Their swords are drawn and their eyes continually scan the terrain. They surround me on every side. The Wilderness of Life is filled with both men and beasts whose delight it is to kill, steal and destroy all who dare to enter this place. I am amazed to find that I feel no fear, but walk in perfect peace.[563]

I lift my eyes and pray, "Father, the Book of Remembrances says that those whose hearts are fixed on You will walk in perfect peace. I am alone in this great wilderness, yet I am not alone because You are with me and so are Your angelic guards. How great is the work that You have done in my heart! May I never forget how far You have brought me."

I walk on. My feet are swollen and bloody. Mercy offers to carry me, but I dare not put such a burden on her. Goodness tries, but finds that she can only go so far before she collapses. "Hardship is part of this life and I will embrace it, "I say, continuing on, bleeding feet and all.

It is early afternoon when I see the One I love coming toward me. Despite my painful feet, I run to Him. He welcomes me with His beautiful smile and open arms. "Your horses ran away," I say, laying my head against His chest.

"And I gave Mine to a stranger in need," He responds. "Come, My love, and let us walk together. You can lean on Me."

"It would be my pleasure," I reply.

With my Beloved by my side, I am in need of nothing. The Captain and his men appear to have relaxed a little, but only a little. They continue to carry their swords unsheathed and scan the path before and behind us.

By late afternoon, my fatigue is so great and my feet are so painful that I cannot take another step. We stop and He tears a strip from the hem of His garment and wraps my feet. We continue on and I must fully lean on my Beloved in order to walk. With His arm supporting me, He says, "Even in the midst of this fallen world, even in your weakness, you are lovely to Me, My sister, My bride."[564]

"And You are my strong tower."

"My bride, there is a day coming when I will go away, but I will return for you."

"You have gone before and have always returned. How long will You be gone this time?"

"I will be gone for an extended time, for I must go and prepare a place for you, that you may be where I am. As for exactly how long I will be gone—only My Father knows the answer to that question."[565]

Stopping to look into His eyes, I say, "But, I don't need another home. There is nothing wrong with the one I have. I am perfectly content there...as long as You are there with me, that is."

I can feel the tears forming in my eyes.

He gently runs the back of His hand across my cheek. "Let not your heart be troubled; My love will sustain you. For My love is as strong as death. My jealousy is as severe as Sheol; its flashes are flashes of fire, for I am a jealous Bridegroom, and I will watch over your soul.[566] Many waters cannot quench My love nor will rivers overflow it."[567]

I slip my trembling hand in His steady one. My Beloved's strong, yet gentle voice interrupts my anxious thoughts. "My bride, there is a jealousy that is holy and full of zeal, which is what I feel concerning you. My jealousy is as pure as My love. I will not compete with another lover. I will not share you with anything or anyone. I have purposed, from the beginning of time, to have you all to Myself, for that is the only way you will ever be fulfilled. My love is as pure as the sun, as fierce as a raging river."[568]

I reply, "You are the only one I want. If I were to search the entire earth, I would find that there is no one even remotely like You. You alone satisfy my every need, my every desire. You alone are my reason, my hope and my future."

He gives my hand a gentle squeeze, then leads me on. Tripping over a rock, I stumble, but my Beloved catches me. My Beloved spreads His cloak on the grass. He unwraps my feet; the bandage is soaked with blood.

Who is this King that He would love me like this? I was nothing more than an unfaithful peasant girl and the King kneels before me like a servant wrapping my feet with the strips He tears from His very own garment.

Laying my hand on His shoulder, I ask, "Can a beggar be crowned a prince in the courtroom of the King? Can a poor girl come and freely drink of a love that makes her a queen? Can a guilty one go free and from such weight of debt be released? Can a heart that drove in nails and thorns be ransomed, restored and adorned with beauty?

"Can my life begin anew? Can my failures be turned to good? What kind of glory comes from shame? Is beauty birthed through pain? Can this dust be turned to gold? Can the end of my story be rewritten? Can the last become the first of all, the most treasured of all souls, the most beautiful?"

My Bridegroom answers, "The answer is 'yes'! My love can take the least and make them the greatest. Eternal love is the other side of the story; it turns the dust into glory. Your Savior's love is heaven's beautiful mystery. I will open the doors of heaven and show you heaven's side of the story. There is another side to the story, My love. For the King of heaven will come; He will come not to proud but to humble of hearts. He will take you away to a glorious place where all your lost dreams and hopes are redeemed at a cross, a beautiful cross."

I cry out, "My Savior's love, heaven's beautiful mystery! The other side of the story! You are the One I love, the One I adore!"

He exclaims, "I have loved you with an everlasting love! I love you! I love you! I love you!"

"The more I hear Your words of love, the more I want to hear them. Tell me once more just how You feel about me, Jesus! I want to hear Your love song over me. Won't You sing, won't You sing over me?" I ask.

Still kneeling, He looks deep into my eyes and nods. He sings, with a rich, full voice, "I love you! I love you! I love you! I am the One who loves you most, the One who loved you first! You are altogether beautiful to Me! You make My heart beat faster with just once glance of your eye."

I ask, "Who are You that You would love me this way? Tell me again, Jesus, tell me again."

My Beloved replies in song, "This is who I am — I am compassionate and gracious, abounding in lovingkindness and slow to anger. I am meek and lowly. I am humble of heart. Come to Me all who are weary and I will give you rest. Come to the One who loves you most, the One who loved you first."

"I can hear Your love song over me," I softly sing.

"I love you! I love you! I love you!" He sings.

I sing out, "Who am I that You would love me so? You chose me, tell me why You chose me!"

"This is who you are, My sister, My bride—you are altogether beautiful! You are the one I love, the one I choose! This is who you are—you're the one I died for, you are My beautiful one. You're the apple of My eye! You are precious in My sight! You're the one I love! This is who you are, this is who you are in Me!" He sings.

I sing in response, "Your love is better than any other love I have ever known. How can I resist this love? You are so kind, so gracious, so faithful, so forgiving! Who could I compare you to? You are unlike anyone I have ever known. You are fairer than the sons of men, outstanding among ten thousand! The way You love me is so beautiful! And I love Your love, amazing love; better than the choicest wine. I love You, Lord. Your love is better than the choicest wine. So, I sing, 'I love You, Lord.'"

He sings, "I say that your love is better than the choicest wine! You are the one I love, the one I choose! You are the one I died for, beautiful one! You're the apple of My eye! You make My heart beat faster and I can hear your love song over Me, My bride."

"And I can hear Your love song over me causing me to fall in love again. You captivate my heart. You alone bring the healing I need, Jesus, my King. One touch from my Savior and I am forever transformed! You opened my eyes to who You are, and I fall in love again—just like the first time. You are mine and I am Yours," I sing.

"For every flower that is crushed there is the Savior's hand ready to heal. For every wounded soul there is a healing touch. For every broken heart there is a Hope from heaven. For every searching soul there is a Light that shines in the darkness. For every lonely soul there is a faithful Friend. The Lord, the King of love, He is with you!"

"I can hear Your love song over me," I sing.

"How I love you! Oh, I love you! Yes, I love you! I love you, My sister, My bride!"

"And I love You! I love You! I love You, King of all love!"

Staring into each other's eyes, we whisper, "I can hear your love song over me!"

I am not the only one in awe of this love; the Captain and his men appear to be mesmerized.

The King says, "Allow Me to carry you, My bride."

He lifts me as easily as if He were lifting a feather. He carries me for miles without growing weary.

We step out of the wilderness and into a large, grassy meadow. In the distance, a Man is walking towards us. I strain to identify Him, but cannot.

There is something very familiar about this Man.

My Beloved sets me down. I lean against His chest. Quite unexpectedly, the Man shouts, "Who is this coming up from the wilderness, leaning on her Beloved?"[569]

"O, is it?" I ask, "Could it be? Is that Comforter's voice I hear?"

"It is indeed," my Beloved answers.

"How I have missed my dear Friend!"

Despite my fatigue and the painful condition of my feet, I desperately try to run to Him, but fail. Instead, I skip along as fast as I can. Comforter is running towards me. Embracing me, He spins me around saying, "You have returned from the mission field even more glorious and beautiful than before! I perceive that your love has matured and you have become quite pure of heart, Lovely Lady."

My Beloved looks into my eyes and adds, "My bride returns strong and resolute because she understands that she is totally and completely dependent upon Me. I am the reason she lives, and I am her source of supply. I am the One she looks to and the One she leans on."

Comforter adds, "I see that she returns cloaked in humility and consumed with devotion even in the midst of success and prosperity."

Squeezing Comforter's hand, I say, "Thank You, for Your

kind and encouraging words. You never cease to amaze me; You always lift me up and cover me with lovingkindness. How good it is to see You, my Friend. I have missed You greatly." I lay my head against His chest. His heart sounds exactly like my Beloved's, for Their heart does not beat like others. Their heartbeat sounds like many waters rushing over a precipice. It is the most calming sound I have ever heard and one that I cannot hear enough.

"There is no place like home," I whisper.

"You have come through the wilderness quite victorious, Lovely Lady," He says as He holds me ever so close.

"Comforter, I am weak, my feet are ruined, but I am in love! I have discovered that my strength lies in the knowledge of how awesome and powerful my Bridegroom is. I have done nothing, but my Beloved has done great exploits. I have merely walked the path He asked me to walk and done the things He asked me to do; nothing more and nothing less. And I have done so in the strength of His mercy and grace. I could talk of His love all day long and would never grow tired."

"You are successful because you are loved and you love. You have learned how to lean on your Beloved, Lovely Lady," Comforter answers.

The King turns to the Captain and says, "We will camp here for the night."

The Captain and his men quickly busy themselves with all that is involved in setting up camp and securing the area. Mercy and Goodness prepare the evening meal. My Beloved carries me to a smooth rock. Removing my sandals, He props my dirty feet on His lap. Wrapping His waist with a towel, He takes up a basin of water, which Comforter provides, then proceeds to wash my feet.

I am completely overwhelmed. This should not be; I should be the one washing His feet. "My King, you should not be washing my feet! "

I pull my feet away. He responds, "If I do not wash your feet, then you have no part with Me."

Quickly placing my feet back on His lap, I say, "Lord, if washing my feet allows me to have a part in Your life, then I say not my feet only, but also my hands and my head."[570]

Rhonda Calhoun

He smiles in response and says, "You are already clean."

Then proceeds to gently and tenderly wash away the caked dirt and blood. He gently dries my feet with the towel from around His waist. Taking a horn from His pouch, He pours oil over my blistered and cut feet. Then, ever so gently, wraps them with strips of cloth that He again tears from the bottom of His robe.

I am humbled and impacted to the core of my being by His lovingkindness. Once again, my Beloved placed Himself in the role of a servant and not of a King.

What kind of love is this that would pour itself out in this fashion and to this degree? It is a love that is not of this world, one that I long to possess.

He carefully props my feet up on His folded cloak and hurries away to bring me food and drink. Feeling quite hungry, I eagerly devour my meal. I am satisfied.

My Beloved carries me to my sleeping mat where He sits beside me, singing of His great love for me, His bride-to-be.

Chapter Thirty-six
FIERY SEAL OF LOVE

Put Me like a seal over your heart.

I sleep ever so peacefully and wake fully rested. My feet do not feel nearly as sore. After breakfast, we continue on our way.

Just before noon we have to stop because my feet are now throbbing. Sitting at the base of the Lebanon Mountains, the King unwraps the bandages. Looking up at the rugged terrain before me, I cannot imagine how my blistered, bleeding feet will ever make it to our lofty home.

My Beloved pours more oil over them. Tearing another strip from His garment, He says, "My love, remember that the purpose of the wilderness is to expose weakness. It is not meant to show you how strong you are, but rather how weak. You will never make it through this life without Me; I designed it that way. You need Me to guide you, to bind up your wounds, to heal your heart and save you.

"I do not call you to do what is possible, but to do the impossible. The impossible will always require faith and will require you to lean on Me, which is exactly what I desire. My grace will always be enough in every situation, and I will always help you.

Rhonda Calhoun

"So, rise up, My love, and let us climb this mountain. Let us do the impossible...together."

I proclaim, "I will not give up; I will not quit. I will rise up and go with You. I will pay the price in this life that I might have a crown to cast at Your feet in the next life. I know that You will strengthen me and hold me up, for You will not forsake me."

With renewed faith, we arrive at our mountain home just before sunset. My Beloved stops to allow me to rest by my favorite rock, which overlooks Hope Valley. Sitting beside me, He says, "I am the One who awakened your heart. I initiated everything. I sought you out and pursued you. I adorned you with beauty and grace. I sent My Spirit to prepare you. I surrounded you with angels to protect you. Mercy and Goodness have followed you and My Father has loved you. I am the One responsible for your growth and beauty. I fed you from My garden, bringing refreshment to your soul. I have been all you need.

"Always remember that the strength of your life is *not* your commitment to Me, but the strength of your life is *My* commitment to *you*.[571]

"I entrusted you to Comforter's care and to the care of My shepherds. They have taught you that it is vital to lean on Me, not just in seasons of adversity, but also in seasons of prosperity. And your reward is the power to love."[572]

He continues, "I am preparing you for what is to come. I will be going away, but I will not leave you alone. Comforter will be with you. You must put Me like a seal over your heart, which is the seat of your emotions and will. Put Me like a seal over your arm, which are your acts of service in the kingdom. Let Me be the seal that sets you apart, for My love is as strong as death and its flashes are flashes of fire; the very flame of the Lord."[573]

"Love is as strong as death, as strong as the grave," I repeat.

I think back to how my King gave up everything and laid aside His glory, in order to purchase me as His bride.

"How do I love like this?"

"See how I have inscribed your name in the palm of My hands." He lays His open hands before me.

I remember our betrothal celebration; my hands are still stained red and will be for as long as I live.

I trace the outline of each letter with my fingertips. He continues, "Just as your name is written in the palm of My hand, allow Comforter to inscribe My name in the very depths of your heart. Set Me as a seal upon your heart, as a seal upon your arm. My perfect love is the seal that creates wholehearted, fiery devotion for Me and wholehearted love for people, which are the first and second greatest commandments in My kingdom.[574]

Holding up His signet ring, He continues, "Whenever I seal an important document, I pour hot wax on it, firmly pressing My ring into it, which marks it as belonging to Me. From that moment on, I am bound to protect it and see that it is delivered safely to its destination. During this time, it remains under My authority and belongs to Me. The Captain and My mighty men help to protect all that bears My seal. You bear My seal; therefore, I am responsible to protect and deliver you safely to My Father on the day of our wedding.

"This seal is none other than My power and My love being released in the human heart. Your past victories are not the seal. Discipline over your flesh is not the seal. This seal is not a list of do's and don'ts, neither is it your past record of failures or accomplishments. This seal comes from Me and is progressive; it grows within you for the rest of your life.

"I desire ownership over not only your thoughts and your will, but also your emotions. You are a privately owned, locked garden, My love. You have been purchased and marked as Mine and no other is allowed entrance. Therefore, guard your gaze and protect your heart. You are My possession and My inheritance.

"Do not depend on anything other than Me—not horses, not chariots, not people, not gold, not even your gifts and talents. I want to be your source of life. I want you to look to Me as the One who protects your heart and your ministry. The strength you need must come from Me. I am your guarantee. I am the One who will keep and sustain you when you are victorious

Rhonda Calhoun

and when you are defeated. Victories can be as detrimental to you as defeat, for pride loves to jump on your back after a victory and condemnation often follows defeat. Run to Me when you succeed and run to Me when you fall. I will pick you up and wash you off."

I respond, "My spirit is willing, but my heart is so very weak. How will I ever live up to such a standard as this?"

"Get low and fall in love. Humble yourself, stay on your face before the King of Glory, for it is there, as you glimpse My face, that you will fall in love. In that place, Comforter will ignite your heart with greater love and greater desire, if you only ask."

Comforter stands with His hand on my shoulder even now. Looking into His kind eyes, I plead, "Comforter, I beg You to impart this Divine love into my spirit and into my heart that I might be completely transformed into my Beloved's image! I offer you my impressionable heart, a heart like wax, which awaits Your seal. Be the love that burns within; be the seal over who I am and all that I do!

"Apply the King's signet ring to my heart and press it hard, even if it means that I must suffer trials and hardships, for my King suffered greatly in becoming this seal for me. May all that I am and everything I do bear His seal that He may be glorified."[575]

Comforter responds, "Your King's love is as strong as death, is deeper than the deepest sea, and higher than the highest heavens.[576] Nothing escapes His love.

"Lovely Lady, this Bridegroom can be trusted completely and loved without reservation—for this is how He loves."

Turning my attention back to my Beloved, I say, "Give me Your love which is stronger than death that I might trust You completely and love You without reservation, that I might remain true to You while awaiting Your return."

My King answers, "I will give you this gift of love, which is like a fire. It consumes everything, the dross and the chaff within, and causes vehement passion in the soul.[577] My love is possessive. I do not want just a little part of you. I desire all of you, all the time. My fiery seal overcomes all disorderly affections. My love is holy, jealous and violent, possessing the soul.[578] I will not be a part-time Spouse and neither should you.

"Many waters cannot quench this love, nor will rivers overflow it. I am a consuming ocean of fiery love, which nothing can overcome—not obstacles, or temptations, or crises, or persecutions, or even death. Absolutely nothing is greater than My love. My love will enable you to repel and triumph over the temptations from the smiles of the world and also from its frowns."[579]

I tremble at His words.

He continues, "Fear not; I have redeemed you. I have called you by name; you are Mine! When you pass through the waters, I will be with you; and through the rivers, they will not overflow you. When you walk through the fire, you will not be scorched, nor will the flame burn you."[580]

Falling at His feet, I look up into His passionate eyes and respond, "I have been crucified with You; and it is no longer I who live, but You live in me. This life that I now live, I live by faith in the One who loved me and delivered Himself up for me.[581] My life is no longer centered around me. You are my center, my focus and I revolve around You."

Jumping to my feet, I exclaim, "I am Yours and Your desire is for me! I will no longer live focused on myself!"[582]

My voice echoes throughout the valley, returning to me several times. My Beloved and Comforter stand with Their eyes closed, not moving. No one speaks until the echoes of my voice ascend to the highest heavens. My King takes my hand and says, "Your devotion has pierced My heart, My bride."

Comforter takes my other hand and says, "Allow Me to tell you a story, Lovely Lady.

"There was a man who had a daughter who was sick and dying. He took her to the physician. After an examination, the doctor said, 'Your daughter will surely die without treatment, but the good news is that I have the skill and medicine needed to heal her. The bad news is that the treatment is very expensive. If you want her to live, you will have to sell everything you have, holding nothing back, then bring the money to me.'

"Without a second thought, the man hurried home to sell his every possession. The following day, he returned with

Rhonda Calhoun

the money and, true to his word, the physician healed his daughter.

"The weeks passed and word spread throughout the village about what this father had done. One day, while in the market, an old friend approached the father saying, 'I heard how you gave up everything for your daughter, and I would like to host a banquet in your honor. I will invite the elders of the city and shout from the rooftops the price you paid. '

"The father quickly lowered his head and replied, 'Dear friend, please don't mention what I have done. I've done nothing spectacular or heroic; I only did what was necessary to save my daughter whom I love so desperately. I would despise any recognition or praise shown to me because I did what I did for love and nothing more."[583]

Taking my hand, my Beloved asks, "Do you understand what Comforter is saying, My dove?"

"I think so, but maybe not."

Comforter explains, "This is a story of extravagant, sacrificial devotion flowing from a heart filled with love. Love is a gift, not a reward for service. My gift to you is the power to love like that father—you will not only love your Bridegroom with your whole heart, but you will also love others in the same way. When others try to praise you or draw attention to your life of sacrificial devotion, you will utterly despise it. Why? Because you live for Love, not for the recognition or applause of man."[584]

Looking deeply into my Beloved's eyes, I say, "I see clearly now what my life is all about—I was born to love You, to receive Your love and give it away. I will "waste" my life on You.

"I desire to lead others to You, my King. Do You remember Esther and the young girls who sat at my feet the night the two strangers surrendered their lives to You?"

"I remember them well," He answers.

"They love You, but are so young and immature that they do not yet understand that they may have a personal, intimate relationship with You.[585] I think of Esther, her heart is especially tender and eager to know Your love, my King. What can we do to help her?"[586]

"What do you think, My love?"

I take a moment to reflect, then answer, "Well, if Esther desires to shepherd Your people, then we will pour into her the ability to strengthen and encourage others based on the power of redemption.[587] But if she is a teacher or one who desires to bring others into the kingdom, then we will surround her with Your very presence and power."[588]

"Very good, but what if Esther is too weak and immature for even that? What if she still has areas of compromise in her life?" my Beloved asks.

"Then we will surround her with truth and love, protecting her until she matures and is able to surrender completely.[589] But if she is mature and strong, then we will build on her the truths of Your redemption and bridal love."[590]

"You have rightly spoken and have grown in wisdom and truth, My bride."

"I am who I am because of Your goodness and mercy, in spite of my weaknesses. You have made me like a wall, like a tower, so that I have been able to protect and sustain others. I have loved them with Your love. You have graced me with the ability to nurture and encourage others, and I have poured out my intercessions on their behalf.[591]

"In Your eyes, I have become as one who is highly favored. I now find my identity in You and not in my accomplishments. Everything I do is for You. I no longer struggle, but trust You to fulfill my destiny. I have no fear of man, but live for Your pleasure and delight. I fix my gaze on You and You alone.[592]

My Beloved lays His arm around Comforter's shoulder and says, "Look at her, My Friend. Is she not stunning? Her virtues and love are delightful. She has become so lovely and so pure of heart. My Bride grows in grace and beauty from glory to glory forevermore!"

"She is indeed most lovely, delighting the very heart of God!" Comforter responds.

"My Bridegroom, it is You who is altogether beautiful and I will tell all who will listen until the day I die," I say, standing. I feel no pain; I have no fear. "My Beloved, I am fully Yours according to the covenant You made with me. I know that Your desire is for me. You treasure me and You are mine in every way. For the remainder of my life, I will fix my gaze upon the King who wore a crown of thorns that I might wear a crown of glory."

Taking His hand in mine, I continue, "I will crown You again one day, but next time I will crown You with a crown of pure devotion, for You provide all this poor soul will ever need."

My Beloved exclaims, "I am in love with you!"

"And I am in love with You!" I reply.

Neither of us move. We are lost in pure love, One with the other. Unaware of anything but Him, I close my eyes. Suddenly, I feel the sharpest of pains. I look down and see that my chest is open and my heart has been removed. It lays on an altar nearby, bloody and consumed by disease and selfishness. I suddenly realize there is nothing I can do to save myself; I am hopeless. Desperate, I cry out, "I cannot live without a heart! Is there anyone who can help me?"

Just seconds later, I hear a sound behind me like that of fine crystal being tapped. I turn and see a beautiful golden heart on another altar. This heart is highly polished like a mirror and is absolutely flawless. It is gold yet it is alive! Never have I ever seen anything like it. *I would love to have a heart like that!*

Comforter steps into my vision and cradles the golden heart in His hand. Glancing my way, His eyes ask the million dollar question, "Would you like this heart?"

Who would be so foolish as to refuse something so valuable, so rare, so perfect? I cannot speak, but merely nod.

In response, He places the heart into my empty chest. The moment he does, eternal Life and perfect Love fill me. Joy overwhelms me. Giddy, I run and twirl and dance saying, "I am alive! I am saved! I am free!"

But then something catches my attention. I hear something. *What . . . who is it?* I turn around just as my Beloved picks up my dead, cold, shriveled heart; a diseased heart consumed by greed, selfishness, apathy and sin. Yet, He holds it as if it is the finest of treasures. I suddenly realize what He is about to do and everything in me wants to stop Him, but I am unable to move, unable to speak.

This is not fair! Why should He take my sin-filled heart into

His sinless being? I am the one who is the criminal, not Him. I am the one who deserves to die, not Him.

I step forward; He steps back. I reach out to Him. He looks into my questioning eyes. In doing so, I see the depth, the height, the width, and the length of His love for me, His bride. I understand, should He not make this Divine exchange, it would be much more painful to Him than the momentary sting He will feel in doing so.

With a nod of His head, He smiles and then places my lifeless heart into the gaping hole in His chest. My cold, lifeless heart looks so small, so pitiful and so completely out of place within His glorious, perfect being. With a final nod, He turns and walks away saying, "For the joy set before Me."

Where is He going? There are two paths before Him. He chooses the one that leads to a hilltop.

Time seems to stand still. I collapse on the ground and wait. Suddenly, deep, deep darkness surrounds me. The ground shakes violently beneath me and my entire being trembles. That is when I hear His cry, "Father, forgive them for they don't know what they are doing!"

I lay face down on the ground. *Perfect Love is dying for me. Oh, how can it be?*

Again, His voice fills heaven and earth, "Father, it is finished....into Your hands I commit My Spirit!"

Nothing can be heard except silence. The Divine exchange has been made; it is complete. I live because He died. I am free because He was bound. I am perfect because He became flawed. I will ascend because He descended. I am complete because He was emptied.

My Beloved no longer lives. It is finished; or so I think.

It is the morning of the third day when the ground shakes once more. Thick, white clouds surround me. Out of a cloud steps my King! He is even more beautiful than before. His robe is torn; I see that He has a large gaping hole in His side.

'Tell me of your wound, my Friend," I say, as tears fill my eyes.

"This wound is the wound of perfect Love. It has served its purpose, for it has made the way for My bride to enter the

Rhonda Calhoun

heart of her Father. Because of this wound, she will be perfect, and without spot, wrinkle or blemish."

I feel drawn into the opening. "Come, My bride. You may now enter the very heart of God," He says, His arms spread wide.

I step into His side and travel deep into His perfect heart. I am lost in His fiery, jealous love. My sins are consumed and will never be seen again. Gold is being formed within me. I begin to shine like the Son and find myself thinking only the purest of thoughts and feeling only the holiest of emotions. O, how glorious, how beautiful the loving heart of God makes one to be!

Suddenly, the hand of my Father reaches in and draws me out. He places me on a Rock. I am dressed in the finest white linen and prepared as a bride for her Husband. My Father asks, "Do you really love Me? Are you really loyal? Do you truly trust Me? From whose hand do you eat and drink? Where do you go for comfort?"

I answer, "My answer is yes! For the rest of my life, I will feed at Your table and drink from Your hand. I will run to You when I am sad, mad or glad, when I am guilty, stubborn and feeling prideful. I will go to You alone for everything, my God and my King!"

"I will pour out My Spirit without measure on the people whose single-minded devotion, love and loyalty are given to the Lord."

"Make me one of those," I whisper.

I open my eyes. My Beloved and Comforter are standing over me. "Was I dreaming?" I ask, somewhat shaken.

My Beloved responds, "My love, you were not dreaming. I merely opened your spiritual eyes to see what is and what was and what is to come."

He lays His hand on my shoulder. I am instantly calm. He continues, "God reached into Adam, the first man created, and, as he slept, He removed his bride from the opening in his side. I, like Adam, slept and My Father reached into the opening in My side and removed My bride.

"It is real! What I saw was real!" Glory fills my soul. "Isn't He lovely! Isn't He beautiful! Isn't He wonderful!" I sing.

Comforter exclaims, "Isn't she lovely! Isn't she beautiful!

Isn't she wonderful!"

My Beloved looks like One who is perfectly content and fully satisfied.

I turn to my Beloved and say, "Shall we continue on our journey? We have much to do and much to see! After all, I have a new heart and can't wait to try it out!"

Chuckling, He answers, "By all means." With the greatest of ease, He lifts me in His arms and carries me to our wonderful home. Mercy meets us at the front door. Upon seeing my blistered and bleeding feet, she cries out, "Child, what have you done?"

"Mercy, I have done nothing. It is my Bridegroom who has accomplished this work of love. I have merely gone the way of the cross. I have walked the same path my Beloved walked, and I have never been happier, for I have a new heart!"

"It is obvious that your path has been the way of the King. Come, let me tend to your feet, child."

Within minutes, she has my feet soaking in very warm water. Goodness brings herbs from the garden adding them to the bowl. The herbs ease the pain and disinfect the wound.

After a good soaking, she carefully dries them and rubs salve over them. Mercy finishes her task by wrapping my feet with strips of white cloth that Comforter provides. And all the while, my Beloved looks on.

His face reflects His obvious pleasure.

Rhonda Calhoun

Chapter Thirty-seven
MY VINEYARD

My very own vineyard is at my disposal.[593]

The following morning, eager to meet the day, I carefully place my bandaged feet on the floor, To my surprise, there is no pain. Removing the wrappings, I am overjoyed to discover that my feet are completely healed!

The King has healed me...again!

Remembering the precious gift that beats within, I run my hand over my chest.

I have a new heart, and not just any heart, but the heart of the King! O, what a glorious day this is going to be!

Skipping breakfast, I run through the orchard anxious to see how the children are and how my vineyard is doing. Upon reaching the clearing, I come to an abrupt stop. I can not believe my eyes! All of the vines that Comforter and I planted have not only budded, but are heavy-laden with huge clusters of grapes!

How can this be? These plants are barely a year old! This is impossible!

Seeing Comforter walking among the vines, I run after Him asking, "Comforter, what has happened? How is this possible?"

Rhonda Calhoun

"Lovely, isn't she?"

"But, how did the vines grow so fast, Comforter? This is not possible."

"This vineyard, Lovely Lady, is a picture of the kingdom and also of you. See how fruitful you have become in such a short time."

Laying His hand under my chin and lifting my face, He smiles. "The vine has budded and its blossoms have opened. Your vineyard brings forth much fruit.[594] You have taken excellent care of your heart, Lovely Lady, and have nurtured your relationship with the King."[595]

Comforter's words are like water to my thirsty soul. "*You* worked a miracle in my heart, Comforter," I respond.

"This miracle was birthed out of the 'yes' in your heart, Lovely Lady. If you had chosen to go your own way none of this would be possible. Salvation into this kingdom is always a partnership. Yes, your Beloved paid the price for your entrance, but He never forces anyone to accept it," He says, handing me a cluster of the deep purple grapes.

"O, Comforter, they are so sweet and full of flavor! I believe these are the best grapes I've ever tasted!"

"I would have to agree."

"And what of the precious orphans? How are they?" I ask, turning towards the houses we built.

"Come and see for yourself."

We walk through the vineyard and just before we come to the clearing, I hear the musical sound of children laughing. Tears pool in my eyes. I look at Comforter. He, too, has tears filling His eyes.

As we step into the clearing, numerous children of various ages run and play and laugh with my dear, dear Father, the Ancient of Days. I watch for a long time just absorbing the scene.

Comforter whispers, "See how He loves them! See how He cares!"

"I see," I whisper in response, my voice breaking.

A little girl, not more than three years old, falls and skins her knee. Father immediately runs to her side, scooping her up in His big, strong arms and kisses her cute little face. With just a touch of His hand, the knee is instantly healed. He puts her down, after she plants a big, wet kiss on His cheek.

I turn to Comforter and say, "As much as I would like to stay, I can't, for I must find my Beloved. It is time to present our gift to Him."

"Before you go, I have something to give you."

We walk to the edge of the vineyard where He opens a rather large chest. "This is the fruit of your labors, Lovely Lady. I sold some of your grapes."

"How can this be?" I ask, looking at the numerous money bags filling the chest. I open one and see that it is filled with silver coins.

"This treasure represents your service to the King. You are much more beautiful and fruitful than you know, Lovely Lady."

"Would You keep charge of this money for me, please?"

"Of course."

I run a short distance, then turn and shout, "O, Comforter, I cannot contain my excitement a moment longer; I must find my Beloved!"

Running as fast as I can, I find the King sitting among the sheep in a nearby pasture. "Good King, will You come with me? Your gift is ready!"

"And what is this gift?"

"I shall not tell You. You must come and see," I answer.

"Then let us be off," He responds, chuckling.

We hurry through the garden and into the orchard. My excitement grows to unbearable proportions; I am chattering about anything and everything. As we are nearly through the orchard, I run ahead to make certain that my vineyard is still full of ripe grapes. Relieved to see that it looks the same, I run back to His side more excited than ever.

Laughing, He asks, "So, tell me, what is this gift that has you so excited, My love?"

"It is a secret. You must be patient — patience is something to be desired, You know," I answer playfully.

"Yes, patience is something I know well. After all, I have been waiting for My bride for what seems like an eternity," He

Rhonda Calhoun

says, reaching out for my hand.

"You grow lovelier every day, My dove. I remember when you were but a child, and now look at you—your love has matured and you have come to know Me in the most intimate way. Your devotion to Me and others is consistently filled with sacrificial love. You died with Me so that you could live with Me! What a glorious bride you are!"

"And what a glorious King You are!"

We step out of the orchard stopping just this side of the vineyard. The sun casts its golden light on my Beloved's face. He stares at the natural beauty before us, but my gaze is fixed on Him.

As stunning as our surroundings are, my Beloved is so much more glorious. As bright as the sun is, my Beloved is so much more radiant. The birds fill the air with heavenly songs, but one word from His mouth transforms my life. The grass is green and the flowers are stunning, but the King is more desirable than them all! O, how good and how perfect He is!

"I love You," I whisper.

He faces me and says, "And I love you with an everlasting, all consuming love."

Kissing my forehead, He whispers, "I infinitely love you."

I stand amazed at this King. "I will never understand how You, my King, could love me so."

"You are easy to love, for I created you! Can an artist despise his greatest masterpiece? Can a musician reject his best piece of music? Can a writer throw out his best loved story? Can a singer despise her voice?

"They might, but I never would. I am the One who formed you and chose you. I delight in loving you."

"Your ways are so far beyond my comprehension. I will never understand how You can see such tremendous value in weak, flawed human beings," I respond.

"You are part of Me and always will be. I have waited for you since before the foundation of the world. You are My Masterpiece, the love of My life, the jewel in My crown, the beat in My heart. You are My dream come true!"

I stare into His eyes, drinking of eternity.

His love and compassion has no beginning and no end.

"As a child, I believed that You, the King, were You too holy to be approached and never dreamed of this day. You are amazing!"

"Now, what was that about a surprise?" He asks.

I tug on His hand and answer, "I trust You fully. I give You *my* garden, *my* life. From this moment on, it is no longer mine. From this day forward, it is *Your* garden. May my Beloved come into *His* garden and eat from its choice fruits! I fully surrender to You."[596]

I escort Him over the top of the hill. Stretching out as far as the eye can see is the vineyard. It lays before us, mature and heavy-laden with fruit. On its perimeter are cottages for the children.

Trembling with excitement, I say, "With Comforter's help, I planted grape vines in the field that You gave me. We tended it well that I might have something of value to give You.[597] We built homes for orphans because every child should have someone to call 'mom' and 'dad'.

"Today, I give You my life and all that it holds. I give You everything I have and all that I am or ever will be."

My Bridegroom surveys the vineyard and homes. His face reflects His emotions; He is more than pleased. "What a wonderful, wonderful gift — the gift of a surrendered heart, a fruitful life!" He exclaims.

Comforter approaches, saying, "She has grown to be extremely beautiful and ever so fruitful, has she not?"

"Indeed she has. You have excelled in making her so," the Bridegroom replies.

"All that We do, We do for love," Comforter responds.

"Well said!" He says.

The three of us walk down the hill to the vineyard. Unable to contain my excitement any longer, I run ahead and quickly choose the choicest of grapes. Like a child with a prized gift, I run back and offer them to my Beloved, saying, "They are pleasant to the eye and sweet to the taste."

"A good tree cannot produce bad fruit, can it? Grapes are not gathered from thorn bushes are they?" He says as He

Rhonda Calhoun

pops a grape in His mouth.[598]

Interlocking His fingers with mine, He says, "I am taking possession of *My* garden. Your gift of love exhilarates My soul and I am strengthened."

Holding a grape up to the sunlight, He says, "You can tell if a tree is good or bad by its fruit."

I hold my breath as He inspects the grape. Nothing escapes His keen eyes.

"Your fruit of your life is good, My love. I am satisfied."[599]

"O, that I could give You this and so much more. I long to give You something that would adequately demonstrate my great love and gratitude for all that You are to me," I respond.

"You have given Me your voluntary love and that is what I most desire."

Taking my hand, He says, "Come and enjoy the fruit of your labors."

Comforter walks before us. My Beloved hands me a grape, saying, "I am the Vine and you are the branches. If you abide in Me and I in you, then you will bear much fruit. Apart from Me, you can do nothing. If you abide in Me, and My words abide in you, ask whatever you wish, and it shall be done for you."[600]

I ponder His words as we walk in silence through the entire vineyard. Then we walk the perimeter, stopping at each house so that He can greet each family. The children are thrilled to meet the King.

As we say farewell to the last family, my Beloved takes my hands and says, "I accept your gift and your life and I offer you Mine in return."

"And I accept!"

We are headed back home when I see a family dressed in rags camping in the furthermost edges of the orchard.

"May we go to them?" I ask.

"I would have it no other way, My dove."

A little girl plays in the dirt near the tent. She sees us and fear fills her eyes. She quickly runs and hides behind her mother's skirt. Peering out from her place of safety, she watches us. I can see pain in her eyes.

I introduce myself to the girl's mother and father.

Discovering that they have not eaten in several days, I look around for my Beloved, but discover that He and Comforter have disappeared.

I must do something; I just can't let them go hungry. What should I do, Father?

An idea pops into my head. "The King owns a vineyard just past this orchard. Why don't we go and pick some grapes? And when I get home, I'll send you food from our garden."

They were a bit hesitant, but after I convinced them that the King would not mind they agreed.

As we work side by side, filling several baskets, I tell them about the Bridegroom King.

The little girl's father responds, "I have heard of this King, but having never met Him or anybody who knew Him, I didn't believe that He was real. If He is real and if He is as kind as you say, then do you suppose He would accept someone like me into His family?"

"Of course He would!"

"But I'm not like you; I've made a lot of wrong choices and I am just a poor man with nothing to offer. I'm a simple man without job or home. I've lost everything except my family, and I fear that I may lose them if I can't feed them."

Holding back the tears, I answer, "I know the King will more than accept you; He accepted me when I was nothing more than a peasant with a divided heart. He is eager for all to come to Him and never rejects anyone. The only person who cannot come to the King is the person who refuses to do so."

Hearing a sound behind me, I turn and nearly jump out of my skin because the King is standing directly behind me. Without saying a word this father falls at my Beloved's feet. His wife soon joins him. Between sobs, they confess their need for a Savior. My Beloved lovingly responds, "Your sins are forgiven. Now come, and follow Me."

He then leads them to a cozy cottage just on the far side of the orchard. The little girl, whose name is Ruth, no longer timid, skips alongside, holding tightly to my hand.

What a joy it is to be able to lead others to my Bridegroom King and to watch Him embrace them with life-changing love!

Rhonda Calhoun

I look up and see Comforter standing in the open door of the cottage with His arms open wide. I remember the day when my Beloved led me to a cottage very much like this one, and Comforter welcomed me into my new home. Tears fill my eyes, for I know the joys and delights awaiting this precious family.

Walking home hand in hand with my Beloved, who loves rich and poor, old and young, friends and enemies, I cannot help but wonder at His endless love and kindness.

How did One so good and so pure ever come to love me so completely?

I do not understand, but I will never forget how far my Beloved has brought me, for one who is forgiven much, loves much. I will always remember how deep the pit was that He drew me out of.

O, how I love my Bridegroom and how I love being His friend and partner![601]

The following morning, I wake to the sound of furious activity outside my window. I quickly dress. Running out, I see that the Captain has saddled the horses. Goodness and Mercy wait nearby. My Beloved steps out from around the corner of the house, singing. Before I can ask, He answers, "It is time for us to go, My love. We have much to do and very little time."

Comforter walks up with my bags in hand.

"Where are we going?" I ask.

"That remains to be seen, Lovely Lady," Comforter answers.

In less than an hour, we are on our way. Riding beside my Beloved, I ask, "Is there anything wrong in the village?"

"There are great needs in the village just as there are in every place, My love. But, that is not where we are going. We are headed to a vineyard in Baal-hamon where many from My kingdom have gathered."

"What will we do there?" I ask.

"We will speak the truth and shower them with My love. We will show them Who I am and who they are, for most people live in ignorance of both. Few in My kingdom understand that I am a Bridegroom and that they are destined to rule and reign with Me as My bride. I am a Bridegroom King who desires a partner in both this life and the one tò come.

"Many know Me as a Shepherd and a Savior, but there is so much more to Me than that. I am a King who longs for intimacy, just as the Ancient of Days is a Father who longs for a family."

We ride for quite some time in silence as I meditate on His words. Comforter comes alongside me and I ask, "How can we explain to those outside the kingdom just how wonderful and majestic the King is?"

"You will show them, Lovely Lady. They will watch your devotion, your dedication and your sacrificial lifestyle, which will cause many to desire to know Him as you do. Just focus on loving your King with all your heart, soul, strength and all your mind, and love others in the same way as I have loved you."

"You are good at what You do, Comforter."

"That is because I am perfect Love," He answers.

When we arrive at the vineyard, I am surprised to see that a great multitude is camped all around its perimeters. I have never seen so many people in one place. I suddenly feel extremely nervous and quickly whisper a prayer for help.

Over the course of the next seven days, the King and I move from camp to camp speaking with and expressing our love to the people. It is true that many do not understand that the Shepherd they serve is also their Bridegroom King. We also find many among the crowd who have never met my Shepherd. It is such a delight to share the good news with them and watch the transformation that happens after being embraced by the great King of all the ages.

This morning we are ministering to the last group. I am already excited about sharing the good news, but when I see my friends from my home village, joy floods my soul. Like a child, I run from person to person, hugging and kissing them. Just when I think everyone has been greeted, I see Martha sitting cross-legged on the grass just a short distance away. Close by her side are two little girls.

Hurrying over, she looks up just before I reach her. I fall on my knees before her. Her face is filled with peace and her eyes sparkle with joy. We hug, laugh and cry all at the same

Rhonda Calhoun

time. Once we are somewhat composed, I ask, "Martha, who are these precious little girls?"

"I would like you to meet Rachel and Sarah, my adopted daughters," she says, smiling from ear to ear.

I lean down and say, "And what pretty girls you are!"

They giggle and hide behind their mother. Hearing someone call my name, I turn. Esther is running toward me with arms open wide. She runs right into my arms, knocking me over. I fall onto the grass with Esther tumbling on top of me. We laugh and hug and laugh and hug some more.

Esther sits up and brushes back the hair from her face. Martha chuckles as she announces, "And you have just been tackled by my other daughter, Esther."

"You adopted Esther, too! O, how wonderful!"

Esther quickly sits on her mother's lap. Clapping her hands, she announces, "Our prayers worked! I now have the best mother in the whole, wide world!"

"And your mother has the best daughter in the whole, wide world," I add.

I grab Martha's hand, tears filling my eyes. "I am so very happy for you, dear friend."

"I never thought I'd ever love again, but look at me; my cup runs over," she says surrounded by happy little faces.

The King approaches and Martha runs to meet Him. He holds her in a long, tender embrace. Martha's three daughters, unable to wait any longer, "attack" Him all at once, and they all tumble to the ground, laughing and squealing with delight.

Once the girls run off to play, our King stands and says, "Martha, taking care of orphans is My definition of pure and undefiled religion."[602]

"It is my delight to love these little ones. They have brought me great joy and much healing," Martha answers.

"It is indeed a delight; one that will last for all eternity," He replies.

Just before lunch, David gathers everyone under the shade of the nearby trees. We hurry to join him. My Beloved stands before the crowd and motions for me to speak. I speak of His great love and tell them of His tender mercies.

I stand before them in weakness, but realize that my words are delivered with great authority and power.

I end by saying, "The King has a vineyard in Baal-hamon This vineyard is you and I. We have been given the incredible honor and privilege of being entrusted as caretakers of this vineyard. Each of us has been instructed to cultivate the soil and tend the vines. As we faithfully use our gifts and talents in His vineyard, we will see His kingdom prosper and will present Him a fruitful harvest. Our harvest is not measured by how many people respond to our message or ministry, but rather by the faithfulness of our hearts.[603]

"The Lord has entrusted to every believer certain gifts and talents for which we will give an account."[604]

Looking into the faces of friends and strangers, I continue, "It is not our gifts and talents that cause us to be fruitful or determine our reward, but it is our willingness to say 'yes' to whatever He should ask and walk with Him wherever He leads.

"When I first began my journey with the Master Shepherd, I did not take care of my own vineyard, my own heart. I was so busy trying to please others that I neglected my relationship with the King. I longed for the approval of men, which caused me to pursue worldly things. In doing so, I neglected to pursue my Beloved.

"I soon grew weak and gave into Compromise, which thrust me into a pit of despair and hopelessness. But, my gracious Shepherd rescued me. He brought me to a place where I could learn to love Him without being distracted. It was there that I came to know Him intimately. There He restored me. Everyone else, myself included, saw me as dark, but He convinced me that I was lovely. His lovingkindness has made me not only beautiful, but also fruitful."

I turn to Comforter to ask for the chest of silver and see it sitting by His feet.

Comforter is amazing! He is always one step ahead of me and always knows exactly what I need and when I need it.

I remove all but two of the leather pouches. Placing them at my Beloved's feet, I say, "My very own vineyard is before me. My future is secure because of You. I have tremendous

Rhonda Calhoun

opportunities for loving others, and I will spend my life doing so.[605] Here, my King, are one thousand shekels. I give them to You. Everything I have is Yours, and I choose to extravagantly pour out my life for Your sake. I have given You my full devotion and obedience knowing that one day I will stand before You to give a full account of all that has been entrusted to my care. I desire to waste my life on You. These coins are for You, my King, for You have made me fruitful."[606]

Picking up the last two pouches, I walk over to David and say, "I have learned the importance of submitting to those the King places over my life. Comforter taught me that we are to give honor to whom honor is due. These coins are for you, David." I hand him the two pouches, which contain two hundred shekels.

He receives them with great joy.

I return to my Beloved's side.

Smiling, He says, "My bride, you dwell in the gardens among My people rather than in isolation. You love not only Me, but also those near and far. You have truly become My partner as we have run together on the hills and on the mountains.

"There are many who need to hear what you have to say. Your voice is no longer an echo, but has become My voice. When you speak, remember that you are speaking primarily to an audience of One and that is Me."[607]

He takes my hand and continues, "My darling, you came to love Me in private, in My garden where you grew in grace and beauty while gazing on My face. Now that you will be spending more time in the world among the people, remember to speak with Me often and listen for My still, small voice. Your greatest battle will always be maintaining intimacy with Me. Do not ever become so busy that you forget the One Who loved you first and loves you most. You are always welcome in My garden, and I will meet with you there anytime."

He turns to the watching crowd and says, "This is My commandment, that you love one another, just as I have loved you. Greater love has no one than this, that one lay down his life for his friends. You are My friends, if you do what I command you.

"You did not choose Me, but I chose you. I appointed

you that you should go and bear fruit and that your fruit should remain. Whatever you ask of the Father in My name, He will give to you. This I command you, that you love one another. If you want others to know that you are My disciples, then love one another even as I have loved you."[608]

Looking back at me, He says, "It is time, My bride; I must go and prepare a place for you."[609]

Sorrow fills my heart at His words. "Must You go?"

Gently squeezing my hand, He asks, "My darling, My perfect one, do you love Me?"

"O, my Beloved, You know all things. You know that I love You."

"Then feed My lambs, shepherd My flock and take care of My sheep."[610]

He speaks with such tenderness and love that I fall at His feet. My heart aches knowing that He is about to leave for what sounds like a long time. I ache for the day when I will never again be separated from my beloved Bridegroom King.

He says, "Truly, truly, I say to you, whoever believes in Me, the works that I do, they will do also; and greater works than these shall they do because I go away."[611]

"Because You are going away, we will do greater works than You did?" I ask, completely perplexed.

"It is true," He answers. Laying His hand on my shoulder, He continues, "My peace I leave with you. My peace I give to you, not as the world gives do I give to you. Let not your heart be troubled or fearful, for I will surely come back for you."[612]

He turns, but suddenly stops. I reach up and take His hand. My eyes plead with Him to stay. "In my Father's house are many dwelling places; I go to prepare a place for you. I will come again and take you back to My Father's house that where I am, there you may be also."[613]

"But my Beloved, I still don't understand why it must be this way. Why must You go to prepare a place for me? Your Father has a grand palace in Hope Valley and the home You built for me on the high places is better than anything I have ever dreamed of. I am perfectly content; I do not need anything more than You. Please, do not go. Stay here with me," I plead.

His eyes are filled with compassion as He looks at me. He says, "I tell you the truth, it is to your advantage that I go away. I am only one Person and can only be in one place at a time. If I go, My Father will send Comforter to live within you and He won't be limited to one physical body, but will be in each of you, empowering you to do the works of the kingdom."[614]

Taking a deep breath, I look into His wonderful eyes and say, "From the first day that I met You, You never once focused on my weaknesses or failures; You never even mentioned them. Instead, You only spoke of my beauty and incredible value. You spoke into existence what was not. Your unconditional love is making me the bride You said I would be. I owe You my everything. I will tend Your vines and love Your sheep, but all the while I will be longing and watching for Your return. You are my first Love and always will be."

Wiping the tears from my cheeks, He responds, "My kingdom is like ten virgins who took their lamps and went out to meet their Bridegroom. Five of them were foolish and five were wise. For when the foolish took their lamps, they took no oil with them, but the wise took extra flasks of oil along with their lamps.

"Now when the Bridegroom took longer to arrive than they expected, they all became drowsy and soon fell asleep. At midnight there was a shout, 'Behold, the Bridegroom! Come out to meet Him!'

"The virgins rose and trimmed their lamps. The foolish said to the wise, 'Give us some of your oil, for our lamps are going out.'

"But the wise answered, saying, 'No, there will not be enough for us and you. Go instead to the dealers and buy some for yourselves.'

"And while they were going away to make the purchase, the Bridegroom came and those who were ready went in with Him to the wedding feast and the door was shut. Later, the other virgins came, saying, 'Lord, Lord, open the door for us.' But He answered and said, 'Truly I say to you, I do not know you.'"

Taking my hand, He raises me up, saying, "Live your life

like the five wise virgins.[615] Stay in a close, intimate relationship with Me so that your life will be filled with a love that is 'oil-based'. If someone throws water on an oil-based fire, instead of putting it out, it spreads the flame. This kind of love cannot be quenched or overcome.[616]

"In My presence, you will find an inexhaustible source of fragrant oil, which will keep you in the midst of peace or persecution, riches or poverty, comfort or tragedy, whether I return tomorrow or delay for a long season.[617] While I am away, Comforter will remind you of all that I have said and done."[618]

Tenderly kissing my forehead, He looks to heaven and prays, "Father, I do not ask on behalf of these alone, but for all who shall come after them, those who shall believe in Me through them. I ask that they may all be one; even as You, Father, are in Me and I in You, that the world may believe that You sent Me.[619]

"Father, I desire that those You have given Me may be with Me where I am, that they may behold My glory, which You have given Me."[620]

He steps away; I hold to His hand as long as possible. With a final wave, He says, "Farewell, My sister, My bride, My darling, My dove, My perfect one!"[621]

I watch Him go. Tears pour down my face. Already longing for His return, I cry out, "Make haste, my Beloved, and run on the mountains of spices like the gazelle; run like a young stag that allows itself to be seen from time to time, for my thirsty soul will never be fully satisfied until You have come and all sin is destroyed and all corruption has been removed."[622]

A gust of wind hits me; I brace myself against its onslaught. My Beloved stops and looks back. I see the love in His eyes. *O, how I will miss those eyes!*

I run a short distance toward Him and shout, "You are my King, and I will bow my knee to none other!"

Suddenly, the clouds part before my very eyes and my beautiful Bridegroom King, shining like the sun, ascends into the heavens. I fall to my knees transfixed.

"Make haste, my Beloved, and return,"[623] I whisper.

"Behold, I come quickly!" He announces.[624]

My King then disappears in a cloud of glory.

Suddenly, two men in white clothing appear beside me, one on each side. "Why do you stand looking into the sky?" they ask.

A thousand questions fill my mind, but I ask none of them.

The men say, "This Jesus, Who has been taken into heaven, will return in the same way as He left."[625]

"And when will He return?" I ask, thinking that surely heavenly beings would know. Hearing no answer, I look to my right and to my left, but they are nowhere to be seen.

Turning to Comforter, I ask, "When will my Beloved return?"

Taking my hand in His, He replies, "Only the Father knows, Lovely Lady; only the Father knows."[626]

"I will betroth you to Me forever;
Yes, I will betroth you to Me
in righteousness and in justice,
in lovingkindness and in compassion,
And I will betroth you to Me in faithfulness.
Then you will know the LORD."

Hosea 2:19

"For I am jealous for you with a godly jealousy,
for I betrothed you to one husband,
so that to Christ I might present you as a pure virgin."

2 Corinthians 11:2

Let us rejoice and be glad
and give the glory to Him,
for the marriage of the Lamb has come
and His bride has made herself ready."

Revelation 19:7

"He who testifies of these things says,
"Yes I am coming quickly!"

Revelation 22:11

Rhonda Calhoun

An Invitation
*Jesus loves you and desires to spend eternity with **you**!*

To better understand the longing in God's heart for a personal relationship with you, it is helpful to think in terms of a wedding proposal. Whether the man is proposing to the woman or the woman to the man, if both parties do not say 'yes', the marriage never happens.

Jesus said 'yes' in the Garden of Gethsemane. He said 'yes' on the cross, becoming the bridal price required for us to enter into a covenant with the King of kings. This covenant is a spiritual union that will last for all eternity.

Whether male or female, old or young, rich or poor, the Son of God desires to be your Savior, your Redeemer, your King and your Bridegroom. He excludes no one from this eternal partnership. He desires relationship, not dictatorship. He will not go against your will. He will not force you. Why? Because that would not be love!

The God of the universe loves you so much that He paid the bridal price for you and that price was the life of His Son. He has given us a gift that we do not deserve and could never earn.

If you have never accepted His invitation to become part of God's family, now is the perfect time. He is waiting for you right now, right where you are. The beauty of this invitation is that He doesn't expect you to 'clean up your act' before coming to Him. He accepts you just as you are; He loves sinners. After all, sinners are the ones He died for.

Don't wait until tomorrow, tomorrow may never be. Eternity is forever and there are no fences to straddle there. Either you spend eternity with a beautiful, glorious, kind Father, His Son and the Holy Spirit, or you will spend it with an evil, accusing, tormenting adversary named Satan. Which will you choose? It is your choice. Will you choose life? Think long and hard, for this is the most important decision you will ever make in this life.

You can know Him just as the shepherdess did. You can have an intimate, personal relationship with the King of kings. He invites you today to become part of His family, to enter into a covenant relationship with Him like unto a marriage.

It all begins with a 'yes'. Talk to Him just as you would a friend. He loves the sound of your voice. Tell Him what you feel. Tell Him that you need a Savior. Ask Him to forgive your sins and fill you with His Holy Spirit and then tell someone about the decision you made to live for Him. Romans 10:9-10 reads, "If you confess with your mouth Jesus as Lord, and believe in your heart that God raised Him from the dead, you shall be saved; for with the heart man believes, resulting in righteousness, and with the mouth he confesses, resulting in salvation."

It is important that you find a group of people that loves Jesus Christ and each other. They will help you. I encourage you to also read the Bible, for it is, among other things, our King's love letter to you, His bride.

Perhaps, you are one who said 'yes' to Jesus in your past, but you are not walking with Him right now. You can start over. You can renew your commitment to Him today. He loves you and is eagerly waiting to welcome you back into His home without any condemnation or guilt or shame. He will set you free from your past mistakes and sins.

"If we confess our sins, He is faithful and righteous to forgive us our sins and to cleanse us from all unrighteousness." (I John 1:9).

Not only are you forgiven, but you are also cleansed, made pure and spotless, white as snow. It is not too late. You haven't gone too far. Come home to perfect Love and true freedom. Let the King wash you today.

Father, I pray that You would grant each reader the grace to know You intimately and live for you completely. Kiss them with kisses of Your mouth as they read Your word. Transform them into Your image that they might look like You and live like You lived. Capture everything in their lives that would keep them from fiery devotion to the King of kings, the Lord of lords. Hold them close and pour out Your Holy Spirit on them this day, I pray.

It is in the precious name of our Messiah, our Bridegroom King that we pray. Amen.

Rhonda Calhoun

ENDNOTES

1 Song of Solomon 1:4b
2 Matthew 5:45
3 Song of Solomon 1:2a
4 Song of Solomon 1:2b
5 Song of Solomon 1:3a
6 Song of Solomon 1:3b
7 Matthew 25:1-13
8 Song of Solomon 1:3c
9 Song of Solomon 1:4a
10 Song of Solomon 1:4b
11 Genesis 3:22; Revelation 22:2
12 John 17:24
13 Hebrews 13:8
14 Song of Solomon 1:4c
15 Psalm 27:4

16 Song of Solomon 1:2b
17 Song of Solomon 1:2b

18 Song of Solomon 1:6d
19 Song of Solomon 1:6d
20 Song of Solomon 1:6c
21 Song of Solomon 2:15

22 Song of Solomon 1:6b
23 Song of Solomon 1:6c, d
24 Matthew 24:12

25 Song of Solomon 1:7 d, e

26 Song of Solomon 4:6
27 Psalm 23:2
28 Song of Solomon 1:6c
29 Song of Solomon 2:1b
30 Luke 7:37-38
31 Song of Solomon 1:6a
32 Song of Solomon 1:6b
33 Isaiah 61:10
34 Psalm 103:12
35 Hebrews 6:18
36 Lamentations 3:22-25

CHAPTER SIX: DARK BUT LOVELY—page 43

37 Song of Solomon 1:5a
38 'mother' represents the church, which gives birth to the bride
39 church leadership
40 Song of Solomon 1:6
41 Song of Solomon 1:5c
42 Song of Solomon 1:5d
43 Song of Solomon 1:5a; Song of Solomon 2:1-2

CHAPTER SEVEN: MOST BEAUTIFUL AMONG WOMEN—page 47

44 Song of Solomon 1:7
45 Song of Solomon 2:2; John 10:4-5; 27
46 Song of Solomon 1:7; the 'shepherds' are pastors, leaders.
47 Song of Solomon 1:8
48 Song of Solomon 1:8
49 Hebrews 13:5
50 Psalm 145:8
51 Psalm 121:5-8
52 Song of Solomon 2:1
53 Song of Solomon 1:17
54 John 14:26
55 Song of Solomon 1:17; 2:14a
56 Song of Solomon 1:9
57 Song of Solomon 1:10a
58 Song of Solomon 1:10b
59 Father, Son, and the Holy Spirit
60 Song of Solomon 1:11
61 Song of Solomon 1:8b

Rhonda Calhoun

[98] Song of Solomon 1:16a, b
[99] Matthew 11:28-29
[100] Zechariah 14:11
[101] Song of Solomon 1:3
[102] John 3:16
[103] I John 3:1

CHAPTER TEN: THE KING'S GARDEN—page 79

[104] Song of Solomon 2:3
[105] Song of Solomon 1:2a
[106] Galatians 5:22-23
[107] I Corinthians 13:13
[108] Galatians 5: 22-23
[109] James 4:6
[110] Matthew 7:13-14
[111] Matthew 17:20
[112] I Corinthians 13
[113] I Corinthians 13:13
[114] Matthew 13:11
[115] I Corinthians 13:2-3
[116] Psalm 119:3-4
[117] Romans 14:17
[118] Ephesians 3:17
[119] John 8:12
[120] John 7:38
[121] John 12:24
[122] Matthew 21:44
[123] Matthew 7:13
[124] Song of Solomon 2:3c; Psalm 17:8; Isaiah 32:2
[125] Song of Solomon 2:1; Matthew 6:33
[126] Song of Solomon 2:3d
[127] Song of Solomon 2:2
[128] Song of Solomon 2:3a, b
[129] Psalm 46:10
[130] Esther 5:3
[131] Psalm 27:4
[131a] Hebrews 12:2
[132] John 1:1
[133] Song of Solomon 2:3c, d
[134] John 4:14; Revelations 22:17
[135] Luke 15:11-30

Rhonda Calhoun

[169] Song of Solomon 2:8-9a
[170] Psalm 24:8
[171] I Timothy 6:15-16
[172] Song of Solomon 2:9
[173] Song of Solomon 2:10; "first bridal proposal"
[174] Song of Solomon 2:11a
[175] Song of Solomon 2:11b-12a
[176] Song of Solomon 2:12b
[177] Song of Solomon 2:12c
[178] II Corinthians 3:18
[179] Psalm 2:8
[180] Song of Solomon 2:13c, d
[181] Song of Solomon 2:14a, b, c
[182] Song of Solomon 2:14d, e
[183] Song of Solomon 2:15
[184] Song of Solomon 2:16-17a
[185] John 21:19-22
[186] John 16:16
[187] Song of Solomon 2:17b, c

CHAPTER THIRTEEN: I MUST ARISE—page 117

[188] Song of Solomon 3:1
[189] Song of Solomon 3:1; Psalm 30:7-8
[190] Psalm 84:10
[191] Song of Solomon 2:8-9a
[192] Song of Solomon 2:9b
[193] Song of Solomon 2:13-14
[194] Song of Solomon 2:10-14; John 15:1-11
[195] Song of Solomon 2:14
[196] Song of Solomon 2:15-16
[197] Song of Solomon 1:9
[198] Song of Solomon 1:8
[199] Song of Solomon 3:2
[200] Song of Solomon 3:2
[201] Song of Solomon 3:3
[202] Song of Solomon 3:3
[203] Song of Solomon 3:3b
[204] Song of Solomon 3:3a
[205] Song of Solomon 6:2
[206] Song of Solomon 3:4a, b
[207] Psalm 73:25-28

Rhonda Calhoun

[208] Song of Solomon 3:4c
[209] Song of Solomon 3:4d; "mother" represents the church
[210] Song of Solomon 3:4d, e
[211] Song of Solomon 3:4e
[212] Hebrews 7:25
[213] Luke 10:40
[214] Luke 10:38-42
[215] Song of Solomon 3:5
[216] John 1:1
[217] Matthew 16:24

PART FIVE: THE SAFE SAVIOR—page 129

CHAPTER FOURTEEN: HOW BEAUTIFUL YOU ARE—page 131

[218] Song of Solomon 3:6
[219] Psalm 27:10
[220] Isaiah 25:8
[221] Mark 16:1-19
[222] Song of Solomon 3:6a, b; Exodus 13:21
[223] Gethsemane means "oil press"
[224] Romans 6:9
[225] Song of Solomon 3:6
[226] Song of Solomon 3:7
[227] Song of Solomon 3:7
[228] Song of Solomon 3:8
[229] Song of Solomon 3:6
[230] Song of Solomon 3:9-10
[231] Song of Solomon 3:10d, e
[232] Song of Solomon 3:11; II Corinthians 11:2
[233] Song of Solomon 4:1a, b
[234] Song of Solomon 4:1c
[235] Song of Solomon 4:1d, e
[236] Song of Solomon 4:2
[237] Song of Solomon 4:3a, b
[238] Song of Solomon 4:3c, d
[239] Song of Solomon 4:4; Ephesians 6:10
[240] Song of Solomon 4:5
[241] Song of Solomon 2:17
[242] Song of Solomon 4:6
[243] Hosea 2:14-16

CHAPTER FIFTEEN: THE MOUNTAIN OF MYRRH—page 141

[244] Song of Solomon 4:6c, d
[245] Song of Solomon 4:6
[246] Psalm 121:1-4; Matthew 6:26-34
[246a] John 8:32
[247] Matthew 25:1-13; Song of Solomon 1:2-3
[248] John 12:24
[249] Mark 2:19-20
[250] Esther 2:12
[251] John 3:30
[252] Song of Solomon 4:6d; 6:10

CHAPTER SIXTEEN: THE HILL OF FRANKINCENSE—page 151

[253] Song of Solomon 4:6
[254] I Corinthians 6:20; 7:23
[255] Psalm 24:3
[256] Psalm 24:4, 5
[257] Zechariah 12:10
[258] Matthew 25:1-13
[259] Joel 2:1
[260] Matthew 25:31-46
[261] Song of Solomon 4:13-14
[262] Song of Solomon 4:14a
[263] Song of Solomon 4:14a
[264] Song of Solomon 4:14a
[265] Song of Solomon 4:14a
[266] Hebrews 5:8
[267] Song of Solomon 4:13-14
[268] Psalm 45:13-15
[269] Romans 8:28

CHAPTER SEVENTEEN: THE BRIDAL PROPOSAL—page 161

[270] Song of Solomon 4:8a
[271] Song of Solomon 4:7
[272] Song of Solomon 4:6c, d; Esther 2:12
[273] Song of Solomon 4:7a, b
[274] Song of Solomon 4:8a, b
[275] Song of Solomon 4:8c, d
[276] Song of Solomon 4:8e, f second "bridal proposal"
[277] She says, "yes" to His invitation, unlike chapter 2:17

Rhonda Calhoun

[278] Song of Solomon 4:9
[279] James 4:7
[280] Psalm 91:11-12
[280a] Matthew 24:4-14
[281] Exodus 20:5
[282] Psalm 139

PART SIX: THE BRIDEGROOM KING—page 169

CHAPTER EIGHTEEN: A LOCKED GARDEN—page 171

[283] Song of Solomon 4:10
[284] Song of Solomon 4:6
[285] Song of Solomon 2:17b
[286] Song of Solomon 4:9
[287] Song of Solomon 4:9
[288] Song of Solomon 4:10a
[289] Song of Solomon 1:2b
[290] Song of Solomon 4:10b; Jesus drank the cup in Gethsemane.
[291] Song of Solomon 1:3a
[292] Song of Solomon 4:10c ,d
[293] Song of Solomon 4:10c, d
[294] Song of Solomon 4:11a, b
[295] Song of Solomon 4:11c, d, e
[296] Psalm 4:3
[297] Song of Solomon 4:12; Isaiah 58:11
[298] Song of Solomon 4:12
[299] Song of Solomon 4:13a
[300] Song of Solomon 4:13b-14
[301] Song of Solomon 4:15a
[302] Song of Solomon 4:15b
[303] Song of Solomon 4:15
[304] Song of Solomon 4:16a
[305] Song of Solomon 4:16b, c, d
[306] Song of Solomon 4:16a, b
[307] Song of Solomon 4:16e
[308] Song of Solomon 4:16e, f
[309] Song of Solomon 5:1b
[310] Song of Solomon 5:1b
[311] Song of Solomon 5:1c, d
[312] Song of Solomon 5:1e, f

Rhonda Calhoun

[343] Song of Solomon 1:8
[344] Song of Solomon 5:2a; Matthew 25:5
[345] Song of Solomon 5:2a, b
[346] Song of Solomon 5:6c
[347] Song of Solomon 5:2c, d
[348] Song of Solomon 5:2c, d
[349] Song of Solomon 5:2e, f
[350] Song of Solomon 5:4
[351] Song of Solomon 5:4
[352] Song of Solomon 5:3
[353] Song of Solomon 5:4-5; the lock was located on the inside; there was an opening where the owner, if he had the key, could reach in and open the door. In this case, the Bridegroom chooses not to open the door but waits for her to open to Him.
[354] Song of Solomon 5:4-5
[355] Song of Solomon 5:6a, b, c A custom in Solomon's time: when a man came to visit and found the woman wasn't home or refused to answer the door, he would cover the lock with sweet-smelling ointment as a token of his affections
[356] Song of Solomon 5:5b,c
[357] Song of Solomon 5:6a
[358] Song of Solomon 5:6b
[359] Song of Solomon 5:6

CHAPTER TWENTY-THREE: DARK NIGHT OF THE SOUL—page 215

[360] Song of Solomon 5:8d
[361] John 16:22
[362] I Peter 4:12
[363] Song of Solomon 7:10
[364] Song of Solomon 5:10
[365] Psalm 23
[366] Song of Solomon 5:8d
[367] Ecclesiastes 3:1-4
[368] Ecclesiastes 3:11

CHAPTER TWENTY-FOUR: DEATH VALLEY—page 225

[369] Song of Solomon 5:6d
[370] Song of Solomon 2:14
[371] Song of Solomon 4:8
[372] Job 23:10-17
[373] Song of Solomon 2:15

[374] Psalm 23:4
[375] Matthew 24:12
[376] Song of Solomon 4:6
[377] Psalm 18:31-33
[378] Habakkuk 3:17-19; Song of Solomon 2:12-13; 6:11
[379] Matthew 21:44
[380] John 3:30
[381] II Corinthians 12:9
[382] Psalm 71:3
[383] Job 13:15
[384] I John 4:19
[384a] Psalm 37:23
[384b] Luke 15:31
[384c] John 11:2
[384d] John 15:9
[385] Psalm 18:2
[386] Psalm 27:4; Psalm 23:6; Matthew 6:25-34
[387] Romans 8:34-36

PART EIGHT: THE MAJESTIC GOD—page 243

CHAPTER TWENTY-FIVE: HAVE YOU SEEN HIM?—page 245

[388] Song of Solomon 5:16
[389] Song of Solomon 5:6d, e
[390] Song of Solomon 5:7a
[391] Matthew 22:34-39
[392] Song of Solomon 5:7b
[393] Psalm 71:10-12
[394] represents place of ministry
[395] Song of Solomon 5:7c
[396] Song of Solomon 1:4a
[397] Psalm 73:23-28
[398] Hebrews 13:5
[399] Song of Solomon 5:8
[400] Song of Solomon 5:9a, b
[401] Song of Solomon 5:9
[402] Song of Solomon 5:10a
[403] Song of Solomon 5:10b
[404] Song of Solomon 5:11a
[405] Song of Solomon 5:11b, c
[406] Song of Solomon 5:11
[407] Song of Solomon 1:15c

Rhonda Calhoun

[408] Song of Solomon 5:12
[409] Song of Solomon 5:13a
[410] Song of Solomon 5:13b
[411] Song of Solomon 5:13c
[412] Song of Solomon 5:13d
[413] Song of Solomon 5:14a, b
[414] Song of Solomon 5:14c, d
[415] Song of Solomon 5:15a
[416] Song of Solomon 5:15b
[417] Song of Solomon 5:15c
[418] Song of Solomon 5:15d
[419] Song of Solomon 5:16a
[420] Song of Solomon 5:16b
[421] Song of Solomon 5:16c
[422] Song of Solomon 6:1
[423] Song of Solomon 5:1
[424] Song of Solomon 6:2a, b
[425] Song of Solomon 6:2c, d
[426] Song of Solomon 5:1
[427] Song of Solomon 5:16
[428] Song of Solomon 6:3b
[429] Song of Solomon 6:3
[430] Song of Solomon 6:4a, b
[431] Song of Solomon 6:4c
[432] Song of Solomon 6:5
[433] Song of Solomon 6:4-9
[434] Song of Solomon 6:5c, d
[435] II Corinthians 4:17
[436] Song of Solomon 6:6
[437] Song of Solomon 6:7a
[438] Song of Solomon 6:7b; Psalm 34:18
[439] Mark 10:15
[440] Song of Solomon 6:9d, e
[441] Song of Solomon 6:8
[442] Song of Solomon 6:9a, b, c
[442a] John 10:14
[442b] Isaiah 60:1

CHAPTER TWENTY-SIX: MY BETROTHAL CELEBRATION—page 261

[443] Song of Solomon 6:10
[444] Psalm 23:6

[445] Isaiah 55:11
[446] I Corinthians 13:7
[447] Song of Solomon 1:11
[448] Revelation 19:8; Isaiah 61:3
[449] II Corinthians 3:18
[450] Song of Solomon 3:9
[451] Psalm 119:11
[452] Song of Solomon 6:10
[453] Song of Solomon 6:10
[454] I Corinthians 6:20; Rev. 21:9-11
[455] John 8:6
[456] Song of Solomon 6:9a,b
[457] II Corinthians 11:2
[458] Song of Solomon 6:9a; Ephesians 5:27
[459] Ephesians 5:26
[459a] Revelation 19:7
[460] Psalm 126:5
[461] Isaiah 49:16
[462] Luke 1:38
[463] Hosea 2:19-20; Jeremiah 31:3
[464] Song of Solomon 8:6
[465] song used by permission (Kenny Bartimioli)
[465a] Hebrews 13:5
[466] Song of Solomon 1:1
[467] Romans 8:38-39
[467a] I Corinthians 2:9

CHAPTER TWENTY-SEVEN: MOUNTAINS OF LEBANON—page 279

[468] Song of Solomon 6:10
[468a] Colossians 3:3
[469] Luke 22:15-20; Mark 14:24-25
[470] Isaiah 64:10
[471] Matthew 22:14
[472] King Solomon literally built a summer home for his bride in Lebanon
[473] I Kings 7:1-12
[474] Song of Solomon 3:9
[475] Psalm 56:11
[476] Psalm 23:6
[477] Song of Solomon 5:7
[478] Song of Solomon 7:4
[479] Song of Solomon 2:11-13

Rhonda Calhoun

CHAPTER TWENTY-EIGHT: THE ORCHARD—page 289

[480] Song of Solomon 6:11; the orchard represents various mercy ministries
[481] Psalm 34:18; Isaiah 54:10
[482] Romans 8:28
[483] Matthew 5:4

CHAPTER TWENTY-NINE: THE VILLAGE—page 297

[484] Song of Solomon 6:11
[485] I John 4:19
[486] Song of Solomon 6:11b, c; 'budding vines' are immature ministries
[487] Matthew 6:19
[488] Song of Solomon 6:11d; 'pomegranates' represent individuals
[488a] Matthew 5:45

CHAPTER THIRTY: COME BACK!—page 303

[489] Song of Solomon 6:12
[489a] John 17:13-18
[490] Song of Solomon 6:12a
[491] Song of Solomon 6:13a, b; Shulamite means, "peaceful one"
[492] Song of Solomon 6:13c
[493] Song of Solomon 6:13d
[494] Song of Solomon 7:1a
[495] Song of Solomon 7:1c, d
[496] Song of Solomon 7:2a, b
[497] Song of Solomon 7:2c, d
[498] Song of Solomon 7:3a, b
[499] Song of Solomon 7:4a
[500] Song of Solomon 7:4b, c
[501] Song of Solomon 7:4d, e
[502] Song of Solomon 7:5a
[503] Song of Solomon 7:5b
[504] Song of Solomon 6:5
[505] Song of Solomon 7:5c
[506] Song of Solomon 7:6
[507] Song of Solomon 7:7a
[508] Song of Solomon 7:7b
[509] Song of Solomon 2:5b
[510] Song of Solomon 7:7b
[511] John 14:12-16
[512] Song of Solomon 7:8a, b

513 Matthew 22:9
514 Song of Solomon 7:8c
515 Song of Solomon 7:8d
516 Song of Solomon 7:9a
517 Song of Solomon 7:9b
518 Song of Solomon 7:9b, c
519 John 15:16
520 Song of Solomon 7:10

CHAPTER THIRTY-ONE: COME AND LET US GO—page 313

521 Song of Solomon 7:12
522 Romans 11:33; Song of Solomon 3:11
523 Ephesians 4:1
524 James 1:17
525 Song of Solomon 7:11a
526 Song of Solomon 7:11b
527 Song of Solomon 7:12a
528 Song of Solomon 7:12
529 Matthew 10:24
530 Song of Solomon 7:12b, c, d
531 I John 4:19
532 Song of Solomon 7:12
533 Song of Solomon 7:13
534 Song of Solomon 7:11-12

CHAPTER THIRTY-TWO: RUNNING WITH MY BELOVED—page 323

535 Song of Solomon 7:13
536 Genesis 18:14
536a Romans 1:18
537 Song of Solomon 7:13a
538 Song of Solomon 7:13a
539 Psalms 27:4
540 John 20:27-29
541 Luke 12:7
542 Song of Solomon 7:13a, b
542a Psalm 103:12
543 Song of Solomon 4:7
544 Song of Solomon 2:15
545 Song of Solomon 1:11
546 Song of Solomon 1:4

Rhonda Calhoun

[547] Song of Solomon 7:13c

CHAPTER THIRTY-THREE: AMAZING LOVE—page 329

[548] Song of Solomon 8:1
[549] Matthew 7:13-14
[550] Matthew 11:28-29; John 14:6
[551] Song of Solomon 8:1a, b
[552] Song of Solomon 8:1c, d
[553] Song of Solomon 8:1
[554] Song of Solomon 8:2
[555] Song of Solomon 8:3
[556] Song of Solomon 7:6
[557] Song of Solomon 8:4

PART NINE: THE CONSUMING FIRE—page 335

CHAPTER THIRTY-FOUR: BEAUTY FOR ASHES—page 337

[558] Song of Solomon 7:10
[559] Jeremiah 33:11; Luke 18:19
[559a] Psalm 84
[559b] John 15: 14-15
[560] Isaiah 58:7-10
[561] John 14:27
[561a] Psalm 34:18
[561b] Song of Solomon 8:5

CHAPTER THIRTY-FIVE: LEANING ON MY BELOVED—page 345

[562] Song of Solomon 8:5
[563] Luke 1:79
[564] Hebrews 4:15
[565] Mark 12:41-44
[566] John 14:2
[567] Song of Solomon 8:6
[568] Song of Solomon 8:7; Isaiah 43:2
[568a] II Corinthians 11:2
[569] Song of Solomon 8:5
[570] John 13:5-10

CHAPTER THIRTY-SIX: FIERY SEAL OF LOVE—page 353

[571] Song of Solomon 8:5c
[572] Song of Solomon 8:5d, e
[573] Song of Solomon 8:6
[574] Song of Solomon 8:6a, b; Matthew 22:37-39
[575] Song of Solomon 8:6a,b
[576] Song of Solomon 8:6c
[577] Song of Solomon 8:6c, d
[578] Song of Solomon 8:6e, f
[579] Song of Solomon 8:7a, b
[580] Isaiah 43:1-2
[581] Galatians 2:20
[582] Song of Solomon 7:10
[583] Song of Solomon 8:7c, d
[584] Song of Solomon 8:7c, d
[585] Song of Solomon 8:8a, b
[586] Song of Solomon 8:8c, d
[587] Song of Solomon 8:9a, b
[588] Song of Solomon 8:9c, d
[589] Song of Solomon 8:9c, d
[590] Song of Solomon 8:9a, b
[591] Song of Solomon 8:10
[592] Song of Solomon 8:10b

CHAPTER THIRTY-SEVEN: MY VINEYARD—page 365

[593] Song of Solomon 8:12
[594] Song of Solomon 7:12
[595] Song of Solomon 1:6
[596] Song of Solomon 4:16e, f
[597] Song of Solomon 1:6d, e
[598] Luke 6:43-44
[599] Matthew 7:17-20
[600] John 15:1-11
[601] Song of Solomon 1:4a
[602] Song of Solomon 8:12
[603] James 1:27
[604] Song of Solomon 8:11
[605] Song of Solomon 8:11
[606] Song of Solomon 8:12
[607] Song of Solomon 8:13

Rhonda Calhoun

[608] John 15:12-17; John 13:35
[609] John 14:1-3
[610] John 21:15-17
[611] John 14:12-13
[612] John 14:27
[613] John 14:1-4
[614] John 16:7
[615] Matthew 25:1-13
[616] Song of Solomon 8:6-7
[617] Song of Solomon 1:3
[618] John 14:25-26
[619] John 17: 20-21
[620] John 17:24
[621] Song of Solomon 5:2c, d
[622] Song of Solomon 8:14
[623] Song of Solomon 8:14
[624] Revelations 22:20
[625] Acts 1:11
[626] Matthew 24:3
[627] John 10:27-30

May God Bless You

Thank you for purchasing this book.
If you would like to read more great books
written by Rhonda Calhoun, please visit our
on-line bookstore at: *www.harvesthome.org*
or phone *816-522-9011.*

100% of the proceeds from the sale
of Rhonda's books help support Our Father's Farm,
which is a ministry that reaches out
to primarily women and children in crisis.

For more information on *Our Father's Farm*,
please visit our website or phone Danny at *816-522-9011.*

Harvest Home is a 501 (c) (3) not for profit organization.
Our Father's Farm is an outreach of Harvest Home.
www.harvesthome.org

Rhonda Calhoun

Rhonda Calhoun

Rhonda Calhoun

Rhonda Calhoun